A FATHER READS TO HIS CHILDREN

A Father Reads
to His Children

An Anthology of Prose and Poetry

EDITED AND WITH AN INTRODUCTION

by ORVILLE PRESCOTT

New York 〰 〰 〰

E. P. DUTTON & CO., INC.

FIRST EDITION

ACKNOWLEDGMENTS

Permission to use the following material is gratefully acknowledged by Mr. Prescott and the Publisher:

THE EMPEROR'S NEW CLOTHES From *The Tales of Grimm and Andersen,* Introduced by W. H. Auden. Copyright 1952 by W. H. Auden. Reprinted by permission of Random House, Inc.

THE FISHERMAN AND HIS WIFE From *The Tales of Grimm and Andersen,* Introduced by W. H. Auden. Copyright 1952 by W. H. Auden. Reprinted by permission of Random House, Inc.

THE UNICORN From the book *The Flattered Flying Fish* by E. V. Rieu. Copyright, ©, 1962 by E. V. Rieu. Reprinted by permission of E. P. Dutton & Co., Inc., and Methuen & Co., Ltd.

THE WANDERING MOON From the book *The Wandering Moon* by James Reeves. Published 1960 by E. P. Dutton & Co., Inc., and reprinted with their permission, and with the permission of William Heinemann, Ltd.

ADVENTURES OF ODYSSEUS From *The Children's Homer* by Padraic Colum. Reprinted with permission of The Macmillan Co. Copyright by The Macmillan Co. 1918, renewed 1946 by Padraic Colum and Willy Pogany.

THE BALLAD OF THE HARP-WEAVER From *Collected Poems,* Harper & Row. Copyright 1923, 1951 by Edna St. Vincent Millay and Norma Millay Ellis.

KING ARTHUR AND THE SABLE KNIGHT From *The Story of King Arthur and His Knights* by Howard Pyle. By courtesy of Charles Scribner's Sons.

THE VALE OF THORNS From *The Story of Roland* by James Baldwin. By courtesy of Charles Scribner's Sons.

PUCK'S SONG From *Rudyard Kipling's Verse: Definitive Edition.* Reprinted by permission of Mrs. George Bambridge, Doubleday & Company, Inc., and The Macmillan Co. of Canada, Ltd.

MISS LARK'S ANDREW From *Mary Poppins* by P. L. Travers, copyright, 1934, 1962, by P. L. Travers. Reprinted by permission of Harcourt, Brace & World, Inc.

RIKKI-TIKKI-TAVI From *The Jungle Book* by Rudyard Kipling. Reprinted by permission of Mrs. George Bambridge, Doubleday & Company, Inc., and The Macmillan Co. of Canada, Ltd.

BAMBI From *Bambi* by Felix Salten. Copyright, ©, 1928, 1956, by Simon and Schuster, Inc. Reprinted by permission of the publishers.

EDUCATION IN THE FOREST SAUVAGE From *The Once and Future King* by T. H. White. Copyright 1939, 1940 by T. H. White. © 1958 by T. H. White. Reprinted by permission of G. P. Putnam's Sons, the Executors of the Estate of T. H. White, International Authors N. V. and Hornro N. V., and William Collins Sons & Co., Ltd.

THE WRASTLING MATCH BETWEEN LORD GOLDRY BLUSZCO AND GORICE XI, KING OF WITCHLAND From the book *The Worm Ouroboros* by E. R. Eddison. Copyright, 1926, by E. P. Dutton & Co., Inc. Renewal, 1954, by Winifred Grace Eddison and Jean Gudrun Rucker. Reprinted by permission of the publishers.

THE LISTENERS From *The Listeners and Other Poems* by Walter de la Mare. Reprinted by permission of The Literary Trustees of Walter de la Mare and the Society of Authors as their representative.

A MISERABLE, MERRY CHRISTMAS From *The Autobiography of Lincoln Steffens*, copyright, 1931, by Harcourt, Brace & World, Inc.; renewed, 1959, by Peter Steffens. Reprinted by permission of the publishers.

OLD SLEWFOOT From *The Yearling* by Marjorie Kinnan Rawlings, pp. 22–44. Copyright 1938 Marjorie Kinnan Rawlings. Reprinted with the permission of Charles Scribner's Sons.

THE HIGHWAYMAN From *Collected Poems* by Alfred Noyes. Copyright 1906, 1934 by Alfred Noyes. Published by J. B. Lippincott Company. Reprinted with the permission of the publisher and Hugh Noyes.

THE SEEING EYE From *Horses I Have Known* by Will James. Copyright 1940 Will James. Reprinted with the permission of Charles Scribner's Sons.

THE WAY OF A LION From *The Way of a Lion* by Alden Stevens. Copyright 1939 by J. B. Lippincott Company. Published by J. B. Lippincott Company.

IN PANOPLY OF SPEARS From *The Kindred of the Wild* by Charles G. D. Roberts. Copyright 1902 by L. C. Page. Reprinted with the permission of (Page) Farrar, Straus & Cudahy, Inc.

AFTER TWENTY YEARS From *The Four Million* by O. Henry. Reprinted by permission of Doubleday & Company, Inc.

A REPROOF OF GLUTTONY From *New Cautionary Tales* by Hilaire Belloc. Copyright, 1931 by Hilaire Belloc. Renewal © 1959 by Eleanor Jebb Belloc, Elizabeth Belloc, and Hilary Belloc. Reprinted with the permission of Alfred A. Knopf, Inc., and A. D. Peters & Co.

THE MONKEY'S PAW Reprinted with the permission of The Society of Authors as the literary representative of the Estate of the late W. W. Jacobs.

LEPANTO From *The Collected Poems of G. K. Chesterton*. Copyright, 1932, by Dodd, Mead & Company, Inc. Reprinted by permission of Dodd, Mead & Company, Inc., and Miss D. E. Collins.

For my grandchildren,

    Alison, Antonia and David,

who soon will be old enough to listen to these stories

Contents

Introduction

This book is a collection of twenty-four stories and twenty-four poems chosen for fathers to read aloud to their children. Why such a purpose? Because I believe that the joy, pleasure, information, and intellectual stimulation to be found in books is one of the truly great enrichments of life, and that it is much easier to learn to love reading as a child than later. When all the world is fresh and new and the ancient art of storytelling seems most magical, boys and girls can most naturally acquire the habit of reading, which, once acquired, can never lose its power to delight and to inform.

But few children learn to love books by themselves. Someone has to lure them into the wonderful world of the written word; someone has to show them the way. And fathers, who usually spend less time with their children than mothers, can do this by reading aloud. Not much time is necessary. A half hour on two weekdays and an hour on Sundays should be more than enough. And one enormous benefit is the shared pleasure of reading aloud. This is something parent and child can do together. It is something that strengthens bonds of family affection. And it offers fathers an opportunity to answer questions, to comment and to explain. By doing so, fathers are actually teaching without either father or child realizing it.

The selections included here are all easy to read aloud. There are no tongue twisters, no breathless sentences. Since two children of the same age have rarely reached the same level of reading interest and understanding, I have not thought of this book as planned for a particular age. The first selections are simple and should present no difficulty to a child of eight. They steadily increase in maturity of content so that most of this book should interest a boy or girl of thirteen. Some of the stories are world famous, some comparatively little known. Nearly all of them are taken from books that fathers and children would enjoy reading from beginning to end.

So here is richness and variety: fairy stories, ancient myths, stories about knights and heroes, fanciful stories about animals and realistic stories about animals, stories with surprise endings (one only in-genious, one horrible), stories about Indians in the Old West and about Zulus in Africa. When I was a boy I loved many of these stories. Others I discovered in my work as a literary critic or while searching for material for this book.

And since this is a book for men and for boys and girls who live in a world of crisis, I have not hesitated to include stories that stress the danger and violence inherent in all life, human as well as animal. Most children are surprisingly tough-minded. I have no patience with people who think that the young should read only about an unrecognizable nursery world. That is the way to boredom, as well as to falsification.

There is poetry here, too, because a taste for poetry even more than for fiction is most easily acquired early. All the poems are conventional in rhyme and rhythm, and stress the enchantment of musical sound. These are poems to roll on the tongue and even to chant. They are romantic, old-fashioned, fanciful, and heroic. Some of them sing of the lost world of faery fantasy. Some praise courage and patriotism and individual defiance of fate. Many are immortal and perhaps overly familiar to some fathers. But I believe that any child who encounters these poems will be glad that he did so for the rest of his life. When he is older, it is time enough to decide that some of them are overly simple or even naïve. A college undergraduate who has studied the difficult and symbolical poetry of our century may well scorn Henly's "Invictus." But if a child reads "Invictus" at the age of ten, he may well be inspired.

Several of these poems, which look simple, are not. But if no father and no learned critic can be certain about their exact meaning, it doesn't matter. They are songs. They are appeals to the imagination. They are casements opening into the world of poetry.

Children whose parents read to them are fortunate. I hope that this book will help spread the noble pleasure of fathers reading aloud to their children.

ORVILLE PRESCOTT

The Emperor's New Clothes

HANS CHRISTIAN ANDERSEN

⇌ ⇌ ⇌ This is the best loved and most famous of Andersen's fairy stories. Its gentle satire is easy to understand.

Many years ago there was an Emperor who was so excessively fond of new clothes that he spent all his money on them. He cared nothing about his soldiers, nor for the theatre, nor for driving in the woods except for the sake of showing off his new clothes. He had a costume for every hour in the day. Instead of saying as one does about any other king or emperor, "He is in his council chamber," the people here always said, "The Emperor is in his dressing room."

Life was very gay in the great town where he lived. Hosts of strangers came to visit it every day, and among them one day were two swindlers. They gave themselves out as weavers and said that they knew how to weave the most beautiful fabrics imaginable. Not only were the colors and patterns unusually fine, but the clothes that were made of this cloth had the peculiar quality of becoming invisible to every person who was not fit for the office he held, or who was impossibly dull.

"Those must be splendid clothes," thought the Emperor. "By wearing them I should be able to discover which men in my kingdom are unfitted for their posts. I shall distinguish the wise men from the fools. Yes, I certainly must order some of that stuff to be woven for me."

The Emperor paid the two swindlers a lot of money in advance, so that they might begin their work at once.

They did put up two looms and pretended to weave, but they had nothing whatever upon their shuttles. At the outset they asked for a quantity of the finest silk and the purest gold thread, all of which they put into their own bags while they worked away at the empty looms far into the night.

"I should like to know how those weavers are getting on with their cloth," thought the Emperor, but he felt a little queer when he reflected that anyone who was stupid or unfit for his post would not be able to see it. He certainly thought that he need have no fears for himself, but still he thought he would send somebody else first to see how it was getting on. Everybody in the town knew what wonderful power the stuff possessed, and everyone was anxious to see how stupid his neighbor was.

"I will send my faithful old minister to the weavers," thought the Emperor. "He will be best able to see how the stuff looks, for he is a clever man and no one fulfills his duties better than he does."

So the good old minister went into the room where the two swindlers sat working at the empty loom.

"Heaven help us," thought the old minister, opening his eyes very wide. "Why, I can't see a thing!" But he took care not to say so.

Both the swindlers begged him to be good enough to step a little nearer, and asked if he did not think it a good pattern and beautiful coloring. They pointed to the empty loom. The poor old minister stared as hard as he could, but he could not see anything, for of course there was nothing to see.

"Good heavens," thought he. "Is it possible that I am a fool? I have never thought so, and nobody must know it. Am I not fit for my post? It will never do to say that I cannot see the stuff."

"Well, sir, you don't say anything about the stuff," said the one who was pretending to weave.

"Oh, it is beautiful—quite charming," said the minister, looking through his spectacles. "Such a pattern and such colors! I will certainly tell the Emperor that the stuff pleases me very much."

"We are delighted to hear you say so," said the swindlers, and then they named all the colors and described the peculiar pattern. The old minister paid great attention to what they said, so as to be able to repeat it when he got home to the Emperor.

Then the swindlers went on to demand more money, more silk, and more gold, to be able to proceed with the weaving. But they put it all into their own pockets. Not a single strand was ever put into the loom, but they went on as before, weaving at the empty loom.

The Emperor soon sent another faithful official to see how the stuff was getting on and if it would soon be ready. The same thing happened to him as to the minister. He looked and looked, but as there was only the empty loom, he could see nothing at all.

"Is not this a beautiful piece of stuff?" said both the swindlers, showing and explaining the beautiful pattern and colors which were not there to be seen.

"I know I am no fool," thought the man, "so it must be that I am unfit for my good post. It is very strange, though. However, one must not let it appear." So he praised the stuff he could not see, and assured them of his delight in the beautiful colors and the originality of the design.

"It is absolutely charming," he said to the Emperor. Everybody in the town was talking about this splendid stuff.

Now the Emperor thought he would like to see it while it was still on the loom. So, accompanied by a number of selected courtiers, among whom were the two faithful officials who had already seen the imaginary stuff, he went to visit the crafty impostors, who were working away as hard as ever they could at the empty loom.

"It is magnificent," said both the honest officials. "Only see, Your Majesty, what a design! What colors!" And they pointed to the empty loom, for they each thought no doubt the others could see the stuff.

"What?" thought the Emperor. "I see nothing at all. This is terrible! Am I a fool? Am I not fit to be Emperor? Why, nothing worse could happen to me!"

"Oh, it is beautiful," said the Emperor. "It has my highest approval." And he nodded his satisfaction as he gazed at the empty loom. Nothing would induce him to say that he could not see anything.

The whole suite gazed and gazed, but saw nothing more than all the others. However, they all exclaimed with His Majesty. "It is very beautiful." And they advised him to wear a suit made of this wonderful cloth on the occasion of a great procession which was just about to take place. "Magnificent! Gorgeous! Excellent!" went from mouth to mouth. They were all equally delighted with it. The Emperor gave each of the rogues an order of knighthood to be worn in their buttonholes and the title of "Gentleman Weaver."

The swindlers sat up the whole night before the day on which the procession was to take place, burning sixteen candles, so that people might see how anxious they were to get the Emperor's new clothes ready. They pretended to take the stuff off the loom. They cut it out in the air with a huge pair of scissors, and they stitched away with needles without any thread in them.

At last they said, "Now the Emperor's new clothes are ready."

The Emperor with his grandest courtiers went to them himself, and both swindlers raised one arm in the air, as if they were holding something. They said, "See, these are the trousers. This is the coat. Here is the mantle," and so on. "It is as light as a spider's web. One might think one had nothing on, but that is the very beauty of it."

"Yes," said all the courtiers, but they could not see anything, for there was nothing to see.

"Will Your Imperial Majesty be graciously pleased to take off your clothes?" said the impostors. "Then we may put on the new ones, along here before the great mirror."

The Emperor took off all his clothes, and the impostors pretended to give him one article of dress after the other of the new ones which they had pretended to make. They pretended to fasten something around his waist and to tie on something. This was the train, and the Emperor turned round and round in front of the mirror.

"How well His Majesty looks in the new clothes! How becoming they are!" cried all the people round. "What a design, and what colors! They are most gorgeous robes."

"The canopy is waiting outside which is to be carried over Your Majesty in the procession," said the master of the ceremonies.

"Well, I am quite ready," said the Emperor. "Don't the clothes fit well?" Then he turned round again in front of the mirror, so that he should seem to be looking at his grand things.

The chamberlains who were to carry the train stooped and pretended to lift it from the ground with both hands, and they walked along with their hands in the air. They dared not let it appear that they could not see anything.

Then the Emperor walked along in the procession under the gorgeous canopy, and everybody in the streets and at the windows, exclaimed, "How beautiful the Emperor's new clothes are! What a splendid train! And they fit to perfection!" Nobody would let it appear that he could see nothing, for then he would not be fit for his post, or else he was a fool.

None of the Emperor's clothes had been so successful before.

"But he has got nothing on," said a little child.

"Oh, listen to the innocent," said its father. And one person whispered to the other what the child had said. "He has nothing on—a child says he has nothing on!"

"But he has nothing on!" at last cried all the people.

The Emperor writhed, for he knew it was true. But he thought, "The procession must go on now." So he held himself stiffer than ever, and the chamberlains held up the invisible train.

The Fairies

WILLIAM ALLINGHAM

Up the airy mountain,
    Down the rushy glen,
We daren't go a-hunting
    For fear of little men;
Wee folk, good folk,
    Trooping all together;
Green jacket, red cap,
    And white owl's feather!

Down along the rocky shore
    Some make their home,
They live on crispy pancakes
    Of yellow tide-foam;
Some in the reeds
    Of the black mountain lake
With frogs for their watch-dogs,
    All night awake.

High on the hill-top
    The old King sits;
He is now so old and gray
    He's nigh lost his wits.
With a bridge of white mist
    Columbkill he crosses,

On his stately journeys
    From Slieveleague to Rosses;
Or going up with music
    On cold starry nights
To sup with the Queen
    Of the gay Northern Lights.

They stole little Bridget
    For seven years long;
When she came down again
    Her friends were all gone.
They took her lightly back,
    Between the night and morrow,
They thought that she was fast asleep,
    But she was dead with sorrow.
They have kept her ever since
Deep within the lake,
On a bed of flag-leaves,
    Watching till she wake.

By the craggy hill-side,
    Through the mosses bare,
They have planted thorn-trees
    For pleasure here and there.
If any man so daring
    As dig them up in spite,
He shall find their sharpest thorns
    In his bed at night.

Up the airy mountain,
    Down the rushy glen,
We daren't go a-hunting
    For fear of little men;
Wee folk, good folk,
    Trooping all together;
Green jacket, red cap,
    White owl's feather!

The Fisherman and His Wife

THE BROTHERS GRIMM

≈ ≈ ≈ *Many of the world-famous Grimm fairy tales are ex-*
tremely gruesome. But some are humorous and poke good-
natured fun at human folly. This joke about greed and
vanity is one of the most amusing.

There was once a fisherman who lived with his wife in a miserable little hovel close to the sea. He went to fish every day, and he fished and fished, and at last one day as he was sitting looking deep down into the shining water, he felt something on his line. When he hauled it up, there was a big flounder on the end of the line.

The flounder said to him, "Listen, fisherman, I beg you not to kill me. I am no common flounder. I am an enchanted prince! What good will it do you to kill me? I shan't be good to eat. Put me back into the water and leave me to swim about."

"Ho! ho!" said the fisherman. "You need not make so many words about it, I am quite ready to put back a flounder that can talk." And so saying, he put back the flounder into the shining water and it sank down to the bottom, leaving a streak of blood behind it. Then the fisherman got up and went back to his wife in the hovel.

"Husband," she said, "have you caught anything today?"

"No," said the man. "All I caught was one flounder. And he said he was an enchanted prince, so I put him back into the water."

"Did you not wish for anything then?" asked the goodwife.

"No," said the man. "What was there to wish for?"

"Alas," said his wife, "isn't it bad enough always to live in this wretched hovel? You might at least have wished for a nice clean cottage. Go back and call him! Tell him I want a pretty cottage. He will surely give us that."

"Alas," said the man, "what am I to go back there for?"

"Well," said the woman, "it was you who caught him and let him go again. He will certainly do that for you. Be off now."

22

The man was still not very willing to go, but he did not want to vex his wife and at last he went back to the sea.

He found the sea no longer bright and shining, but dull and green. He stood by it and said:

> "Flounder, flounder in the sea,
> Prythee, hearken unto me:
> My wife, Ilsebil, must have her own will,
> And sends me to beg a boon of thee."

The flounder came swimming up, and said, "Well, what do you want?"

"Alas," said the man. "I had to call you, for my wife said I ought to have wished for something as I caught you. She doesn't want to live in our miserable hovel any longer. She wants a pretty cottage."

"Go home again then," said the flounder. "She has her wish fully."

The man went home and found his wife no longer in the old hut, but a pretty little cottage stood in its place and his wife was sitting on a bench by the door.

She took him by the hand and said, "Come and look in here. Isn't this much better?"

They went inside and found a pretty sitting room, a bedroom with a bed in it, a kitchen, and a larder furnished with everything of the best in tin and brass and every possible need. Outside there was a little yard with chickens and ducks and a little garden full of vegetables and fruit.

"Look!" said the woman. "Is not this nice?"

"Yes," said the man, "and so let it remain. We can live here very happily."

"We will see about that," said the woman. With that they ate something and went to bed.

Everything went well for a week or more, and then the wife said, "Listen, husband, this cottage is too cramped and the garden is too small. The flounder could have given us a bigger house. I want to live in a big stone castle. Go to the flounder and tell him to give us a castle."

"Alas, wife," said the man, "the cottage is good enough for us. What should we do with a castle?"

"Never mind," said his wife. "You just go to the flounder and he will manage it."

"No, wife," said the man. "The flounder gave us the cottage. I don't want to go back. As likely as not he'll be angry."

"Go, all the same," said the woman. "He can do it easily enough and willingly into the bargain. Just go!"

The man's heart was heavy and he was very unwilling to go. He said to himself, "It's not right." But at last he went. He found the sea was no longer green: it was still calm, but dark violet and gray. He stood by it and said:

> "Flounder, flounder in the sea,
> Prythee, hearken unto me:
> My wife, Ilsebil, must have her own will,
> And sends me to beg a boon of thee."

"Now what do you want?" said the flounder.

"Alas," said the man, half scared, "my wife wants a big stone castle."

"Go home again," said the flounder. "She is standing at the door of it."

Then the man went away thinking he would find no house; but when he got back he found a great stone palace, and his wife was standing at the top of the steps waiting to go in. She took him by the hand and said, "Come in with me."

With that they went in and found a great hall paved with marble slabs, and numbers of servants in attendance who opened the great doors for them. The walls were hung with beautiful tapestries and the rooms were furnished with golden chairs and tables, while rich carpets covered the floors and crystal chandeliers hung from the ceilings. The tables groaned under every kind of delicate food and the most costly wines. Outside the house there was a great courtyard, with stables for horses and cows, and many fine carriages. Beyond this there was a great garden filled with the loveliest flowers and fine fruit trees. There was also a park half a mile long, and in it were stags and hinds and hares, and everything that one could wish for.

"Now," said the woman, "is not this worth having?"

"Oh yes," said the man, "and so let it remain. We will live in this beautiful palace and be content."

"We will think about that," said his wife, "and sleep upon it."

With that they went to bed.

Next morning the wife woke up first. Day was just dawning, and from her bed she could see the beautiful country around her. Her husband was still asleep, but she pushed him with her elbow and said, "Husband, get up and peep out of the window. See here, now, could we not be King over all this land? Go to the flounder. We will be King."

"Alas, wife," said the man, "why should we be King? I don't want to be King."

"Ah," said his wife, "if you will not be King, I will. Go to the flounder. I will be King."

"Alas, wife," said the man, "why do you want to be King? I don't want to ask the flounder."

"Why not?" said the woman. "Go you must. I insist I will be King."

So the man went, but he was quite sad because his wife would be King.

"It is not right," he said. "It is not right."

When he reached the sea, he found it dark, gray, and rough, and evil-smelling. He stood there and said:

> "Flounder, flounder in the sea,
> Prythee, hearken unto me:
> My wife, Ilsebil, must have her own will,
> And sends me to beg a boon of thee."

"Now what does she want?" said the flounder.

"Alas," said the man, "she wants to be King now."

"Go back. She is King already," said the flounder.

So the man went back, and when he reached the palace he found that it had grown much larger and a great tower had been added with handsome decorations. There was a sentry at the door and numbers of soldiers were playing drums and trumpets. As soon as he got inside the house he found everything was marble and gold, and the hangings were of velvet with great gold tassels. The doors of the salon were thrown wide open, and he saw the whole court assembled. His wife was sitting on a lofty throne of gold and diamonds. She wore a golden crown and carried in one hand a scepter of pure gold. On each side of her stood her ladies in a long row, every one a head shorter than the next.

He stood before her and said, "Alas, wife, are you now King?"

"Yes," she said, "now I am King."

He stood looking at her for some time, and then he said. "Ah, wife, it is a fine thing for you to be King. Now we will not wish to be anything more."

"No, husband," she answered, quite uneasily, "I find that time hangs very heavy on my hands. I can't bear it any longer. Go back to the flounder. King I am, but I must also be Emperor."

"Alas, wife," said the man, "why do you now want to be Emperor?"

"Husband," she answered, "go to the flounder. Emperor I will be."

"Alas, wife," said the man, "Emperor he can't make you, and I won't ask him. There is only one emperor in the country, and Emperor the flounder cannot make you. That he can't."

"What?" said the woman. "I am King, and you are but my husband. To him you must go and that right quickly. If he can make a king, he can also make an emperor. Emperor I will be, so go quickly."

He had to go, but he was quite frightened. And as he went he thought, "This won't end well. Emperor is too shameless. The flounder will make an end of the whole thing."

With that he came to the sea, but now he found it quite black and heaving up from below in great waves. It tossed to and fro and a sharp wind blew over it, and the man trembled. So he stood there and said:

> "Flounder, flounder in the sea,
> Prythee, hearken unto me:
> My wife, Ilsebil, must have her own will,
> And sends me to beg a boon of thee."

"What does she want now?" said the flounder.

"Alas," he said, "my wife wants to be Emperor."

"Go back," said the flounder. "She is Emperor."

So the man went back, and when he got to the door he found that the whole palace was made of polished marble, with alabaster figures and golden decorations. Soldiers marched up and down before the doors, blowing their trumpets and beating their drums. Inside the palace, counts, barons, and dukes walked about as attendants, and they opened to him the doors, which were of pure gold.

He went in and saw his wife sitting on a huge throne made of solid gold. It was at least two miles high. She had on her head a great golden crown set with diamonds, three yards high. In one hand she held the scepter, and in the other the orb of empire. On each side of her stood the gentlemen-at-arms in two rows, each one a little smaller than the other, from giants two miles high down to the tiniest dwarf no bigger than my little finger. She was surrounded by princes and dukes.

Her husband stood still and said, "Wife, are you now Emperor?"

"Yes," said she. "Now I am Emperor."

Then he looked at her for some time and said, "Alas, wife, how much better off are you for being Emperor?"

"Husband," she said, "what are you standing there for? Now I am Emperor, I mean to be Pope! Go back to the flounder."

"Alas, wife," said the man, "what won't you want next? Pope you cannot be. There is only one pope in Christendom. That's more than the flounder can do."

"Husband," she said, "Pope I will be, so go at once! I must be Pope this very day."

"No, wife," he said, "I dare not tell him. It's no good. It's too monstrous altogether. The flounder cannot make you Pope."

"Husband," said the woman, "don't talk nonsense. If he can make an emperor, he can make a pope. Go immediately. I am Emperor, and you are but my husband, and you must obey."

So he was frightened and went, but he was quite dazed. He shivered and shook and his knees trembled.

A great wind arose over the land, the clouds flew across the sky, and it grew dark as night. The leaves fell from the trees, and the water foamed and dashed upon the shore. In the distance, the ships were being tossed to and fro on the waves, and he heard them firing signals of distress. There was still a little patch of blue in the sky among the dark clouds, but towards the south they were red and heavy, as in a bad storm. In despair, he stood and said:

> "Flounder, flounder in the sea,
> Prythee, hearken unto me:
> My wife, Ilsebil, must have her own will,
> And sends me to beg a boon of thee."

"Now what does she want?" said the flounder.

"Alas," said the man, "she wants to be Pope!"

"Go back. Pope she is," said the flounder.

So back he went, and he found a great church surrounded with palaces. He pressed through the crowd, and inside he found thousands and thousands of lights. And his wife, entirely clad in gold, was sitting on a still higher throne, with three golden crowns upon her head, and she was surrounded with priestly state. On each side of her were two rows of candles, from the biggest as thick as a tower down to the tiniest little taper. Kings and emperors were on their knees before her, kissing her shoe.

"Wife," said the man, looking at her, "are you now the Pope?"

"Yes," said she. "Now I am Pope."

At first she sat as stiff as a post, without stirring. Then he said, "Now, wife, be content with being Pope. Higher you cannot go."

"I will think about that," said the woman, and with that they both went to bed. Still she was not content and could not sleep for her inordinate desires. The man slept well and soundly, for he had walked about a great deal in the day. But his wife could think of nothing but what further grandeur she could demand. When the dawn reddened the sky she raised herself up in bed and looked out of the window, and when she saw the sun rise she said, "Ha! Can I not cause the sun and the moon to rise? Husband!" she cried, digging her elbow into his side, "wake up and go to the flounder. I will be Lord of the Universe."

Her husband, who was still more than half asleep, was so shocked that he fell out of bed. He thought he must have heard wrong. He rubbed his eyes and said, "Alas, wife, what did you say?"

"Husband," she said, "if I cannot be Lord of the Universe, and cause the sun and moon to set and rise, I shall not be able to bear it. I shall never have another happy moment."

She looked at him so wildly that it caused a shudder to run through him.

"Alas, wife," he said, falling on his knees before her. "The flounder can't do that. Emperor and Pope he can make, but this is indeed beyond him. I pray you, control yourself and remain Pope."

Then she flew into a terrible rage. Her hair stood on end. She kicked him and screamed, "I won't bear it any longer. Now go!"

Then he pulled on his trousers and tore away like a madman. Such a storm was raging that he could hardly keep his feet. Houses and trees quivered and swayed, and mountains trembled, and the rocks rolled into the sea. The sky was pitchy black. It thundered and lightened, and the sea ran black waves mountain high, crested with white foam. He shrieked out, but could hardly make himself heard:

"Flounder, flounder in the sea,
Prythee, hearken unto me:
My wife, Ilsebil, must have her own will,
And sends me to beg a boon of thee."

"Now what does she want?" asked the flounder.

"Alas," said he, "she wants to be Lord of the Universe."

"Now she must go back to her old hovel," said the flounder, "and there she is!" So there they are to this very day.

The Unicorn

E . V . RIEU

≈ ≈ ≈

The Unicorn stood, like a king in a dream,
On the bank of a dark Senegambian stream;
And flaming flamingoes flew over his head,
As the African sun rose in purple and red.

Who knows what the thoughts of a unicorn are
When he shines on the world like a visiting star;
When he comes from the magical pages of story
In the pride of his horn and a halo of glory?

He followed the paths where the jungle beasts go,
And he walked with a step that was stately and slow;
But he threw not a shadow and made not a sound,
And his foot was as light as the wind on the ground.

The lion looked up with his terrible eyes,
And growled like the thunder to hide his surprise.
He thought for a while, with a paw in the air;
Then tucked up his tail and turned into his lair.

The gentle giraffe ran away to relate
The news to his tawny and elegant mate,
While the snake slid aside with a venomous hiss,
And the little birds piped: 'There is something amiss!'

But the Unicorn strode with his head in a cloud
And uttered his innocent fancies aloud.
'What a wonderful world!' he was heard to exclaim;
'It is better than books: it is sweeter than fame!'

And he gazed at himself, with a thrill and a quiver,
Reflected in white by the slow-flowing river:
'Oh, speak to me, dark Senegambian stream,
And prove that my beauty is more than a dream!'

He had paused for a word in the midst of his pride,
When a whisper came down through the leaves at his side
From a spying, malevolent imp of an ape
With a twist in his tail and a villainous shape:

'He was made by the stroke of a fanciful pen;
He was wholly invented by ignorant men.
One word in his ear, and one puff of the truth—
And a unicorn fades in the flower of his youth.'

The Unicorn heard, and the demon of doubt
Crept into his heart, and the sun was put out.
He looked in the water, but saw not a gleam
In the slow-flowing deep Senegambian stream.

He turned to the woods, and his shadowy form
Was seen through the trees like the moon in a storm.
And the darkness fell down on the Gambian plain;
And the stars of the Senegal sought him in vain.

He had come like a beautiful melody heard
When the strings of the fiddle are tunefully stirred;
And he passed where the splendours of melody go
When the hand of the fiddler surrenders the bow.

The Gorgon's Head

NATHANIEL HAWTHORNE

≈ ≈ ≈ *The Greek myths about gods and heroes still enthrall readers thousands of years after they were first told. The story of Perseus is one of the best. Hawthorne's version of it is the best of those he retold in his perennially popular* A Wonder Book *and* Tanglewood Tales.

Perseus was the son of Danaë, who was the daughter of a king. And when Perseus was a very little boy, some wicked people put his mother and himself into a chest, and set them afloat upon the sea. The wind blew freshly, and drove the chest away from the shore, and the uneasy billows tossed it up and down; while Danaë clasped her child to her bosom, and dreaded that some big wave would dash its foamy crest over them both. The chest sailed on, however, and neither sank nor was upset; until, when night was coming, it floated so near an island that it got entangled in a fisherman's nets, and was drawn out high and dry upon the sand. The island was called Seriphus, and it was reigned over by King Polydectes, who happened to be the fisherman's brother.

The fisherman, I am glad to tell you, was an exceedingly humane and upright man. He showed great kindness to Danaë and her little boy; and continued to befriend them, until Perseus had grown to be a handsome youth, very strong and active, and skilful in the use of arms. Long before this time, King Polydectes had seen the two strangers—the mother and her child—who had come to his dominions in a floating chest. As he was not good and kind, like his brother the fisherman, but extremely wicked, he resolved to send Perseus on a dangerous enterprise, in which he would probably be killed, and then to do some great mischief to Danaë herself. So this bad-hearted king spent a long while in considering what was the most dangerous thing that a young man could possibly undertake to perform. At last, having hit upon an enterprise that promised to turn out as fatally as he desired, he sent for the youthful Perseus.

The young man came to the palace and found the king sitting upon his throne.

"Perseus," said King Polydectes, smiling craftily upon him, "you are grown up a fine young man. You and your good mother have received a great deal of kindness from myself as well as from my worthy brother the fisherman, and I suppose you would not be sorry to repay some of it."

"Please your Majesty," answered Perseus, "I would willingly risk my life to do so."

"Well, then," continued the king, with a cunning smile on his lips, "I have a little adventure to propose to you; and, as you are a brave and enterprising youth, you will doubtless look upon it as a great piece of good luck to have so rare an opportunity of distinguishing yourself. You must know, my good Perseus, I think of getting married to the beautiful Princess Hippodamia; and it is customary, on these occasions, to make the bride a present of some far-fetched and elegant curiosity. I have been a little perplexed, I must honestly confess, where to obtain anything likely to please a princess of her exquisite taste. But, this morning, I flatter myself, I have thought of precisely the article."

"And can I assist your Majesty in obtaining it?" cried Perseus eagerly.

"You can, if you are as brave a youth as I believe you to be," replied King Polydectes, with the utmost graciousness of manner. "The bridal gift which I have set my heart on presenting to the beautiful Hippodamia is the head of the Gorgon Medusa, with the snaky locks; and I depend on you, my dear Perseus, to bring it to me. So, as I am anxious to settle affairs with the princess, the sooner you go in quest of the Gorgon, the better I shall be pleased."

"I will set out to-morrow morning," answered Perseus.

"Pray do so, my gallant youth," rejoined the king. "And, Perseus, in cutting off the Gorgon's head, be careful to make a clean stroke, so as not to injure its appearance. You must bring it home in the very best condition, in order to suit the exquisite taste of the beautiful Princess Hippodamia."

Perseus left the palace, but was scarcely out of hearing before Polydectes burst into a laugh; being greatly amused, wicked king that he was! to find how readily the young man fell into the snare. The news quickly spread abroad, that Perseus had undertaken to cut off the head of Medusa with the snaky locks. Everybody was rejoiced; for most of the inhabitants of the island were as wicked as the king himself, and would have liked nothing better than to see some enormous mischief happen to Danaë and her son. The only good man in this unfortunate island of Seriphus appears to have been the fisherman. As Perseus walked along, therefore, the people pointed after him, and made mouths, and winked to one another, and ridiculed him as loudly as they dared.

"Ho, ho!" cried they; "Medusa's snakes will sting him soundly!"

Now, there were three Gorgons alive, at that period; and they were the most strange and terrible monsters that had ever been seen since the world was made, or that have been seen in afterdays, or that are likely to be seen in all time to come. I hardly know what sort of creature or hobgoblin to call them. They were three sisters, and seem to have borne some distant resemblance to women, but were really a very frightful and mischievous species of dragon. It is, indeed, difficult to imagine what hideous beings these three sisters were. Why, instead of locks of hair, if you can believe me, they had each of them a hundred enormous snakes growing on their heads, all alive, twisting, wriggling, curling, and thrusting out their venomous tongues, with forked stings at the end! The teeth of the Gorgons were terribly long tusks; their hands were made of brass; and their bodies were all over scales, which, if not iron, were something as hard and impenetrable. They had wings, too, and exceedingly splendid ones, I can assure you; for every feather in them was pure, bright, glittering, burnished gold, and they looked very dazzling, no doubt, when the Gorgons were flying about in the sunshine.

But when people happened to catch a glimpse of their glittering brightness, aloft in the air, they seldom stopped to gaze, but ran and hid themselves as speedily as they could. You will think, perhaps, that they were afraid of being stung by the serpents that served the Gorgons instead of hair—or of havng their heads bitten off by their ugly tusks—or of being torn all to pieces by their brazen claws. Well, to be sure, these were some of the dangers, but by no means the greatest, nor the most difficult to avoid. For the worst thing about these abominable Gorgons was, that, if once a poor mortal fixed his eyes full upon one of their faces, he was certain, that very instant, to be changed from warm flesh and blood into cold and lifeless stone!

Thus, as you will easily perceive, it was a very dangerous adventure that the wicked King Polydectes had contrived for this innocent young man. Perseus himself, when he had thought over the matter, could not help seeing that he had very little chance of coming safely through it, and that he was far more likely to become a stone image than to bring back the head of Medusa with the snaky locks. For, not to speak of other difficulties, there was one which it would have puzzled an older man than Perseus to get over. Not only must he fight with and slay this golden-winged, iron-scaled, long-tusked, brazen-clawed, snaky-haired monster, but he must do it with his eyes shut, or, at least, without so much as a glance at the enemy with whom he was contending. Else, while his arm was lifted to strike, he would stiffen into stone, and stand with that uplifted arm for centuries, until time, and the wind and weather, should crumble him quite away. This would be a very sad thing to befall a young man who wanted to perform a great many brave deeds, and to enjoy a great deal of happiness, in this bright and beautiful world.

So disconsolate did these thoughts make him, that Perseus could not bear to tell his mother what he had undertaken to do. He therefore took his shield, girded on his sword, and crossed over from the island to the main land, where he sat down in a solitary place, and hardly refrained from shedding tears.

But, while he was in this sorrowful mood, he heard a voice close beside him.

"Perseus," said the voice, "why are you sad?"

He lifted his head from his hands, in which he had hidden it, and behold! all alone as Perseus had supposed himself to be, there was a stranger in the solitary place. It was a brisk, intelligent, and remarkably shrewd-looking young man, with a cloak over his shoulders, an odd sort of cap on his head, a strangely-twisted staff in his hand, and a short and very crooked sword hanging by his side. He was exceedingly light and active in his figure, like a person much accustomed to gymnastic exercises, and well able to leap and run. Above all, the stranger had such a cheerful, knowing, and helpful aspect (though it was certainly a little mischievous, into the bargain), that Perseus could not help feeling his spirits grow livelier, as he gazed at him. Besides, being really a courageous youth, he felt greatly ashamed that anybody should have found him with tears in his eyes, like a timid little schoolboy, when after all, perhaps there might be no occasion for despair. So Perseus wiped his eyes, and answered the stranger pretty briskly, putting on as brave a look as he could.

"I am not so very sad," he said; "only thoughtful about an adventure that I have undertaken."

"Oho!" answered the stranger, "Well, tell me all about it, and possibly I may be of service to you. I have helped a good many young men through adventures that looked difficult enough beforehand. Perhaps you may have heard of me. I have more names than one; but the name of Quicksilver suits me as well as any other. Tell me what your trouble is, and we will talk the matter over, and see what can be done."

The stranger's words and manner put Perseus into quite a different mood from his former one. He resolved to tell Quicksilver all his difficulties, since he could not easily be worse off than he already was, and very possibly his new friend might give him some advice that would turn out well in the end. So he let the stranger know, in a few words, precisely what the case was; how that King Polydectes wanted the head of Medusa with the snaky locks as a bridal gift for the beautiful Princess Hippodamia, and how that he had undertaken to get it for him, but was afraid of being turned into stone.

"And that would be a great pity," said Quicksilver, with his mischievous smile. "You would make a very handsome marble statue, it is true, and it would be a considerable number of centuries before you crumbled away; but, on the whole, one would rather be a young man for a few years than a stone image for a great many."

"O, far rather!" exclaimed Perseus, with the tears again in his eyes. "And, besides, what would my dear mother do, if her beloved son were turned into a stone?"

"Well, well; let us hope that the affair will not turn out so very badly," replied Quicksilver, in an encouraging tone. "I am the very person to help you, if anybody can. My sister and myself will do our utmost to bring you safe through the adventure, ugly as it now looks."

"Your sister?" repeated Perseus.

"Yes, my sister," replied the stranger. "She is very wise, I promise you; and as for myself, I generally have all my wits about me, such as they are. If you show yourself bold and cautious, and follow our advice, you need not fear being a stone image yet awhile. But, first of all, you must polish your shield, till you can see your face in it as distinctly as in a mirror."

This seemed to Perseus rather an odd beginning of the adventure; for he thought it of far more consequence that the shield should be strong enough to defend him from the Gorgon's brazen claws, than that it should be bright enough to show him the reflection of his face. However, concluding that Quicksilver knew better than himself, he immediately set to work, and scrubbed the shield with so much diligence and goodwill, that it very quickly shone like the moon at harvest time. Quicksilver looked at it with a smile, and nodded his approbation. Then, taking off his own short and crooked sword, he girded it about Perseus, instead of the one which he had before worn.

"No sword but mine will answer your purpose," observed he: "the blade has a most excellent temper, and will cut through iron and brass as easily as through the slenderest twig. And now we will set out. The next thing is to find the Three Grey Women, who will tell us where to find the Nymphs."

"The Three Grey Women!" cried Perseus, to whom this seemed only a new difficulty in the path of his adventure; "pray who may the Three Grey Women be? I never heard of them before."

"They are three very strange old ladies," said Quicksilver, laughing. "They have but one eye among them, and only one tooth. Moreover, you must find them out by starlight, or in the dusk of the evening; for they never show themselves by the light either of the sun or moon."

"But," said Perseus, "why should I waste my time with these Three Grey Women? Would it not be better to set out at once in search of the terrible Gorgons?"

"No, no," answered his friend. "There are other things to be done, before you can find your way to the Gorgons. There is nothing for it but to hunt up these old ladies; and when we meet them, you may be sure that the Gorgons are not a great way off. Come, let us be stirring!"

Perseus, by this time, felt so much confidence in his companion's sagacity, that he made no more objections, and professed himself ready to begin the adventure immediately. They accordingly set out, and walked at a pretty brisk pace; so brisk, indeed, that Perseus found it rather difficult to keep up with his nimble friend Quicksilver. To say the truth, he had a singular idea that Quicksilver was furnished with a pair of winged shoes, which, of course, helped him along marvellously. And then, too, when Perseus looked sideways at him, out of the corner of his eye, he seemed to see wings on the side of his head; although, if he turned a full gaze, there were no such things to be perceived, but only an odd kind of cap. But, at all events, the twisted staff was evidently a great convenience to Quicksilver, and enabled him to proceed so fast, that Perseus, though a remarkably active young man, began to be out of breath.

"Here!" cried Quicksilver, at last—for he knew well enough, rogue that he was, how hard Perseus found it to keep pace with him—"take you the staff, for you need it a great deal more than I. Are there no better walkers than yourself in the island of Seriphus?"

"I could walk pretty well," said Perseus, glancing slyly at his companion's feet, "if I had only a pair of winged shoes."

"We must see about getting you a pair," answered Quicksilver.

But the staff helped Perseus along so bravely, that he no longer felt the slightest weariness. In fact, the stick seemed to be alive in his hand, and to lend some of its life to Perseus. He and Quicksilver now walked onward at their ease, talking very sociably together; and Quicksilver told so many pleasant stories about his former adventures, and how well his wits had served him on various occasions, that Perseus began to think him a very wonderful person. He evidently knew the world; and nobody is so charming to a young man as a friend who has that kind of knowledge. Perseus listened the more eagerly, in the hope of brightening his own wits by what he heard.

At last, he happened to recollect that Quicksilver had spoken of a sister, who was to lend her assistance in the adventure which they were now bound upon.

"Where is she?" he inquired. "Shall we not meet her soon?"

"All at the proper time," said his companion. "But this sister of mine, you must understand, is quite a different sort of person from myself. She is very grave and prudent, seldom smiles, never laughs, and makes it a rule not to utter a word unless she has something particularly profound to say. Neither will she listen to any but the wisest conversation."

"Dear me!" ejaculated Perseus; "I shall be afraid to say a syllable."

"She is a very accomplished person, I assure you," continued Quicksilver, "and has all the arts and sciences at her fingers' ends. In short, she is so immoderately wise, that many people call her wisdom personified. But to tell you the truth, she has hardly vivacity enough for my taste; and I think you would scarcely find her so pleasant a travelling companion as myself. She has her good points, nevertheless; and you will find the benefit of them, in your encounter with the Gorgons."

By this time it had grown quite dusk. They were now come to a very wild and desert place, overgrown with shaggy bushes, and so silent and solitary that nobody seemed ever to have dwelt or journeyed there. All was waste and desolate in the grey twilight, which grew every moment more obscure. Perseus looked about him rather disconsolately, and asked Quicksilver whether they had a great deal further to go.

"Hist! hist!" whispered his companion. "Make no noise! This is just the time and place to meet the Three Grey Women. Be careful that they do not see you before you see them; for, though they have but a single eye among the three, it is as sharp-sighted as half-a-dozen common eyes."

"But what must I do," asked Perseus, "when we meet them?"

Quicksilver explained to Perseus how the Three Grey Women managed with their one eye. They were in the habit, it seemed, of changing it from one to another, as if it had been a pair of spectacles, or—which would have suited them better—a quizzing glass. When one of the three had kept the eye a certain time, she took it out of the socket and passed it to one of her sisters, whose turn it might happen to be, and who immediately clapped it into her own head, and enjoyed a peep at the visible world. Thus it will easily be understood that only one of the Three Gray Women could see, while the other two were in utter darkness; and, moreover, at the instant when the eye was passing from hand to hand, neither of the poor old ladies was able to see a wink. I have heard of a great many strange things, in my day, and have witnessed not a few; but none, it seems to me, that can compare with the oddity of these Three Grey Women, all peeping through a single eye.

So thought Perseus likewise, and was so astonished that he almost fancied his companion was joking with him, and that there were no such old women in the world.

"You will soon find out whether I tell the truth or no," observed Quicksilver. "Hark! hush! hist! hist! There they come now!"

Perseus looked earnestly through the dusk of the evening, and there, sure enough, at no great distance off, he descried the Three Grey Women. The light being so faint, he could not well make out what sort of figures they were—only he discovered that they had long grey hair; and, as they came nearer, he saw that two of them had but the empty socket of an eye in the middle of their foreheads. But, in the middle of the third sister's forehead, there was a very large, bright and piercing eye, which sparkled like a great diamond in a ring; and so penetrating did it seem to be, that Perseus could not help thinking it must possess the gift of seeing in the darkest midnight just as perfectly as at noonday. The sight of three persons' eyes was melted and collected into that single one.

Thus the three old dames got along about as comfortably, upon the whole, as if they could all see at once. She who chanced to have the eye in her forehead led the other two by the hands, peeping sharply about her, all the while; insomuch that Perseus dreaded lest she should see right through the thick clump of bushes behind which he and Quicksilver had hidden themselves. My stars! it was positively terrible to be within reach of so very sharp an eye!

But, before they reached the clump of bushes, one of the Three Grey Women spoke,—

"Sister! Sister Scarecrow!" cried she, "you have had the eye long enough. It is my turn now!"

"Let me keep it a moment longer, Sister Nightmare," answered Scarecrow. "I thought I had a glimpse of something behind that thick bush."

"Well, and what of that?" retorted Nightmare, peevishly. "Can't I see into a thick bush as easily as yourself? The eye is mine, as well as yours; and I know the use of it as well as you, or may be a little better. I insist upon taking a peep immediately!"

But here the third sister, whose name was Shakejoint, began to complain, and said it was her turn to have the eye, and that Scarecrow and Nightmare wanted to keep it all to themselves. To end the dispute, old Dame Scarecrow took the eye out of her forehead, and held it forth in her hand.

"Take it, one of you," cried she, "and quit this foolish quarrelling. For my part, I shall be glad of a little thick darkness. Take it quickly, however, or I must clap it into my own head again!"

Accordingly, both Nightmare and Shakejoint put out their hands, groping eagerly to snatch the eye out of the hand of Scarecrow. But, being both alike blind, they could not easily find where Scarecrow's hand was; and Scarecrow, being now just as much in the dark as Shakejoint and Nightmare, could not at once meet either of their hands, in order to put the eye into it. Thus (as you will see with half an eye, my wise little auditors), these good old dames had fallen into a strange perplexity. For, though the eye shone and glistened like a star, as Scarecrow held it out, yet the Grey Women caught not the least glimpse of its light, and were all three in utter darkness, from too impatient a desire to see.

Quicksilver was so much tickled at beholding Shakejoint and Nightmare both groping for the eye, and each finding fault with Scarecrow and one another, that he could scarcely help laughing aloud.

"Now is your time!" he whispered to Perseus. "Quick, quick, before they can clap the eye into either of their heads. Rush out upon the old ladies, and snatch it from Scarecrow's hand!"

In an instant, while the Three Grey Women were still scolding each other, Perseus leaped from behind the clump of bushes, and made himself master of the prize. The marvellous eye, as he held it in his hand, shone very brightly, and seemed to look up into his face with a knowing air, and an expression as if it would have winked, had it been provided with a pair of eyelids for that purpose. But the Grey Women knew nothing of what had happened; and, each supposing that one of her sisters was in possession of the eye, they began their quarrel anew. At last, as Perseus did not wish to put these respectable dames to greater inconvenience than was really necessary, he thought it right to explain the matter.

"My good ladies," said he, "pray do not be angry with one another. If anybody is at fault, it is myself; for I have the honour to hold your very brilliant and excellent eye in my own hand!"

"You! you have our eye! And who are you then?" screamed the Three Grey Women, all in a breath; for they were terribly frightened, of course, at hearing a strange voice, and discovering that their eyesight had gone into the hands of they could not guess whom. "O! what shall we do, sisters? what shall we do? We are all in the dark! Give us our eye! Give us our one, precious, solitary eye! You have two of your own! Give us our eye!"

"Tell them," whispered Quicksilver to Perseus, "that they shall have back the eye as soon as they direct you where to find the Nymphs who have the flying slippers, the magic wallet, and the helmet of darkness."

"My dear, good admirable old ladies," said Perseus, addressing the Grey Women, "there is no occasion for putting yourselves into such a fright. I am by no means a bad young man. You shall have back your eye, safe and sound, and as bright as ever, the moment you tell me where to find the Nymphs."

"The Nymphs! Goodness me, sisters! what Nymphs does he mean?" screamed Scarecrow. "There are a great many Nymphs, people say; some that go a-hunting in the woods, and some that live inside of trees, and some that have a comfortable home in fountains of water. We know nothing at all about them. We are three unfortunate old souls, that go wandering about in the dusk, and never had but one eye amongst us, and that one you have stolen away. O, give it back, good stranger!—whoever you are, give it back!"

All this while, the Three Grey Women were groping with their outstretched hands, and trying their utmost to get hold of Perseus. But he took good care to keep out of their reach.

"My respectable dames," said he—for his mother had taught him always to use the greatest civility—"I hold your eye fast in my hand, and shall keep it safely for you, until you please to tell me where to find these Nymphs. The Nymphs, I mean, who keep the enchanted wallet, the flying slippers and the—what is it?—the helmet of invisibility."

"Mercy on us, sisters! what is the young man talking about?" exclaimed Scarecrow, Nightmare, and Shakejoint one to another, with great appearance of astonishment. "A pair of flying slippers, quoth he! His heels would quickly fly higher than his head, if he were silly enough to put them on. And a helmet of invisibility! How could a helmet make him invisible, unless it were big enough for him to hide under it? And an enchanted wallet! What sort of a contrivance may that be, I wonder? No, no, good stranger! we can tell you nothing of these marvellous things. You have two eyes of your own, and we but a single one amongst us three. You can find out such wonders better than three blind old creatures, like us."

Perseus, hearing them talk in this way, began really to think that the Grey Women knew nothing of the matter; and, as it grieved him to have put them to so much trouble, he was just on the point of restoring their eye, and asking pardon for his rudeness in snatching it away. But Quicksilver caught his hand.

"Don't let them make a fool of you!" said he. "These Three Grey Women are the only persons in the world that can tell you where to find the Nymphs; and, unless you get that information, you will never succeed in cutting off the head of Medusa with the snaky locks. Keep fast hold of the eye, and all will go well."

As it turned out, Quicksilver was in the right. There are but few things that people prize so much as they do their eyesight; and the Grey Women valued their single eye as highly as if it had been half-a-dozen, which was the number they ought to have had. Finding that there was no other way of recovering it, they at last told Perseus what he wanted to know. No sooner had they done so, than he immediately, and with the utmost respect, clapped the eye into the vacant socket of one of their foreheads, thanked them for their kindness, and bade them farewell. Before the young man was out of hearing, however, they had got into a new dispute, because he happened to have given the eye to Scarecrow, who had already taken her turn of it when their trouble with Perseus commenced.

It is greatly to be feared that the Three Grey Women were very much in the habit of disturbing their mutual harmony by bickerings of this sort; whch was the more pity, as they could not conveniently do without one another, and were evidently intended to be inseparable companions. As a general rule, I would advise all people, whether sisters or brothers, old or young, who chance to have but one eye amongst them, to cultivate forebearance, and not all insist upon peeping through it at once.

Quicksilver and Perseus, in the meantime, were making the best of their way in quest of the Nymphs. The old dames had given them such particular directions, that they were not long in finding them out. They proved to be very different persons from Nightmare, Shakejoint, and Scarecrow; for, instead of being old, they were young and beautiful; and instead of one eye amongst the sisterhood, each Nymph had two exceedingly bright eyes of her own, with which she looked very kindly at Perseus. They seemed to be acquainted with Quicksilver; and when he told them the adventure which Perseus had undertaken, they made no difficulty about giving him the valuable articles that were in their custody. In the first place, they brought out what appeared to be a small purse, made of deer-skin, and curiously embroidered, and bade him be sure and keep it safe. This was the magic wallet. The Nymphs next produced a pair of shoes, or slippers, with a nice little pair of wings at the heel of each.

"Put them on, Perseus," said Quicksilver. "You will find yourself as light-heeled as you can desire for the remainder of our journey."

So Perseus proceeded to put one of the slippers on, while he laid the other on the ground by his side. Unexpectedly, however, this other slipper spread its wings, fluttered up off the ground, and would probably have flown away, if Quicksilver had not made a leap, and luckily caught it in the air.

"Be more careful," said he, as he gave it back to Perseus. "It would frighten the birds, up aloft, if they should see a flying slipper amongst them."

When Perseus had got on both of these wonderful slippers, he was altogether too buoyant to tread on earth. Making a step or two, lo, and behold! upward he popped into the air, high above the heads of Quicksilver and the Nymphs, and found it very difficult to clamber down again. Winged slippers, and all such high-flying contrivances, are seldom quite easy to manage until one grows a little accustomed to them. Quicksilver laughed at his companion's involuntary activity, and told him that he must not be in so desperate a hurry, must wait for the invisible helmet.

The good-natured Nymphs had the helmet, with its dark tuft of waving plumes, all in readiness to put upon his head. And now there happened about as wonderful an incident as anything that I have yet told you. The instant before the helmet was put on, there stood Perseus, a beautiful young man, wth golden ringlets and rosy cheeks, the crooked sword by his side, and the brightly-polished shield upon his arm—a figure that seemed all made up of courage, sprightliness, and glorious light. But when the helmet had descended over his white brow, there was no longer any Perseus to be seen! Nothing but empty air! Even the helmet, that covered him with its invisibility, had vanished!

"Where are you, Perseus?" asked Quicksilver.

"Why, here, to be sure!" ansered Perseus, very quietly, although his voice seemed to come out of the transparent atmosphere. "Just where I was a moment ago. Don't you see me?"

"No, indeed!" answered his friend. "You are hidden under the helmet. But, if I cannot see you, neither can the Gorgons. Follow me, therefore, and we will try your dexterity in using the winged slippers."

With these words, Quicksilver's cap spread its wings, as if his head were about to fly away from his shoulders; but his whole figure rose lightly into the air, and Perseus followed. By the time they had ascended a few hundred feet, the young man began to feel what a delightful thing it was to leave the dull earth so far beneath him, and to be able to flit about like a bird.

It was now deep night. Perseus looked upward, and saw the round, bright, silvery moon, and thought that he should desire nothing better than to soar up thither, and spend his life there. Then he looked downwards again, and saw the earth, with its seas, and lakes, and the silver courses of its rivers, and its snowy mountain-peaks, and the breadth of its fields, and the dark cluster of its woods, and its cities of white marble; and, with the moonshine sleeping over the whole scene, it was as beautiful as the moon or any star could be. And, among other objects, he saw the island of Seriphus, where his dear mother was. Sometimes, he and Quicksilver approached a cloud, that, at a distance, looked as if it were made of fleecy silver; although, when they plunged into it, they found themselves chilled and moistened with grey mist. So swift was their flight, however, that in an instant, they emerged from the cloud into the moonlight again. Once, a high-soaring eagle flew right against the invisible Perseus. The bravest sights were the meteors, that gleamed suddenly out, as if a bonfire had been kindled in the sky, and made the moonshine pale for as much as a hundred miles around them.

As the two companions flew onward, Perseus fancied that he could hear the rustle of a garment close by his side; and it was on the side opposite to the one where he beheld Quicksilver, yet only Quicksilver was visible.

"Whose garment is this," inquired Perseus, "that keeps rustling close beside me, in the breeze."

"O, it is my sister's!" answered Quicksilver. "She is coming along with us, as I told you she would. We could do nothing without the help of my sister. You have no idea how wise she is. She has such eyes, too! Why, she can see you, at this moment, just as distinctly as if you were not invisible; and I'll venture to say, she will be the first to discover the Gorgons."

By this time, in their swift voyage through the air, they had come within sight of the great ocean, and were soon flying over it. Far beneath them, the waves tossed themselves tumultuously in mid-sea, or rolled a white surf-line upon the long beaches, or foamed against the rocky cliffs, with a roar that was thunderous in the lower world; although it became a gentle murmur, like the voice of a baby half asleep, before it reached the ears of Perseus. Just then a voice spoke in the air close by him. It seemed to be a woman's voice, and was melodious, though not exactly what might be called sweet, but grave and mild.

"Perseus," said the voice, "there are the Gorgons."

"Where?" exclaimed Perseus. "I cannot see them."

"On the shore of that island beneath you," replied the voice. "A pebble, dropped from your hand, would strike in the midst of them."

"I told you she would be the first to discover them," said Quicksilver to Perseus. "And there they are!"

Straight downward, two or three thousand feet below him, Perseus perceived a small island, with the sea breaking into white foam all around its rocky shore, except on one side, where there was a beach of snowy sand. He descended toward it, and, looking earnestly at a cluster or heap of brightness, at the foot of a precipice of black rocks, behold, there were the terrible Gorgons! They lay fast asleep, soothed by the thunder of the sea; for it required a tumult that would have deafened everybody else to lull such fierce creatures into slumber. The moonlight glistened on their steely scales, and on their golden wings, which drooped idly over the sand. Their brazen claws, horrible to look at, were thrust out, and clutched the wave-beaten fragments of rock, while the sleeping Gorgons dreamed of tearing some poor mortal all to pieces. The snakes, that served them instead of hair, seemed likewise to be asleep; although, now and then, one would writhe, and lift its head, and thrust out its forked tongue, emitting a drowsy hiss, and then let itself subside among its sister snakes.

The Gorgons were more like an awful, gigantic kind of insect— immense, golden-winged beetles, or dragon-flies, or things of that sort —at once ugly and beautiful—than like anything else; only that they were a thousand and a million times as big. And, with all this, there was something partly human about them, too. Luckily for Perseus, their faces were completely hidden from him by the posture in which they lay; for, had he but looked one instant at them, he would have fallen heavily out of the air, an image of senseless stone.

"Now," whispered Quicksilver, as he hovered by the side of Perseus, "now is your time to do the deed! Be quick; for, if one of the Gorgons should awake, you are too late!"

"Which shall I strike at?" asked Perseus, drawing his sword and descending a little lower. "They all three look alike. All three have snaky locks. Which of the three is Medusa?"

It must be understood that Medusa was the only one of these dragon-monsters whose head Perseus could possibly cut off. As for the other two, let him have the sharpest sword that ever was forged, and he might have hacked away by the hour together, without doing them the least harm.

"Be cautious," said the calm voice which had before spoken to him. "One of the Gorgons is stirring in her sleep, and is just about to turn over. That is Medusa. Do not look at her! The sight would turn you to stone! Look at the reflection of her face and figure in the bright mirror of your shield."

Perseus now understood Quicksilver's motive for so earnestly exhorting him to polish his shield. In its surface he could safely look at the reflection of the Gorgon's face. And there it was—that terrible countenance—mirrored in the brightness of the shield, with the moonlight falling over it, and displaying all its horror. The snakes, whose venomous nature could not altogether sleep, kept twisting themselves over the forehead. It was the fiercest and most horrible face that ever was seen or imagined, and yet with a strange, fearful, and savage kind of beauty in it. The eyes were closed, and the Gorgon was still in a deep slumber; but there was an unquiet expression disturbing her features, as if the monster was troubled with an ugly dream. She gnashed her white tusks, and dug into the sand with her brazen claws.

The snakes, too, seemed to feel Medusa's dream, and to be made more restless by it. They twisted themselves into tumultuous knots, writhed fiercely, and uplifted a hundred hissing heads, without opening their eyes.

"Now, now!" whispered Quicksilver, who was growing impatient. "Make a dash at the monster!"

"But be calm," said the grave, melodious voice at the young man's side. "Look in your shield, as you fly downward, and take care that you do not miss your first stroke."

Perseus flew cautiously downward, still keeping his eyes on Medusa's face, as reflected in his shield. The nearer he came, the more terrible did the snaky visage and metallic body of the monster grow. At last, when he found himself hovering over her within arm's length, Perseus uplifted his sword, while at the same instant each separate snake upon the Gorgon's head stretched threateningly upward, and Medusa unclosed her eyes. But she awoke too late. The sword was sharp; the stroke fell like a lightning-flash; and the head of the wicked Medusa tumbled from her body!

"Admirably done!" cried Quicksilver. "Make haste, and clap the head into your magic wallet."

To the astonishment of Perseus, the small, embroidered wallet, which he had hung about his neck, and which had hitherto been no bigger than a purse, grew all at once large enough to contain Medusa's head. As quick as thought, he snatched it up, with the snakes still writhing upon it, and thrust it in.

"Your task is done," said the calm voice. "Now fly; for the other Gorgons will do their utmost to take vengeance for Medusa's death."

It was, indeed, necessary to take flight; for Perseus had not done the deed so quietly, but that the clash of his sword, and the hissing of the snakes, and the thump of Medusa's head as it tumbled upon the sea-beaten sand, awoke the other two monsters. There they sat, for an instant, sleepily rubbing their eyes with their brazen fingers, while all the snakes on their heads reared themselves on end with surprise, and with venomous malice against they knew not what. But when the Gorgons saw the scaly carcass of Medusa, headless, and her golden wings all ruffled, and half out on the sand, it was really awful to hear what yells and screeches they set up. And then the snakes! They sent forth a hundred-fold hiss with one consent, and Medusa's snakes answered them out of the magic wallet.

No sooner were the Gorgons broad awake, than they hurtled upward into the air, brandishing their brass talons, gnashing their horrible tusks, and flapping their huge wings so wildly, that some of the golden feathers were shaken out, and floated down upon the shore. And there, perhaps, those very feathers lie scattered till this day. Up rose the Gorgons, as I tell you, staring horribly about, in hopes of turning somebody to stone. Had Perseus looked them in the face, or had he fallen into their clutches, his poor mother would never have kissed her boy again! But he took good care to turn his eyes another way; and, as he wore the helmet of invisibility, the Gorgons knew not in what direction to follow him; nor did he fail to make the best use of the winged slippers, by soaring upward a mile or so. At that height, when the screams of those abominable creatures sounded faintly beneath him, he made a straight course for the island of Seriphus, in order to carry Medusa's head to King Polydectes.

I have no time to tell you of several marvellous things that befell Perseus on his way homeward; such as his killing a hideous sea-monster, just as it was on the point of devouring a beautiful maiden; nor how he changed an enormous giant into a mountain of stone, merely by show-ing him the head of the Gorgon. If you doubt this latter story, you may make a voyage to Africa, some day or other, and see the very mountain, which is still known by the ancient giant's name.

Finally, our brave Perseus arrived at the island, where he expected to see his dear mother. But, during his absence, the wicked king had treated Danaë so very ill, that she was compelled to make her escape, and had taken refuge in a temple, where some good old priests were extremely kind to her. These praiseworthy priests, and the kind-hearted fisherman, who had first shown hospitality to Danaë and little Perseus when he found them afloat in the chest, seem to have been the only persons on the island who cared about doing right. All the rest of the people, as well as King Polydectes himself, were remarkably ill-behaved, and deserved no better destiny than that which was now to happen.

Not finding his mother at home, Perseus went straight to the palace, and was immediately ushered into the presence of the king. Polydectes was by no means rejoiced to see him; for he had felt almost certain, in his own evil mind, that the Gorgons would have torn the poor young man to pieces, and have eaten him up out of the way. However, seeing him safely returned, he put the best face he could upon the matter, and asked Perseus how he had succeeded.

"Have you performed your promise?" inquired he. "Have you brought me the head of Medusa, with the snaky locks? If not, young man, it will cost you dear; for I must have a bridal present for the beautiful Princess Hippodamia, and there is nothing else that she would admire so much."

"Yes, please your Majesty," answered Perseus, in a quiet way, as if it were no very wonderful deed for such a young man as he to perform. "I have brought you the Gorgon's head, snaky locks and all!"

"Indeed! Pray let me see it," quoth King Polydectes. "It must be a very curious spectacle, if all that travellers tell about it be true!"

"Your Majesty is right," replied Perseus. "It is really an object that will be pretty certain to fix the regards of all who look at it. And, if your Majesty think fit, I would suggest that a holiday be proclaimed, and that all your Majesty's subjects be summoned to behold this wonderful curiosity. Few of them I imagine, have seen a Gorgon's head before, and perhaps never may again!"

The king well knew that his subjects were an idle set of reprobates, and very fond of sight-seeing, as idle persons usually are. So he took the young man's advice, and sent out heralds and messengers in all directions, to blow the trumpet at the street-corners, and in the market-places, and wherever two roads met, and summon everybody to court. Thither, accordingly, came a great multitude of good-for-nothing vaga-bonds, all of whom, out of pure love of mischief, would have been glad if Perseus had met with some ill-hap in his encounter with the Gorgons. If there were any better people in the island (as I really hope there may have been, although the story tells nothing about any such), they staid quietly at home, minding their own business, and taking care of their little children. Most of the inhabitants, at all events, ran as fast as they could to the palace, and shoved, and pushed, and elbowed one another, in their eagerness to get near a balcony, on which Perseus showed himself, holding the embroidered wallet in his hand.

On a platform, within full view of the balcony, sat the mighty King Polydectes, amid his evil counsellors, and with his flattering courtiers in a semi-circle round about him. Monarch, counsellors, courtiers, and subjects, all gazed eagerly towards Perseus.

"Show us the head! Show us the head!" shouted the people; and there was a fierceness in their cry, as if they would tear Perseus to pieces unless he should satisfy them with what he had to show. "Show us the head of Medusa with the snaky locks!"

A feeling of sorrow and pity came over the youthful Perseus.

"O King Polydectes," cried he, "and ye, many people, I am very loth to show you the Gorgon's head!"

"Ah, the villain and coward!" yelled the people, more fiercely than before. "He is making game of us! He has no Gorgon's head! Show us the head if you have it, or we will take your own head for a football!"

The evil counsellors whispered bad advice in the king's ear; the courtiers murmured with one consent that Perseus had shown disrespect to their royal lord and master; and the great King Polydectes himself waved his hand, and ordered him, with the stern, deep voice of authority, on his peril, to produce the head.

"Show me the Gorgon's head, or I will cut off your own!"

And Perseus sighed.

"This instant," repeated Polydectes, "or you die!"

"Behold it, then!" cried Perseus, in a voice like the blast of a trumpet.

And, suddenly holding up the head, not an eyelid had time to wink before the wicked King Polydectes, his evil counsellors, and all his fierce subjects, were no longer anything but the mere images of a monarch and his people. They were all fixed, forever, in the look and attitude of that moment! At the first glimpse of the terrible head of Medusa, they whitened into marble! And Perseus thrust the head back into his wallet, and went to tell his dear mother that she need no longer be afraid of the wicked King Polydectes.

The Wandering Moon

JAMES REEVES

≈ ≈ ≈

Age after age and all alone,
  She turns through endless space,
Showing the watchers on the earth
  Her round and rocky face.
Enchantment comes upon all hearts
  That feel her lonely grace.

Mount Newton is the highest peak
  Upon the wandering moon,
And there perhaps the witches dance
  To some fantastic tune,
And in the half-light cold and grey
  Their incantations croon.

And there perhaps mad creatures come
  To play at hide-and-seek
With howling apes and blundering bears
  And bats that swoop and squeak.
I cannot see what nameless things
  Go on at Newton Peak.

I cannot tell what vessels move
  Across the Nubian Sea,
Nor whether any bird alights
  On any stony tree.
A quarter of a million miles
  Divide the moon and me.

A quarter of a million miles—
  It is a fearsome way,

But ah! if we could only fly
  On some auspicious day
And land at last on Newton's Peak,
  Ah then, what games we'd play!

What songs we'd sing on Newton Peak,
  On what wild journeys go
By frozen fen or burning waste,
  Or where the moon-flowers grow,
And countless strange and fearful things—
  If only we could know!

Adventures of Odysseus

PADRAIC COLUM

≈ ≈ ≈ *After the fall of Troy the victorious Greeks took to their ships and sailed back to the various kingdoms whence they had come. Odysseus, one of the greatest of the Greek heroes, encountered many adventures before he was shipwrecked on the land of Alcinous. In return for King Alcinous' hospitality he described some of his adventures.*

Then Odysseus spoke before the company and said, "O Alcinous, famous King, it is good to listen to a minstrel such as Demodocus is. And as for me, I know of no greater delight than when men feast together with open hearts, when tables are plentifully spread, when wine-bearers pour out good wine into cups, and when a minstrel sings to them noble songs. This seems to me to be happiness indeed. But thou hast asked me to speak of my wanderings and my toils. Ah, where can I begin that tale? For the gods have given me more woes than a man can speak of!

"But first of all I will declare to you my name and my country. I am Odysseus, son of Laertes, and my land is Ithaka, an island around which many islands lie. Ithaka is a rugged isle, but a good nurse for hardy men, and I, for one, have found that there is no place fairer than a man's own land. But now I will tell thee, King, and tell the Princes and Captains and Councillors of the Phæacians, the tale of my wanderings.

"The wind bore my ships from the coast of Troy, and with our white sails hoisted we came to the cape that is called Malea. Now if we had been able to double this cape we should soon have come to our own country, all unhurt. But the north wind came and swept us from our course and drove us wandering past Cythera.

"Then for nine days we were borne onward by terrible winds, and away from all known lands. On the tenth day we came to a strange country. Many of my men landed there. The people of that land were harmless and friendly, but the land itself was most dangerous. For there grew there the honey-sweet fruit of the lotus that makes all men forgetful of their past and neglectful of their future. And those of my men who ate the lotus that the dwellers of that land offered them became forgetful of their country and of the way before them. They wanted to abide forever in the land of the lotus. They wept when they thought of all the toils before them and of all they had endured. I led them back to the ships, and I had to place them beneath the benches and leave them in bonds. And I commanded those who ate of the lotus to go at once aboard the ships. Then, when I had got all my men upon the ships, we made haste to sail away.

"Later we came to the land of the Cyclôpes, a giant people. There is a waste island outside the harbor of their land, and on it there is a well of bright water that has poplars growing round it. We came to that empty island, and we beached our ships and took down our sails.

"As soon as the dawn came we went through the empty island, starting the wild goats that were there in flocks, and shooting them with our arrows. We killed so many wild goats there that we had nine for each ship. Afterwards we looked across to the land of the Cyclôpes, and we heard the sound of voices and saw the smoke of fires and heard the bleating of flocks of sheep and goats.

"I called my companions together and I said, 'It would be well for some of us to go to that other island. With my own ship and with the company that is on it I shall go there. The rest of you abide here. I will find out what manner of men live there, and whether they will treat us kindly and give us gifts that are due to strangers—gifts of provisions for our voyage.'

"We embarked and we came to the land. There was a cave near the sea, and round the cave there were mighty flocks of sheep and goats. I took twelve men with me and I left the rest to guard the ship. We went into the cave and found no man there. There were baskets filled with cheeses, and vessels of whey, and pails and bowls of milk. My men wanted me to take some of the cheeses and drive off some of the lambs and kids and come away. But this I would not do, for I would rather that he who owned the stores would give us of his own free will the offerings that were due to strangers.

"While we were in the cave, he whose dwelling it was, returned to it. He carried on his shoulder a great pile of wood for his fire. Never in our lives did we see a creature so frightful as this Cyclops was. He was a giant in size, and, what made him terrible to behold, he had but one eye, and that single eye was in his forehead. He cast down on the ground a pile of wood that he carried, making such a din that we fled in terror into the corners and recesses of the cave. Next he drove his flocks into the cave and began to milk his ewes and goats. And when he had the flocks within, he took up a stone that not all our strengths could move and set it as a door to the mouth of the cave.

"The Cyclops kindled his fire, and when it blazed up he saw us in the corners and recesses. He spoke to us. We knew not what he said, but our hearts were shaken with terror at the sound of his deep voice.

"I spoke to him saying that we were Agamemnon's men on our way home from the taking of Priam's City, and I begged him to deal with us kindly, for the sake of Zeus who is ever in the company of strangers and suppliants. But he answered me saying, 'We Cyclôpes pay no heed to Zeus, nor to any of thy gods. In our strength and our power we deem that we are mightier than they. I will not spare thee, neither will I give thee aught for the sake of Zeus, but only as my own spirit bids me. And first I would have thee tell me how you came to our land.'

"I knew it would be better not to let the Cyclops know that my ship and my companions were at the harbor of the island. Therefore I spoke to him guilefully, telling him that my ship had been broken on the rocks, and that I and the men with me were the only ones who had escaped utter doom.

"I begged again that he would deal with us as just men deal with strangers and suppliants, but he, without saying a word, laid hands upon two of my men, and swinging them by the legs, dashed their brains out on the earth. He cut them to pieces and ate them before our very eyes. We wept and we prayed to Zeus as we witnessed a deed so terrible.

"Next the Cyclops stretched himself amongst his sheep and went to sleep by the fire. Then I debated whether I should take my sharp sword in my hand, and feeling where his heart was, stab him there. But second thoughts held me back from doing this. I might be able to kill him as he slept, but not even with my companions could I roll away the great stone that closed the mouth of the cave.

"Dawn came, and the Cyclops wakened, kindled his fire and milked his flocks. Then he seized two others of my men and made ready for his midday meal. And now he rolled away the great stone and drove his flocks out of the cave.

"I had pondered on a way of escape, and I had thought of something that might be done to baffle the Cyclops. I had with me a great skin of sweet wine, and I thought that if I could make him drunken with wine I and my companions might be a match for him. But there were other preparations to be made first. On the floor of the cave there was a great beam of olive wood which the Cyclops had cut to make a club when the wood should be seasoned. It was yet green. I and my companions went and cut off a fathom's length of the wood, and sharpened it to a point and took it to the fire and hardened it in the glow. Then I hid the beam in a recess of the cave.

"The Cyclops came back in the evening, and opening up the cave drove in his flocks. Then he closed the cave again with the stone and went and milked his ewes and his goats. Again he seized two of my companions. I went to the terrible creature with a bowl of wine in my hands. He took it and drank it and cried out, 'Give me another bowl of this, and tell me thy name that I may give thee gifts for bringing me this honey-tasting drink.'

"Again I spoke to him guilefully and said, 'Noman is my name. Noman my father and my mother call me.'

" 'Give me more of the drink, Noman,' he shouted. 'And the gift that I shall give to thee is that I shall make thee the last of thy fellows to be eaten.'

"I gave him wine again, and when he had taken the third bowl he sank backwards with his face upturned, and sleep came upon him. Then I, with four companions, took that beam of olive wood, now made into a hard and pointed stake, and thrust it into the ashes of the fire. When the pointed end began to glow we drew it out of the flame. Then I and my companions laid hold on the great stake and, dashing at the Cyclops, thrust it into his eye. He raised a terrible cry that made the rocks ring and we dashed away into the recesses of the cave.

"His cries brought other Cyclôpes to the mouth of the cave, and they, naming him as Polyphemus, called out and asked him what ailed him to cry. 'Noman,' he shrieked out, 'Noman is slaying me by guile.' They answered him saying, 'If no man is slaying thee, there is nothing we can do for thee, Polyphemus. What ails thee has been sent to thee by the gods.' Saying this, they went away from the mouth of the cave without attempting to move away the stone.

"Polyphemus then, groaning with pain, rolled away the stone and sat before the mouth of the cave with his hands outstretched, thinking that he would catch us as we dashed out. I showed my companions how we might pass by him. I laid hands on certain rams of the flock and I lashed three of them together with supple rods. Then on the middle ram I put a man of my company. Thus every three rams carried a man. As soon as the dawn had come the rams hastened out to the pasture, and, as they passed, Polyphemus laid hands on the first and the third of each three that went by. They passed out and Polyphemus did not guess that a ram that he did not touch carried out a man.

"For myself, I took a ram that was the strongest and fleeciest of the whole flock and I placed myself under him, clinging to the wool of his belly. As this ram, the best of all his flock, went by, Polyphemus, laying his hands upon him, said, 'Would that you, the best of my flock, were endowed with speech, so that you might tell me where Noman, who has blinded me, has hidden himself.' The ram went by him, and when he had gone a little way from the cave I loosed myself from him and went and set my companions free.

"We gathered together many of Polyphemus' sheep and we drove them down to our ship. The men we had left behind would have wept when they heard what had happened to six of their companions. But I bade them take on board the sheep we had brought and pull the ship away from that land. Then when we had drawn a certain distance from the shore I could not forbear to shout my taunts into the cave of Polyphemus. 'Cyclops,' I cried, 'you thought that you had the company of a fool and a weakling to eat. But you have been worsted by me, and your evil deeds have been punished.'

"So I shouted, and Polyphemus came to the mouth of the cave with great anger in his heart. He took up rocks and cast them at the ship and they fell before the prow. The men bent to the oars and pulled the ship away or it would have been broken by the rocks he cast. And when we were further away I shouted to him:

" 'Cyclops, if any man should ask who it was set his mark upon you, say that he was Odysseus, the son of Laertes.'

"Then I heard Polyphemus cry out, 'I call on Poseidon, the god of the sea, whose son I am, to avenge me upon you, Odysseus. I call upon Poseidon to grant that you, Odysseus, may never come to your home, or if the gods have ordained your return, that you come to it after much toil and suffering, in an evil plight and in a stranger's ship, to find sorrow in your home.'

"So Polyphemus prayed, and, to my evil fortune, Poseidon heard his prayer. But we went on in our ship rejoicing at our escape. We came to the waste island where my other ships were. All the company rejoiced to see us, although they had to mourn for their six companions slain by Polyphemus. We divided amongst the ships the sheep we had taken from Polyphemus' flock and we sacrificed to the gods. At the dawn of the next day we raised the sails on each ship and we sailed away.

"We came to the island where Æolus, the Lord of the Winds, he who can give mariners a good or a bad wind, has his dwelling. With his six sons and his six daughters Æolus lives on a floating island that has all around it a wall of bronze. And when we came to his island, the Lord of the Winds treated us kindly and kept us at his dwelling a month. Now when the time came for us to leave, Æolus did not try to hold us on the island. And to me, when I was going down to the ships, he gave a bag made from the hide of an ox, and in that bag were all the winds that blow. He made the mouth of the bag fast with a silver thong, so that no wind that might drive us from our course would escape. Then he sent the West Wind to blow on our sails that we might reach our own land as quickly as a ship might go.

"For nine days we sailed with the West Wind driving us, and on the tenth day we came in sight of Ithaka, our own land. We saw its coast and the beacon fires upon the coast and the people tending the fires. Then I thought that the curse of the Cyclops was vain and could bring no harm to us. Sleep that I had kept from me for long I let weigh me down, and I no longer kept watch.

"Then even as I slept, the misfortune that I had watched against fell upon me. For now my men spoke together and said, 'There is our native land, and we come back to it after ten years' struggles and toils, with empty hands. Different it is with our lord, Odysseus. He brings gold and silver from Priam's treasure chamber in Troy. And Æolus too has given him a treasure in an oxhide bag. But let us take something out of that bag while he sleeps.'

"So they spoke, and they unloosed the mouth of the bag, and behold! All the winds that were tied in it burst out. Then the winds drove our ship toward the high seas and away from our land. What became of the other ships I know not. I awoke and I found that we were being driven here and there by the winds. I did not know whether I should spring into the sea and so end all my troubles, or whether I should endure this terrible misfortune. I muffled my head in my cloak and lay on the deck of my ship.

"The winds brought us back again to the floating island. We landed and I went to the dwelling of the Lord of the Winds. I sat by the pillars of his threshold and he came out and spoke to me. 'How now, Odysseus?' said he. 'How is it thou hast returned so soon? Did I not give thee a fair wind to take thee to thine own country, and did I not tie up all the winds that might be contrary to thee?'

" 'My evil companions,' I said, 'have been my bane. They have undone all the good that thou didst for me, O King of the Winds. They opened the bag and let all the winds fly out. And now help me, O Lord Æolus, once again.'

"But Æolus said to me, 'Far be it from me to help such a man as thou—a man surely accursed by the gods. Go from my Island, for nothing will I do for thee.' Then I went from his dwelling and took my way down to the ship.

"We sailed away from the Island of Æolus with heavy hearts. Next we came to the Æean Island, where we met with Circe, the Enchantress. For two days, and two nights we were on that island without seeing the sign of habitation. On the third day I saw smoke rising up from some hearth. I spoke to my men, and it seemed good to us that part of our company should go to see were there people there who might help us. We drew lots to find out who should go, and it fell to the lot of Eurylochus to go with part of the company, while I remained with the other part.

"So Eurylochus went with two and twenty men. In the forest glades they came upon a house built of polished stones. All round that house wild beasts roamed—wolves and lions. But these beasts were not fierce. As Eurylochus and his men went toward the house the lions and wolves fawned upon them like house dogs.

"But the men were affrighted and stood round the outer gate of the court. They heard a voice within the house singing, and it seemed to them to be the voice of a woman, singing as she went to and fro before a web she was weaving on a loom. The men shouted, and she who had been singing opened the polished doors and came out of the dwelling. She was very fair to see. As she opened the doors of the house she asked the men to come within and they went into her halls.

"But Eurylochus tarried behind. He watched the woman and he saw her give food to the men. But he saw that she mixed a drug with what she gave them to eat and with the wine she gave them to drink. No sooner had they eaten the food and drunk the wine than she struck them with a wand, and behold! The men turned into swine. Then the woman drove them out of the house and put them in the swinepens and gave them acorns and mast and the fruit of the cornel tree to eat.

"Eurylochus, when he saw these happenings, ran back through the forest and told me all. Then I cast about my shoulder my good sword of bronze, and, bidding Eurylochus stay by the ships, I went through the forest and came to the house of the enchantress. I stood at the outer court and called out. Then Circe the Enchantress flung wide the shining doors, and called me to come within. I entered her dwelling and she brought me a chair and put a footstool under my feet. Then she brought me in a golden cup the wine into which she had cast a harmful drug.

"As she handed me the cup I drew my sword, and sprang at her as one eager to slay her. She shrank back from me and cried out, 'Who art thou who art able to guess at my enchantments? Verily, thou art Odysseus, of whom Hermes told me. Nay, put up thy sword and let us two be friendly to each other. In all things I will treat thee kindly.'

"But I said to her, 'Nay, Circe, you must swear to me first that thou wilt not treat me guilefully.'

"She swore by the gods that she would not treat me guilefully, and I put up my sword. Then the handmaidens of Circe prepared a bath, and I bathed and rubbed myself with olive oil, and Circe gave me a new mantle and doublet. The handmaidens brought out silver tables, and on them set golden baskets with bread and meat in them, and others brought cups of honey-tasting wine. I sat before a silver table but I had no pleasure in the food before me.

"When Circe saw me sitting silent and troubled she said, 'Why, Odysseus, dost thou sit like a speechless man? Dost thou think there is a drug in this food? But I have sworn that I will not treat thee guilefully, and that oath I shall keep.'

"And I said to her, 'O Circe, Enchantress, what man of good heart could take meat and drink while his companions are as swine in swinepens? If thou wouldst have me eat and drink, first let me see my companions in their own forms.'

"Circe, when she heard me say this, went to the swinepen and anointed each of the swine that was there with a charm. As she did, the bristles dropped away and the limbs of the man were seen. My companions became men again, and were even taller and handsomer than they had been before.

"After that we lived on Circe's island in friendship with the enchantress. She did not treat us guilefully again and we feasted in her house for a year.

"But in all of us there was a longing to return to our own land. And my men came to me and craved that I should ask Circe to let us go on our homeward way. She gave us leave to go and she told us of the many dangers we should meet on our voyage."

The Ballad of the Harp-Weaver

EDNA ST. VINCENT MILLAY

"Son," said my mother,
  When I was knee-high,
"You've need of clothes to cover you,
  And not a rag have I.

"There's nothing in the house
  To make a boy breeches,
Nor shears to cut a cloth with
  Nor thread to take stitches.

"There's nothing in the house
  But a loaf-end of rye,
And a harp with a woman's head
  Nobody will buy,"
  And she began to cry.

That was in the early fall.
  When came the late fall,
"Son," she said, "the sight of you
  Makes your mother's blood crawl,—

"Little skinny shoulder-blades
  Sticking through your clothes!
And where you'll get a jacket from
  God above knows.

"It's lucky for me, lad,
  Your daddy's in the ground,
And can't see the way I let
  His son go around!"
  And she made a queer sound.

That was in the late fall.
   When the winter came,
I'd not a pair of breeches
   Nor a shirt to my name.

I couldn't go to school,
   Or out of doors to play,
And all the other little boys
   Passed our way.

"Son," said my mother,
   "Come, climb into my lap,
And I'll chafe your little bones
   While you take a nap."

And, oh, but we were silly,
   For half an hour or more,
Me with my long legs
   Dragging on the floor,

A-rock-rock-rocking
   To a mother-goose rhyme!
Oh, but we were happy
   For half an hour's time!

But there was I, a great boy,
   And what would folks say
To hear my mother singing me
   To sleep all day,
   In such a daft way?

Men say the winter
   Was bad that year;
Fuel was scarce,
   And food was dear.

A wind with a wolf's head
   Howled about our door,
And we burned up the chairs
   And sat upon the floor.

All that was left us
   Was a chair we couldn't break,
And the harp with a woman's head
   Nobody would take,
     For song or pity's sake.

The night before Christmas
   I cried with the cold,
I cried myself to sleep
   Like a two-year-old.

And in the deep night
   I felt my mother rise,
And stare down upon me
   With love in her eyes.

I saw my mother sitting
   On the one good chair,
A light falling on her,
   From I couldn't tell where,

Looking nineteen,
   And not a day older,
And the harp with a woman's head
   Leaned against her shoulder.

Her thin fingers moving
   In the thin, tall strings,
Were weav-weav-weaving
   Wonderful things.

Many bright threads,
   From where I couldn't see,
Were running through the harp-strings
   Rapidly,

And gold threads whistling
   Through my mother's hand.
I saw the web grow,
   And the pattern expand.

She wove a child's jacket,
  And when it was done
She laid it on the floor
  And wove another one.

She wove a red cloak
  So regal to see,
"She's made it for a king's son,"
  I said, "and not for me."
  But I knew it was for me.

She wove a pair of breeches
  Quicker than that!
She wove a pair of boots
  And a little cocked hat.

She wove a pair of mittens,
  She wove a little blouse,
She wove all night
  In the still, cold house.

She sang as she worked,
  And the harp-strings spoke;
Her voice never faltered,
  And the thread never broke.
  And when I awoke,—

There sat my mother
  With the harp against her shoulder,
Looking nineteen
  And not a day older,

A smile about her lips,
  And a light about her head,
And her hands in the harp-strings
  Frozen dead.

And piled up beside her
  And toppling to the skies,
Were the clothes of a king's son,
  Just my size.

King Arthur and the Sable Knight

HOWARD PYLE

≈ ≈ ≈ *Arthur, the noblest and most chivalrous king who ever
ruled in Britain, always strove to protect the weak and to
suppress the wicked. Merlin was a wise magician who helped
and advised King Arthur. A "mall" is a hammer, a "portcullis"
a grilled gate, a "truncheon" the base of a lance of which part
has broken off; a "cantel" is a fragment of armor.*

*How King Arthur Fought With the Sable Knight and How He Was
Sorely Wounded. Likewise How Merlin Brought Him Safe Away From
the Field of Battle.*

So King Arthur and Merlin rode together through the forest for a
considerable while, until they perceived that they must be approaching
nigh to the place where dwelt the Sable Knight whom the King sought
so diligently. For the forest, which had till then been altogether a
wilderness, very deep and mossy, began to show an aspect more thin
and open, as though a dwelling-place of mankind was close at hand.

And, after a little, they beheld before them a violent stream of water,
that rushed through a dark and dismal glen. And, likewise, they perceived that across this stream of water there was a bridge of stone, and
that upon the other side of the bridge there was a smooth and level
lawn of green grass, whereon Knights-contestants might joust very
well. And beyond this lawn they beheld a tall and forbidding castle,
with smooth walls and a straight tower; and this castle was built upon
the rocks so that it appeared to be altogether a part of the stone. So
they wist that this must be the castle whereof the page and Sir Griflet
had spoken.

For, midway upon the bridge, they beheld that there hung a sable
shield and a brass mall exactly as the page and Sir
Griflet had said; and that upon the farther side of the *King Arthur
stream was an apple-tree, amid the leaves of which cometh to the
hung a very great many shields of various devices, ex- castle of the
actly as those two had reported: and they beheld that Sable Knight*

some of those shields were clean and fair, and that some were foul and stained with blood, and that some were smooth and unbroken, and that some were cleft as though by battle of knight with knight. And all those shields were the shields of different knights whom the Sable Knight, who dwelt within the castle, had overthrown in combat with his own hand.

"Splendor of Paradise!" quoth King Arthur, "that must, indeed, be a right valiant knight who, with his own single strength, hath overthrown and cast down so many other knights. For, indeed, Merlin, there must be an hundred shields hanging in yonder tree!"

Unto this Merlin made reply, "And thou, Lord mayst be very happy an thy shield, too, hangeth not there ere the sun goeth down this eventide."

"That," said King Arthur, with a very steadfast countenance, "shall be as God willeth. For, certes, I have a greater mind than ever for to try my power against yonder knight. For, consider, what especial honor would fall to me should I overcome so valiant a warrior as this same Sable Champion appeareth to be, seeing that he hath been victorious over so many other good knights."

Thereupon, having so spoken his mind, King Arthur immediately pushed forward his horse and so, coming upon the bridge, he clearly read that challenge writ in letters of red beneath the shield:

WHOSO SMITETH THIS SHIELD

DOETH SO AT HIS PERIL.

Upon reading these words, the King seized the brazen mall, and smote that shield so violent a blow that the sound thereof *King Arthur* echoed back from the smooth walls of the castle, and *challenges* from the rocks whereon it stood, and from the skirts of *the Sable* the forest around about, as though twelve other shields *Knight* had been struck in those several places.

And in answer to that sound, the portcullis of the castle was immediately let fall, and there issued forth a knight, very huge of frame, and clad all in sable armor. And, likewise, all of his apparel and all the trappings of his horse were entirely of sable, so that he presented a most grim and forbidding aspect. And this Sable Knight came across that level meadow of smooth grass with a very stately and honorable gait; for neither did he ride in haste, nor did he ride slowly, but with great pride and haughtiness of mien, as became a champion who, haply, had never yet been overcome in battle. So, reaching the bridge-head, he drew rein and saluted King Arthur with great dignity, and also right haughtily. "Ha! Sir Knight!" quoth he, "why didst thou, having read those words yonder inscribed, smite upon my shield? Now I do tell thee that, for thy discourtesy, I shall presently take thy shield away from thee, and shall hang it up upon yonder apple-tree where thou beholdest all those other shields to be hanging. Wherefore, either deliver thou thy shield unto me without more ado, or else prepare for to defend with thy person—in the which event thou shalt certainly suffer great pain and discomfort to thy body."

"Gramercy for the choice thou grantest me," said King Arthur. "But as for taking away my shield—I do believe that that shall be as Heaven willeth, and not as thou willest. Know, thou unkind knight, that I have come hither for no other purpose than to do battle with thee and so to endeavor for to redeem with my person all those shields that hang yonder upon that apple-tree. So make thou ready straightway that I may have to do with thee, maybe to thy great disadvantage."

"That will I so," replied the Sable Knight. And thereupon he turned his horse's head and, riding back a certain distance across the level lawn, he took stand in such place as appeared to him to be convenient. And so did King Arthur ride forth also upon that lawn, and take his station as seemed to him to be convenient.

Then each knight dressed his spear and his shield for the encounter, and, having thus made ready for the assault, each shouted to his war-horse and drave his spurs deep into its flank.

Then those two noble steeds rushed forth like lightning, coursing across the ground with such violent speed that the earth trembled and shook beneath them, an it were by cause of an earthquake. So those two knights met fairly in the midst of the centre of the field, crashing together like a thunderbolt. And so violently did they smite the one against the other that the spears burst into splinters, even unto the guard and the truncheon thereof, and the horses of the riders staggered back from the onset, so that only because of the extraordinary address of the knights-rider did they recover from falling before that shock of meeting.

King Arthur contests with the Sable Knight

But, with great spirit, these two knights uplifted each his horse with his own spirit, and so completed his course in safety.

And indeed King Arthur was very much amazed that he had not overthrown his opponent, for, at that time, as aforesaid, he was considered to be the very best knight and the one best approved in deeds of arms that lived in all of Britain. Wherefore he marvelled at the power and the address of that knight against whom he had driven, that he had not been overthrown by the greatness of the blow that had been delivered against his defences. So, when they met again in the midst of the field, King Arthur gave that knight greeting, and bespoke him with great courtesy, addressing him in this wise: "Sir Knight, I know not who thou art, but I do pledge my knightly word that thou art the most potent knight that ever I have met in all my life. Now I do bid thee get down straightway from thy horse, and let us two fight this battle with sword and upon foot, for it were pity to let it end in this way."

"Not so," quoth the Sable Knight—"not so, nor until one of us twain be overthrown will I so contest this battle upon foot." And upon this he shouted, "Ho! Ho!" in a very loud voice, and straightway thereupon the gateway of the castle opened and there came running forth two tall esquires clad all in black, pied with crimson. And each of these esquires bare in his hand a great spear of ash-wood, new and well-seasoned, and never yet strained in battle.

So King Arthur chose one of these spears and the Sable Knight took the other, and thereupon each returned to that station wherefrom he had before essayed the encounter.

Then once again each knight rushed his steed to the assault, and once again did each smite so fairly in the midst of the defence of the other that the spears were splintered, so that only the guard and the truncheon thereof remained in the grasp of the knight who held it.

Then as before, King Arthur would have fought the battle out with swords and upon foot, but again the Sable Knight would not have it
The knights break lances a second time so, but called aloud upon those within the castle, whereupon there immediately came forth two other esquires with fresh, new spears of ash-wood. So each knight again took him a spear, and having armed himself therewith, chose each his station upon that fair, level lawn of grass.

And now, for the third time, having thus prepared themselves thereof assault, those two excellent knights hurled themselves together in furious assault. And now, as twice before, did King Arthur strike the Sable Knight so fairly in the centre of his defence that the spear which he held was burst into splinters. But this time, the spear of the Sable

Knight did not so break in that manner, but held; and so violent was the blow that he delivered upon King Arthur's shield that he pierced through the centre of it. Then the girths of the King's saddle burst apart by that great, powerful blow, and both he and his steed were cast violently backward. So King Arthur might have been overcast, had he not voided his saddle with extraordinary skill and knightly address,

King Arthur is over-thrown wherefore, though his horse was overthrown, he himself still held his footing and did not fall into the dust. Ne'theless, so violent was the blow that he received that, for a little space, he was altogether bereft of his senses so that everything whirled around before his eyes.

But when his sight returned to him he was filled with an anger so vehement that it appeared to him as though all the blood in his heart rushed into his brains so that he saw naught but red, as of blood, before his eyes. And when this also had passed he perceived the Sable Knight that he sat his horse at no great distance. Then immediately King Arthur ran to him and catching the bridle-rein of his horse, he cried out aloud unto that Sable Knight with great violence: "Come down, thou black knight! and fight me upon foot and with thy sword."

"That will I not do," said the Sable Knight, "for lo! I have over-thrown thee. Wherefore deliver thou to me thy shield, that I may hang it upon yonder apple-tree, and go thy way as others have done before thee."

"That will I not!" cried King Arthur, with exceeding passion, "neither will I yield myself nor go hence until either thou or I have altogether conquered the other." Thereupon he thrust the horse of the Sable Knight backward by the bridle-rein so vehemently, that the other was constrained to void his saddle to save himself from being overthrown upon the ground.

And now each knight was as entirely furious as the other, wherefore, each drew his sword and dressed his shield, and thereupon rushed together like two wild bulls in battle. They foined, they smote, they traced, they parried, they struck again and again, and the sound of their blows, crashing and clashing the one upon the other, filled the entire surrounding space with an extraordinary uproar.

Nor may any man altogether conceive of the entire fury of that encounter, for, because of the violence of the blows which the one delivered upon the other, whole cantels of armor were hewn from their bodies and many *The knights fight with swords upon foot* deep and grievous wounds were given and received, so that the armor of each was altogether stained with red because of the blood that flowed down upon it.

At last King Arthur waxing, as it were, entirely mad, struck so fierce a blow that no armor could have withstood that stroke had it fallen fairly upon it. But it befell with that stroke that his sword broke at the hilt and the blade thereof flew into three several pieces into the air. Yet was the stroke so wonderfully fierce that the Sable Knight groaned, and staggered, and ran about in a circle as though he had gone blind and knew not whither to direct his steps.

But presently he recovered himself again, and perceiving King Arthur standing near by, and not knowing that his enemy had now no sword for to defend himself withal, he cast aside his shield and took his own sword into both hands, and therewith smote so dolorous a stroke that he clave through King Arthur's shield and through his helmet and even to the bone of his brain-pan.

Then King Arthur thought that he had received his death-wound, for his brains swam like water, his thighs trembled exceedingly, and he sank down to his knees, whilst the blood and sweat, commingled together in the darkness of his helmet, flowed down into his eyes in a lather and blinded him. Thereupon, seeing him thus grievously hurt, the Sable Knight called upon him with great vehemence for to yield himself and to surrender his shield, because he was now too sorely wounded for to fight any more.

King Arthur is sorely wounded

But King Arthur would not yield himself, but catching the other by the sword-belt, he lifted himself to his feet. Then, being in a manner recovered from his amazement, he embraced the other with both arms, and placing his knee behind the thigh of the Sable Knight, he cast him backward down upon the ground so violently that the sound of the fall was astounding to hear. And with that fall the Sable Knight was, awhile, entirely bereft of consciousness. Then King Arthur straightway unlaced the helm of the Sable Knight and so beheld his face, and he knew him in spite of the blood that still ran down his own countenance in great quantities, and he knew that knight was King Pellinore, afore-named in this history, who had twice warred against King Arthur. (It hath already been said how King Arthur had driven that other king from the habitations of men and into the forests, so that now he dwelt in this poor gloomy castle whence he waged war against all the knights who came unto that place.)

Now when King Arthur beheld who it was against whom he had done battle, he cried aloud, "Ha! Pellinore, is it then thou? Now yield thee to me, for thou art entirely at my mercy." And upon this he drew his misericordia and set the point thereof at King Pellinore's throat.

But by now King Pellinore had greatly recovered from his fall, and perceiving that the blood was flowing down in great measure from out his enemy's helmet, he wist that that other must have been very sorely wounded by the blow which he had just now received. Wherefore he catched King Arthur's wrist in his hand and directed the point of the dagger away from his own throat so that no great danger threatened therefrom.

And, indeed, what with his sore wound and with the loss of blood, King Arthur was now fallen exceedingly sick and faint, so that it appeared to him that he was nigh to death. Accordingly, it was with no very great ado that King Pellinore suddenly heaved himself up from the ground and so overthrew his enemy that King Arthur was now underneath his knees.

And by this King Pellinore was exceedingly mad with the fury of the sore battle he had fought. For he was so enraged that his eyes were all beshot with blood like those of a wild boar, *King Pell-* and a froth, like the champings of a wild boar, stood in *inore makes* the beard about his lips. Wherefore he wrenched the *to kill* dagger out of his enemy's hand, and immediately began *King Arthur* to unlace his helm, with intent to slay him where he lay. But at this moment Merlin came in great haste, crying out, "Stay! stay! Sir Pellinore; what would you be at? Stay your sacrilegious hand! For he who lieth beneath you is none other than Arthur, King of all this realm!"

At this King Pellinore was astonished beyond measure. And for a little he was silent, and then after awhile he cried out in a very loud voice, "Say you so, old man? Then verily your words have doomed this man unto death. For no one in all this world hath ever suffered such ill and such wrongs as I have suffered at his hands. For, lo! he hath taken from me power, and kingship, and honors, and estates, and hath left me only this gloomy, dismal castle of the forest as an abiding-place. Wherefore, seeing that he is thus in my power, he shall now presently die; if for no other reason than because if I now let him go free, he will certainly revenge himself when he shall have recovered from all the ill he hath suffered at my hands."

Then Merlin said, "Not so! He shall not die at thy hands, for I, myself, shall save him." Whereupon he uplifted his staff and smote King Pellinore across the shoulders. Then imme- *Merlin lays* diately King Pellinore fell down and lay upon the ground *a spell* on his face like one who had suddenly gone dead. *upon King* *Pellinore*

Upon this, King Arthur uplifted himself upon his elbow and beheld his enemy lying there as though dead, and he cried out, "Ha! Merlin! what is this that thou hast done? I am very sorry, for I do perceive that thou, by thy arts of magic, hath slain one of the best knights in all the world."

"Not so, my lord King!" said Merlin; "for, in sooth, I tell thee that thou art far nigher to thy death than he. For he is but in sleep and will soon awaken; but thou art in such a case that it would take only a very little for to cause thee to die."

And indeed King Arthur was exceeding sick, even to the heart, with the sore wound he had received, so that it was only with much ado that Merlin could help him upon his horse. Having done the which and having hung the King's shield upon the horn of the saddle, Merlin straightway conveyed the wounded man thence across the bridge, and, leading the horse by the bridle, so took him away into the forest.

Now I must tell you that there was in that part of the forest a certain hermit so holy that the wild birds of the woodland would come and rest upon his hand whiles he read his breviary; and so sanctified was he in gentleness that the wild does would come even to the door of his hermitage, and there stand whilst he milked them for his refreshment. And this hermit dwelt in that part of the forest so remote from the habitations of man that when he rang the bell for matins or for vespers, there was hardly ever anyone to hear the sound thereof excepting the wild creatures that dwelt thereabout. Yet, ne'theless, to this remote and lonely place royal folk and others of high degree would sometimes come, as though on a pilgrimage, because of the hermit's exceeding saintliness.

So Merlin conveyed King Arthur unto this sanctuary, *Merlin bringeth* and, having reached that place, he and the hermit *King Arthur to* lifted the wounded man down from his saddle—the *the cell of a* hermit giving many words of pity and sorrow—and *lone hermit* together they conveyed him into the holy man's cell. There they laid him upon a couch of moss and unlaced his armor and searched his wounds and bathed them with pure water and dressed his hurts, for that hermit was a very skilful leech. So for all that day and part of the next, King Arthur lay upon the hermit's pallet like one about to die; for he beheld all things about him as though through thin water, and the breath hung upon his lips and fluttered, and he could not even lift his head from the pallet because of the weakness that lay upon him.

Now upon the afternoon of the second day there fell a great noise and tumult in that part of the forest. For it happened that the Lady Guinevere of Cameliard, together with her Court, both of ladies and of knights, had come upon a pilgrimage to that holy man, the fame of whose saintliness had reached even unto the place where she dwelt. For that lady had a favorite page who was very sick of a fever, and she trusted that the holy man might give her some charm or amulet by the virtue of which he might haply be cured. Wherefore she had come to that place with her entire Court so that all that part of the forest was made gay with fine raiment and the silence thereof was made merry with the sound of talk and laughter and the singing of songs and the chattering of many voices and the neighing of horses. And the Lady Guinevere rode in the midst of her damsels and her Court, and her beauty outshone the beauty of her damsels as the splendor of the morning star outshines that of all the lesser stars that surround it. For then and afterward she was held by all the Courts of Chivalry to be the most beautiful lady in the world.

The Lady Guinevere consults with the priest

Now when the Lady Guinevere had come to that place, she perceived the milk-white war-horse of King Arthur where it stood cropping the green grass of the open glade nigh to the hermitage. And likewise she perceived Merlin, where he stood beside the door of the cell. So of him she demanded whose was that noble war-horse that stood browsing upon the grass at that lonely place, and who was it that lay within that cell. And unto her Merlin made answer, "Lady, he who lieth within is a knight, very sorely wounded, so that he is sick nigh unto death!"

"Pity of Heaven!" cried the Lady Guinevere. "What a sad thing is this that thou tellest me! Now I do beseech thee to lead me presently unto that knight that I may behold him. For I have in my Court a very skilful leech, who is well used to the cure of hurts such as knights receive in battle."

So Merlin brought the lady into the cell, and there she beheld King Arthur where he lay stretched upon the pallet. And she wist not who he was. Yet it appeared to her that in all her life she had not beheld so noble appearing a knight as he who lay sorely wounded in that lonely place. And King Arthur cast his looks upward to where she stood beside his bed of pain, surrounded by her maidens, and in the great weakness that lay upon him he wist not whether she whom he beheld was a mortal lady or whether she was not rather some tall straight angel who had descended from one of the Lordly Courts of Paradise for to visit him in his pain and distresses. And the Lady Guinevere was filled with a great pity at beholding King Arthur's sorrowful estate. Wherefore she called to her that skilful leech who was with her Court. And she bade him bring a certain alabaster box of exceedingly precious balsam. And she commanded him for to search that knight's wounds and to anoint them with the balsam, so that he might be healed of his hurts with all despatch.

The Lady Guinevere biddeth her leech for to heal King Arthur

So that wise and skilful leech did according to the Lady Guinevere's commands, and immediately King Arthur felt entire ease of all his aches and great content of spirit. And when the Lady and her Court had departed, he found himself much uplifted in heart, and three days thereafter he was entirely healed and was as well and strong and lusty as ever he had been in all of his life.

And this was the first time that King Arthur ever beheld that beautiful lady, the Lady Guinevere of Cameliard, and from that time forth he never forgot her, but she was almost always present in his thought. Wherefore, when he was recovered he said thus to himself: "I will forget that I am a king and I will cherish the thought of this lady and will serve her faithfully as a good knight may serve his chosen dame."

And so he did, as ye shall hear later in this book.

The Lady of Shalott

≈ ≈ ≈

Part I

On either side the river lie
Long fields of barley and of rye,
That clothe the world and meet the sky;
And thro' the field the road runs by
　　To many-tower'd Camelot;
And up and down the people go,
Gazing where the lilies blow
Round an island there below,
　　The island of Shalott.

Willows whiten, aspens quiver,
Little breezes dusk and shiver
Thro' the wave that runs for ever
By the island in the river
　　Flowing down to Camelot.
Four gray walls, and four gray towers,
Overlook a space of flowers,
And the silent isle imbowers
　　The Lady of Shalott.

By the margin, willow-veil'd,
Slide the heavy barges trail'd
By slow horses; and unhail'd
The shallop flitteth silken-sail'd
　　Skimming down to Camelot:
But who hath seen her wave her hand?
Or at the casement seen her stand?
Or is she known in all the land,
　　The Lady of Shalott?

Only reapers, reaping early
In among the bearded barley,
Hear a song that echoes cheerly
From the river winding clearly,
      Down to tower'd Camelot;
And by the moon the reaper weary,
Piling sheaves in uplands airy,
Listening, whispers ' 'Tis the fairy
      Lady of Shalott.'

Part II

There she weaves by night and day
A magic web with colors gay.
She has heard a whisper say,
A curse is on her if she stay
      To look down to Camelot.
She knows not what the curse may be,
And so she weaveth steadily,
And little other care hath she,
      The Lady of Shalott.

And moving thro' a mirror clear
That hangs before her all the year,
Shadows of the world appear.
There she sees the highway near
      Winding down to Camelot;
There the river eddy whirls,
And there the surly village-churls,
And the red cloaks of market girls,
      Pass onward from Shalott.

Sometimes a troop of damsels glad,
An abbot on an ambling pad,
Sometimes a curly shepherd-lad,
Or long-hair'd page in crimson clad,
      Goes by to tower'd Camelot;
And sometimes thro' the mirror blue
The knights come riding two and two:

She hath no loyal knight and true,
        The Lady of Shalott.

But in her web she still delights
To weave the mirror's magic sights,
For often thro' the silent nights
A funeral, with plumes and lights
        And music, went to Camelot;
Or when the moon was overhead,
Came two young lovers lately wed:
'I am half sick of shadows,' said
        The Lady of Shalott.

Part III

A bow-shot from her bower-eaves,
He rode between the barley-sheaves,
The sun came dazzling thro' the leaves,
And flamed upon the brazen greaves
        Of bold Sir Lancelot.
A red-cross knight for ever kneel'd
To a lady in his shield,
That sparkled on the yellow field,
        Beside remote Shalott.

The gemmy bridle glitter'd free,
Like to some branch of stars we see
Hung in the golden Galaxy.
The bridle bells rang merrily
        As he rode down to Camelot;
And from his blazon'd baldric slung
A mighty silver bugle hung,
And as he rode his armor rung,
        Beside remote Shalott.

All in the blue unclouded weather
Thick-jewell'd shone the saddle-leather,
The helmet and the helmet-feather
Burn'd like one burning flame together,

As he rode down to Camelot;
As often thro' the purple night
Below the starry clusters bright,
Some bearded meteor, trailing light,
    Moves over still Shalott.

His broad clear brow in sunlight glow'd;
On burnish'd hooves his war-horse trode;
From underneath his helmet flow'd
His coal-black curls as on he rode,
    As he rode down to Camelot.
From the bank and from the river
He flash'd into the crystal mirror,
'Tirra lirra,' by the river
    Sang Sir Lancelot.

She left the web, she left the loom,
She made three paces thro' the room,
She saw the water-lily bloom,
She saw the helmet and the plume,
    She look'd down to Camelot.
Out flew the web and floated wide;
The mirror cracked from side to side;
'The curse is come upon me,' cried
    The Lady of Shalott.

Part IV

In the stormy east-wind straining,
The pale yellow woods were waning,
The broad stream in his banks complaining,
Heavily the low sky raining
    Over tower'd Camelot.
Down she came and found a boat
Beneath a willow left afloat,
And round about the prow she wrote
    The Lady of Shalott.

And down the river's dim expanse
Like some bold seër in a trance,
Seeing all his own mischance—
With a glassy countenance
  Did she look to Camelot.
And at the closing of the day
She loosed the chain, and down she lay;
The broad stream bore her far away,
  The Lady of Shalott.

Lying, robed in snowy white
That loosely flew to left and right—
The leaves upon her falling light—
Thro' the noises of the night
  She floated down to Camelot;
And as the boat-head wound along
The willowy hills and fields among,
They heard her singing her last song,
  The Lady of Shalott.

Heard a carol, mournful, holy,
Chanted loudly, chanted lowly,
Till her blood was frozen slowly
And her eyes were darken'd wholly,
  Turn'd to tower'd Camelot.
For ere she reach'd upon the tide
The first house by the water-side,
Singing in her song she died,
  The Lady of Shalott.

Under tower and balcony,
By garden-wall and gallery,
A gleaming shape she floated by,
Dead-pale between the houses high,
  Silent into Camelot.
Out upon the wharfs they came,
Knight and burgher, lord and dame,
And round the prow they read her name,
  The Lady of Shalott.

Who is this? and what is here?
And in the lighted palace near
Died the sound of royal cheer;
And they crossed themselves for fear,
    All the knights at Camelot:
But Lancelot mused a little space;
He said, 'She has a lovely face;
God in his mercy lend her grace,
    The Lady of Shalott.'

The Vale of Thorns

JAMES BALDWIN

Just as Arthur was the greatest king of England in the days of old, so was Charlemagne the greatest warrior-king of the French. Roland, his nephew, was his bravest knight —except for Oliver, who was equally brave. How Roland blew his ivory horn too late at the Battle of Roncevaux is the story told here. —From The Song of Roland

Seven years passed. In all the world there was not such another king as Charlemagne. Wherever his arms were carried, there victory followed; and neither Pagan nor haughty Christian foe dared lift up hands any more against him. His kingdom stretched from the Baltic Sea to the Italian shores, and from beyond the Rhine to the great Western Ocean. Princes were his servants; kings were his vassals; and even the Pope of Rome did him homage. And now he had crossed the Pyrenees, and was carrying fire and sword into the fair fields and rich towns of the Spanish Moors; for he had vowed to punish Marsilius, king of Spain, for the injuries he had done the French in former years. And he had overrun the whole of that haughty land, and had left neither castle, nor city, nor wall, unbroken, save only the town of Saragossa.

One day Charlemagne sat beneath the blossoming trees of an orchard near Cordova. White was his beard, and flowered was his head; yet still handsome was his body, and proud his form. Around him were the noblest of his knights, Roland and Oliver and old Duke Namon, and fifteen thousand of the choicest men of France. It was a gala-day for the French, and the warriors amused themselves with field-sports, and many pleasant games. Then a party of Moorish messengers were brought to the king. They came from Marsilius at Saragossa, who had sent to beg peace of Charlemagne.

"What will Marsilius give for peace?" asked the king.

"If you will go back to your own country, and cease this unhappy war," answered they, "then Marsilius binds himself to do this: he will

82

go to Aix at Michaelmas, and be baptized; he will do homage then for Spain, and will faithfully hold it in fief from you; he will give you great store of treasures,—four hundred mules loaded with gold, and fifty cartloads of silver, besides numbers of bears and lions and tame greyhounds, and seven hundred camels, and a thousand moulted falcons. Too long has this cruel war been waging. Marsilius would fain have peace."

Charlemagne listened to the words of the messengers, but he was not quick to answer. He called together his peers, and laid the matter before them.

"What think you of the Moor's offers of peace?" asked he.

"Put no trust in Marsilius!" cried Roland. "He is the most faithless of Pagans, and speaks only lies. Carry on the war as you have begun, and talk not of peace until Saragossa is ours."

Charlemagne's face grew dark, yet he said not a word. It was plain that he coveted the treasures which Marsilius had promised. Then Ganelon arose, and with curling lip, thus answered,—

"If Marsilius offers to do fealty for Spain, and to hold it as a gift from you, wherefore should we refuse his plea? He who would advise you otherwise cares not what manner of death we die."

And Namon of Bavaria added, "If the Moor is beaten, and cries for mercy, it would be an unknightly act to continue warring against him. My voice is for peace."

And all the peers, save Roland and Oliver, cried out, "The duke hath spoken wisely. Let us have peace!"

"It is well," answered Charlemagne; "and so it shall be. But whom shall we send to Saragossa to treat with Marsilius, and to receive the pledges of good faith which he shall give?"

Then arose a great dispute among the peers as to which should undertake this dangerous errand. Duke Namon, who was never known to shirk a duty, offered to go; but the king would not consent. He liked not to part with his wise old friend, even for a single day.

"I will carry the message," said Roland.

"Not so, my brother," interrupted Oliver. "Thy pride will get the better of thy judgment, and thou wilt act rashly. Let me undertake the errand."

But Charlemagne refused them both. "Neither of you shall go," said he. "But you may choose one from among these other barons to be the messenger."

"Then send Ganelon of Mayence," said Roland. "He is in favor of peace, and he is most fit to carry the message."

"Yes, send Ganelon of Mayence!" cried all the peers.

Ganelon rose from his seat in rage. Fire flashed from his hazel eyes; his lips quivered; he tore the sable border from his crimson tunic, and stood proudly before Roland. "Fool!" cried he. "Who art thou who wouldst send me to Marsilius? If I but live to come again from Saragossa, I will deal thee such a blow as thou shalt never forget."

"Speak softly, Sir Ganelon," said Roland. "Men know that I care not for threats. If thou art afraid of the danger, mayhap the king will allow me to go in thy place."

Hotter than before was Ganelon's wrath; but he held his tongue, and turned humbly toward the king.

"My lord," said he, "since you will that I bear this message to Marsilius, I go. But I know too well the false-hearted Moor to hope that I shall ever return. I pray you, care for my fair son Baldwin, to whom I leave my lands and all my fiefs. Keep him well, for these eyes of mine shall never see him again."

"Thou art too fearful, and too tender of heart," said the king, as he offered to Ganelon the staff and the glove which messengers were wont to carry as signs of their office. "Go now, and doubt not the issue of thine errand."

Ganelon took the staff; but his hand trembled, and the glove fell to the ground.

"An evil omen is that," whispered the peers who saw it. "It is a sign of no good fortune, either to him or to us."

Then Ganelon bade the king good-by, and went on his way. But he said to himself, "This is Roland's doings, and I shall hate him all my life long: neither shall I love Oliver his brother, nor any other of the twelve peers."

When he reached Saragossa, Ganelon was led into the presence of Marsilius. The Moorish king sat under a pine-tree, and twenty thousand warriors stood around him.

"What answer bring you from your liege-lord Charlemagne?" asked he.

Ganelon had studied well what he should say; and he answered, like one long used to cunning guile, "If thou wilt be baptized and become a Christian, Charlemagne will give thee the half of Spain to hold in fief. If thou will not accept this offer, then he will besiege thee in Saragossa, and take thee prisoner; and he will send thee bound upon the back of a sumter horse to Aix, and there he will have thee put to death. This is the message which Charlemagne sends thee."

Great was the anger of the Moorish king, and he raised his javelin to strike the messenger dead. But Ganelon, no whit daunted, set his back against the trunk of a tree, and drew his sword part way from its scabbard.

"Good sword," said he, "thou art fair and bright, and thou hast done me many a service. Never shall it be said that Ganelon died alone in a strange land."

But the courtiers of King Marsilius stepped in between them. "It were better," said they, "to treat with this man than to slay him. If his face slander him not, he is a man who may be persuaded to help us. Try him."

Then Marsilius called Ganelon to his side, and offered him five hundred pounds of gold for his friendship. And the two sat long together, and plotted bloodshed and treason.

"Indeed, what think you of this Charlemagne?" asked the Moor. "Through how many lands has he carried that old body of his? How many scars are there on his shield? How many kingdoms has he stolen, and how many kings impoverished? Methinks that his days are well-nigh spent. He must be more than two hundred years old."

But Ganelon, although a traitor, would say naught against the king. "None can see him," said he, "but will say that he is a man. None can so praise or honor him, but that there shall yet be in him more worth and goodness."

"Yet, methinks," said the Moor, "that he is very old. His beard is white; his hair is flowered. It is strange that he grows not tired of fighting."

"That he will never do so long as Roland, his nephew, lives," answered Ganelon. "There, too, is Oliver; and there are the other peers of the realm, all of whom the king holds most dear. They alone are worth twenty thousand men."

"I have heard much of Roland," said the Moor; "and I would fain put him out of the way. Tell me how it can be done, and thou shalt have three baggage horse-loads of gold, three of silver, and three of fine silk and red wine and jewels."

Now Ganelon desired, above all things, the death of Roland; and he eagerly made known his plans to Marsilius.

"Send to Charlemagne," said he, "great store of rich gifts, so that every Frenchman shall wonder at your wealth. Send also hostages, and promise him that on next Michaelmas you will be baptized at Aix and do him homage for Spain. Pleased with your promises, he will return to sweet France. But this rearguard, with Roland and Oliver, and twenty thousand Frenchmen, will be long among the passes of the Pyrenees. A hundred thousand Moors could well cope with them there."

Then the two traitors exchanged promises and pledges; and Ganelon, taking with him the keys of Saragossa, and rich presents for Charlemagne, went back to Cordova.

Right glad was Charlemagne to hear the message which the lying traitor brought. He was tired of warring, and he longed to return in peace to his own sweet France. The next day the trumpets sounded throughout the camp. The tents were struck; the baggage was packed on the sumter horses; the knights mounted their steeds; banners and pennons waved thick in the air; the great army began its glad march homeward. Joyful was the beginning of that march; but, ah, how sad the ending! The French did not see the crafty Moors following them through the upper valleys, their banners furled, their helmets closed, their lances in rest.

That first night the king was troubled with sad dreams. He thought that Ganelon seized his lance and shook it, and that it fell in pieces. He thought that he hunted in the forest of Ardennes, and that both a boar and a leopard attacked him. A thousand fearful fancies vexed him. Mountains fell upon him and crushed him; the earth yawned and swallowed him; perils beset him on every side; but amid them all, the face of Ganelon was ever to be seen.

By and by the army came to the Pyrenees, and the great land of France lay just beyond the mountains.

"To whom now," said the king to his peers, "shall we intrust our rearguards while we pass safely through the mountain gates?"

"Give it to Roland, your nephew," said Ganelon. "There is none more worthy than he."

"And who shall lead the vanguard?"

"Ogier, the Dane. Next to Roland, he is the bravest of your barons."

Right willingly did Roland accept the dangerous trust.

"I will see to it," said he, "that no harm come to the French while passing through the gates. Neither pack-horse, nor mule, nor palfrey, nor charger, nor man shall we lose, that shall not be paid for by the blood of our foes."

Then he mounted his steed, and rode back to the rear. And with him went Oliver and Gerin and Gerer and Josse and Berenger and Jastor and Anseis, and Duke Gaifer, and proud Gerard of Rousillon, and Turpin the archbishop, and twenty thousand valiant fighting-men.

High were the mountains, and gloomy the valleys; dark were the rocks, and fearful were the glens. But the day was fair, and the sky was clear; and the bright shields of the warriors glittered in the sunlight like flashes of fire. All at once a sound, as of a thousand trumpets blowing, was heard in the valley below them. The French knights hearkened.

"Comrades," said Oliver, "methinks that we are followed by the Moors."

"And may God grant us battle and victory!" said Roland earnestly. "Well it is that we are here to defend the king. For one should never murmur that he suffers distress for his friends: for them, he should lose, if need be, both blood and flesh and even life itself."

Then Oliver climbed a high pine tree, and looked down into the grassy valley behind them. There he beheld such troops of Pagan folk as he had never seen before.

"Comrades," cried he, "we shall have such a battle as no man has known. The passes are full of armed Moors; their hauberks and glittering helmets fill the lower valleys. Great mischief is in store for us, but may we stand to the field like men!"

"Shame be to him that flees!" said the warriors who heard him.

Bewildered and amazed at sight of so terrible an array of Pagans, Oliver descended from the tree.

"Brother Roland," said he, "I pray thee blow thy horn. The king will hear it, and he will turn about and come to our succor."

"To do so would be to act as a craven," answered Roland. "Never shall it be said that I feared a foe. I will strike strong strokes with Durandal. Ill shall it fare with the Pagan traitors."

"Comrade Roland," again said Oliver, "now blow thy horn. Charlemagne will hear it, and he will make his host return."

"Never," answered Roland, "shall my kinsmen upbraid me, or be blamed by me. But I will strike with Durandal. The brand which the king gave me when he knighted me, that shall be our succor."

Then Oliver prayed him a third time, "Comrade Roland, sound now thine ivory horn. Charlemagne, who is passing the gates, will hear us and come to our aid."

"No man shall ever say," answered Roland, "that I have blown my horn for Pagans. My kinsmen shall not bear that reproach. But when the great battle is joined, then you shall see the lightning flashes of Durandal in the thickest of the fight. A thousand and seven hundred times shall the blade be dyed in the blood of the Moors. Better would it be to perish than suffer shame."

But Oliver was not yet satisfied. "I have seen the Moorish host," said he. "The mountains and the plains, the valleys and the groves, are full of them. Never have we fought against such great odds."

"Friend and brother," answered Roland, "say not another word. The king has left us here, with a rearguard of twenty thousand men, and he esteems every one of us as a hero. Do thou strike with thy lance and thy good blade Haultclear. As for me, Durandal shall serve me well. And, if I die, men shall say, 'This sword belonged to a noble knight.'"

Then the good Archbishop Turpin rode down the ranks, holding a sword in one hand and a crucifix in the other. "Comrades," cried he, "the king has left us here. He trusts in us, and for him we shall die. Cry now your sins to Heaven. Pray God's mercy, and ask his blessing."

In a moment every knight among those twenty thousand horsemen had dismounted. Humbly and reverently every knee was bent, and every head was bowed. And the good archbishop blessed the company in God's name.

"If ye die," said he, "ye shall have places in paradise."

Then the warriors arose, light-hearted and hopeful. They rode into the place which is called Roncevaux, The Vale of Thorns, and there they put themselves in battle-array, and waited the onset of their foes. Roland sat astride of his good war steed, and proudly faced the Moorish host. In his hand he held the bared blade Durandal, pointing toward heaven. Never was seen a more comely knight. Courteously he spoke to the warriors about him. Then, putting spurs to his steed, he cried,—

"Comrades, ride onward! The day shall be ours!"

"Forget not the war-cry of Charlemagne," said Oliver.

At these words the rocks and valleys rang with the cry, "Monjoie! Monjoie!" And every warrior dashed forward to meet the foe.

Long and fierce was the fight, and terrible was the slaughter. With

heart and strength the French knights struck. The Moors were slain by
hundreds and by thousands. For a time victory seemed to be with the
French. Many and valiant were the deeds achieved by Roland and
Oliver and the archbishop and the peers that were with them. But at
length Marsilius came down upon them with a fresh troop of seven
thousand Moors. They hemmed the French heroes in on every side.
Roland saw his knights falling one by one around him. All were slain
save sixty men.

"Oliver, my fair dear comrade," said he, "behold how many brave
vassals have fallen! The battle goes hard with us. If, now, we only
knew how to send news to Charlemagne, he would return and succor
us."

"It is too late," answered Oliver. "Better would we die than suffer
shame."

Then said Roland, "I will sound my ivory horn. Mayhap Charlemagne, who is passing the gates of Spain, will hear it and return."

"Do no such thing," answered Oliver. "Great shame would be upon
you and your kinsmen forever. You would not blow your horn when I
advised it, and now you shall not do so because the day is lost."

Then the archbishop rode up, and said, "The day is indeed lost, and
to blow the horn would now no more avail us. But, should the king
hear it, he will come back through the passes. He will find us dead: his
men will lift us in biers and carry us home to be buried in minsters,
and we shall not be left as food for wolves and dogs."

"Thou sayest well," said Roland. And he placed the horn to his lips.
High were the hills, deep and dark were the gorges, narrow were the
ways among the mountains. Yet the sound of that horn was heard for
thirty leagues. Charlemagne and Duke Namon heard it while yet they
were between the gates.

"Hark!" said the king. "I hear Roland's horn. The felon Moors have
attacked him: he is hard pressed in battle."

"You are foolishly mistaken," said Ganelon. "There is no battle. You
are old, your beard is white, your head flowery, you are growing
childish. You love your silly nephew, Roland, too well. He is only
hunting among the mountains. He would blow his horn all day for a
single hare, and then he would boast before you of his valor. Ride on.
Your own France is not far ahead."

But the king was not to be deceived. He ordered Ganelon to be seized
and bound and given in charge of his cooks, who were to hold him a

close prisoner. They bound him with a great chain, and laid him across the back of a sumter horse; they pulled his beard; they struck him with their fists; they beat him with sticks. Sorry indeed was the traitor's plight, but his punishment was just. As for Charlemagne, he turned and, with all his host, hastened back to the succor of Roland and the valiant rearguard. High were the mountain walls, and darkly did they overhang the way; deep were the mountain gorges; swift and strong were the torrents; narrow and steep was the road. The trumpets sounded: anxiously and with haste the king and horsemen retraced their steps.

Fiercely still the battle raged in the fated Vale of Thorns. One by one the French knights fell; but for every one that was slain ten Pagans bit the dust. At length Oliver was wounded unto death; but still he sat on his horse and struck valiantly about him with his good Haultclear. His eyes lost their strength: he could not see. He met Roland, and struck him a blow which split his helmet down to the nose-piece, but luckily wounded him not.

"Brother," said Roland softly and gently, "thou has not done this willingly. I am Roland, he who has loved thee so long and so well."

"Ah, comrade!" said Oliver, "I hear thee; but I cannot see thee. Pray forgive me if I have harmed thee."

"I am none the worse," answered Roland; "and there is naught to forgive."

Then the two brothers bent over from their steeds, and embraced each other; and amid much love and many hasty words of farewell, they parted.

And now all the French were slain, save only Roland and the archbishop. The hero was wounded in a dozen places: he felt his lifeblood oozing away. Again he drew his ivory horn, and feebly sounded it. He would fain know whether Charlemagne were coming. The king was in the pass, not far away, and he heard the failing blast.

"Ah, Roland!" said he, "the battle goes ill with thee." Then he turned to his host, and said, "Blow loud your trumpets, that the hero may know that succor comes."

At once sixty thousand bugles were blown so loudly that the valleys and the caves resounded, and the rocks themselves trembled. Roland heard it and thanked God. The Pagans heard it and knew that it boded no good to them. They rushed in a body upon Roland and the archbishop. Roland's horse was slain beneath him; his shield was split in twain; his hauberk was broken. The archbishop was mortally wounded, and stretched upon the ground. Again the trumpets of Charlemagne's host were heard, and the Pagans fled in great haste toward Spain.

Then Roland knelt by the side of the dying archbishop. "Kind friend, so good and true," said he, "now the end has come. Our comrades whom we held so dear are all dead. Give me leave to bring them and lay them in order by thee, that we may all have thy blessing."

"It is well," answered the good Turpin. "Do as thou wilt. The field is thine and mine."

So Roland, weak and faint, went all alone through that field of blood, seeking his friends. He found Berenger and Otho and Anseis and Samson, and proud Gerard of Rousillon; and one by one he brought them and laid them on the grass before the archbishop. And lastly he brought back Oliver, pressed gently against his bosom, and placed him on a shield by the others. The archbishop wept; and he lifted up his feeble hands and blessed them: "Sad has it been with you, comrades. May God, the glorious King, receive your souls in his paradise!"

Then Roland, faint with loss of blood, and overcome with grief, swooned and fell to the ground. The good archbishop felt such distress as he had never known before. He staggered to his feet; he took the ivory horn in his hands, and went to fetch water from the brook which flows through the Vale of Thorns. Slowly and feebly he tottered onward, but not far: his strength failed and he fell to the ground. Soon Roland recovered from his swoon and looked about him. On the green grass this side of the rivulet, he saw the archbishop lying. The good Turpin was dead.

And now Roland felt that he, too, was nigh death's door. He took the ivory horn in one hand, and Durandal in the other, and went up a little hill that lies toward Spain. He sat down beneath a pine-tree where were four great blocks of marble. He looked at the blade Durandal. "Ha, Durandal," he said, "how bright and white thou art! Thou shinest and flamest against the sun! Many countries have I conquered with thee, and now for thee I have great grief. Better would it be to destroy thee than to have thee fall into the hands of the Pagan folk."

With great effort he raised himself on his feet again. Ten times he smote with Durandal the great rock before him. But the sword was bright and whole as ever, while the rock was split in pieces. Then the hero lay down upon the grass, with his face toward the foe. He put the sword and the horn under him. He stretched his right glove toward heaven, and an unseen hand came and took it away. Dead was the matchless hero.

Not long after this King Charlemagne with his host came to the death-strewn Vale of Thorns. Great was the grief of the king and of all the French, when they found that they had come too late to save even a single life. Roland was found lying on the grass, his face turned toward Spain. Charlemagne took him up tenderly in his arms, and wept.

"Friend Roland," said he, "worthiest of men, bravest of warriors, noblest of all my knights, what shall I say when they in France shall ask news of thee? I shall tell them that thou art dead in Spain. With great sorrow shall I hold my realm from this time on. Every day I shall weep and bewail thee, and wish that my life, too, were ended."

Then the French buried their dead on the field where they had fallen. But the king brought Roland and Oliver and the archbishop to Blaye in France, and laid them in white marble tombs; and there they lie until this day, in the beautiful little chapel of St. Roman's. And he took the ivory horn to Bordeaux, and filled it with fine gold, and laid it on the altar of the church in that city; and there it is still seen by the pious pilgrims who visit that place.

Puck's Song

RUDYARD KIPLING

See you the ferny ride that steals
Into the oak-woods far?
O that was whence they hewed the keels
That rolled to Trafalgar.

And mark you where the ivy clings
To Bayham's mouldering walls?
O there we cast the stout railings
That stand around St. Paul's.

See you the dimpled track that runs
All hollow through the wheat?
O that was where they hauled the guns
That smote King Philip's fleet.

(Out of the Weald, the secret Weald,
Men sent in ancient years
The horse-shoes red at Flodden Field,
The arrows at Poitiers!)

See you our little mill that clacks,
So busy by the brook?
She has ground her corn and paid her tax
Ever since Domesday Book.

See you our stilly woods of oak,
And the dread ditch beside?
O that was where the Saxons broke
On the day that Harold died.

See you the windy levels spread
About the gates of Rye?
O that was where the Northmen fled,
When Alfred's ships came by.

See you our pastures wide and lone,
Where the red oxen browse?
O there was a City thronged and known,
Ere London boasted a house.

And see you, after rain, the trace
Of mound and ditch and wall?
O that was a Legion's camping-place,
When Cæsar sailed from Gaul.

And see you marks that show and fade,
Like shadows on the Downs?
O they are the lines the Flint Men made,
To guard their wondrous towns.

Trackway and Camp and City lost,
Salt Marsh where now is corn—
Old Wars, old Peace, old Arts that cease,
And so was England born!

She is not any common Earth,
Water or wood or air,
But Merlin's Isle of Gramarye,
Where you and I will fare!

Miss Lark's Andrew

P. L. TRAVERS

≈ ≈ ≈ *In England more than thirty years ago Mary Poppins came to the house in Cherry Tree Lane to be the children's nurse. Lots of children had nurses in those days, but none was so extraordinary as Mary Poppins—as you will agree after reading this story. —From* Mary Poppins

Miss Lark lived Next Door.

But before we go any further I must tell you what Next Door looked like. It was a very grand house, by far the grandest in Cherry-Tree Lane. Even Admiral Boom had been known to envy Miss Lark her wonderful house, though his own had ship's funnels instead of chimneys, and a flagstaff in the front garden. Over and over again the inhabitants of the Lane heard him say, as he rolled past Miss Lark's mansion: "Blast my gizzard! What does *she* want with a house like that?"

And the reason of Admiral Boom's jealousy was that Miss Lark had two gates. One was for Miss Lark's friends and relations, and the other for the Butcher and the Baker and the Milkman.

Once the Baker made a mistake and came in through the gate reserved for the friends and relations, and Miss Lark was so angry that she said she wouldn't have any more bread ever.

But in the end she had to forgive the Baker because he was the only one in the neighbourhood who made those little flat rolls with the curly twists of crust on the top. She never really liked him very much after that, however, and when he came he pulled his hat far down over his eyes so that Miss Lark might think he was somebody else. But she never did.

Jane and Michael always knew when Miss Lark was in the garden or coming along the Lane, because she wore so many brooches and necklaces and earrings that she jingled and jangled just like a brass band. And, whenever she met them, she always said the same thing:

"Good-morning!" (or "Good-afternoon!" if it happened to be after luncheon), "and how are *we* today?"

And Jane and Michael were never quite sure whether Miss Lark was asking how *they* were, or how she and Andrew were.

So they just replied: "Good-afternoon!" (or, of course, "Good-morning!" if it was before luncheon).

All day long, no matter where the children were, they could hear Miss Lark calling, in a very loud voice, things like:

"Andrew, where are you?" or

"Andrew, you mustn't go out without your overcoat!" or

"Andrew, come to Mother!"

And, if you didn't know, you would think that Andrew must be a little boy. Indeed, Jane thought that Miss Lark thought that Andrew *was* a little boy. But Andrew wasn't. He was a dog—one of those small, silky, fluffy dogs that look like a fur necklet, until they begin to bark. But, of course, when they do that you *know* that they're dogs. No fur necklet ever made a noise like that.

Now, Andrew led such a luxurious life that you might have thought he was the Shah of Persia in disguise. He slept on a silk pillow in Miss Lark's room; he went by car to the Hairdresser's twice a week to be shampooed; he had cream for every meal and sometimes oysters, and he possessed four overcoats with checks and stripes in different colours. Andrew's ordinary days were filled with the kind of things most people have only on birthdays. And when Andrew himself had a birthday he had *two* candles on his cake for every year, instead of only one.

The effect of all this was to make Andrew very much disliked in the neighbourhood. People used to laugh heartily when they saw Andrew sitting up in the back seat of Miss Lark's car on the way to the Hairdresser's, with the fur rug over his knees and his best coat on. And on the day when Miss Lark bought him two pairs of small leather boots so that he could go out in the Park wet or fine, everybody in the Lane came down to their front gates to watch him go by and to smile secretly behind their hands.

"Pooh!" said Michael, as they were watching Andrew one day through the fence that separated Number Seventeen from Next Door. "Pooh, he's a ninkypoop!"

"How do you know?" asked Jane, very interested.

"I know because I heard Daddy call him one this morning!" said Michael, and he laughed at Andrew very rudely.

"He is *not* a nincompoop," said Mary Poppins. "And that is that."

And Mary Poppins was right. Andrew wasn't a nincompoop, as you will very soon see.

You must not think he did not respect Miss Lark. He did. He was even very fond of her in a mild sort of way. He couldn't help having a kindly feeling for somebody who had been so good to him ever since he was a puppy, even if she *did* kiss him rather too often. But there was no doubt about it that the life Andrew led bored him to distraction. He would have given half his fortune, if he had one, for a nice piece of raw, red meat, instead of the usual breast of chicken or scrambled eggs with asparagus.

For in his secret, innermost heart, Andrew longed to be a common dog. He never passed his pedigree (which hung on the wall in Miss Lark's drawing-room) without a shudder of shame. And many a time he wished he'd never had a father, nor a grandfather, nor a great-grandfather, if Miss Lark was going to make such a fuss of it.

It was this desire of his to *be* a common dog that made Andrew choose common dogs for his friends. And whenever he got the chance, he would run down to the front gate and sit there watching for them, so that he could exchange a few common remarks. But Miss Lark, when she discovered him, would be sure to call out:

"Andrew, Andrew, come in, my darling! Come away from those dreadful street arabs!"

And of course Andrew would *have* to come in, or Miss Lark would shame him by coming out and *bringing* him in. And Andrew would blush and hurry up the steps so that his friends should not hear her calling him her Precious, her Joy, her Little Lump of Sugar.

Andrew's most special friend was more than common, he was a By-word. He was half an Airedale and half a Retriever and the worst half of both. Whenever there was a fight in the road he would be sure to be in the thick of it; he was always getting into trouble with the Postman or the Policeman, and there was nothing he loved better than sniffing about in drains or garbage tins. He was, in fact, the talk of the whole street, and more than one person had been heard to say thankfully that they were glad he was not *their* dog.

But Andrew loved him and was continually on the watch for him. Sometimes they had only time to exchange a sniff in the Park, but on luckier occasions—though these were very rare—they would have long talks at the gate. From his friend, Andrew heard all the town gossip, and you could see by the rude way in which the other dog laughed as he told it, that it wasn't very complimentary.

Then suddenly Miss Lark's voice would be heard calling from a window, and the other dog would get up, loll out his tongue at Miss Lark, wink at Andrew and wander off, waving his hind-quarters as he went just to show that *he* didn't care.

Andrew, of course, was never allowed outside the gate unless he went with Miss Lark for a walk in the Park, or with one of the maids to have his toes manicured.

Imagine, then, the surprise of Jane and Michael when they saw Andrew, all alone, careering past them through the Park, with his ears back and his tail up as though he were on the track of a tiger.

Mary Poppins pulled the perambulator up with a jerk, in case Andrew, in his wild flight, should upset it and the Twins. And Jane and Michael screamed at him as he passed.

"Hi, Andrew! Where's your overcoat?" cried Michael, trying to make a high, windy voice like Miss Lark's.

"Andrew, you naughty little boy!" said Jane, and her voice, because she was a girl, was much more like Miss Lark's.

But Andrew just looked at them both very haughtily and barked sharply in the direction of Mary Poppins.

"Yap-yap!" said Andrew several times very quickly.

"Let me see. I think it's the first on your right and second house on the left-hand side," said Mary Poppins.

"Yap?" said Andrew.

"No—no garden. Only a back-yard. Gate's usually open."

Andrew barked again.

"I'm not sure," said Mary Poppins. "But I should think so. Generally gets home at tea-time."

Andrew flung back his head and set off again at a gallop.

Jane's eyes and Michael's were round as saucers with surprise.

"What was he saying?" they demanded breathlessly, both together.

"Just passing the time of day!" said Mary Poppins, and shut her mouth tightly as though she did not intend any more words to escape from it. John and Barbara gurgled from their perambulator.

"He wasn't!" said Michael.

"He *couldn't* have been!" said Jane.

"Well, you know best, of course. *As* usual," said Mary Poppins haughtily.

"He must have been asking you where somebody lived, I'm sure he must—" Michael began.

"Well, if you know, why bother to ask me?" said Mary Poppins sniffing. "*I'm* no dictionary."

"Oh, Michael," said Jane, "she'll never tell us if you talk like that. Mary Poppins, do say what Andrew was saying to you, *please*."

"Ask *him*. *He* knows—Mr. Know-All!" said Mary Poppins, nodding her head scornfully at Michael.

"Oh no, I don't. I promise I don't, Mary Poppins. Do tell."

"Half-past three. Tea-time," said Mary Poppins, and she wheeled the perambulator round and shut her mouth tight again as though it were a trap-door. She did not say another word all the way home.

Jane dropped behind with Michael.

"It's your fault!" she said. "Now we'll never know."

"I don't care!" said Michael, and he began to push his scooter very quickly. "I don't want to know."

But he did want to know very badly indeed. And, as it turned out, he and Jane and everybody else knew all about it before tea-time.

Just as they were about to cross the road to their own house, they heard loud cries coming from Next Door, and there they saw a curious sight. Miss Lark's two maids were rushing wildly about the garden, looking under bushes and up into the trees as people do who have lost their most valuable possession. And there was Robertson Ay, from Number Seventeen, busily wasting his time by poking at the gravel on Miss Lark's path with a broom as though he expected to find the missing treasure under a pebble. Miss Lark herself was running about in her garden, waving her arms and calling: "Andrew, Andrew! Oh, he's lost. My darling boy is lost! We must send for the Police. I must see the Prime Minister. Andrew is lost! Oh dear! oh dear!"

"Oh, poor Miss Lark!" said Jane, hurrying across the road. She could not help feeling sorry because Miss Lark looked so upset.

But it was Michael who really comforted Miss Lark. Just as he was going in at the gate of Number Seventeen, he looked down the Lane and there he saw—

"Why, there's Andrew, Miss Lark. See, down there—just turning Admiral Boom's corner!"

"Where, where? Show me!" said Miss Lark breathlessly, and she peered in the direction in which Michael was pointing.

And there, sure enough, *was* Andrew, walking as slowly and as casually as though nothing in the world was the matter; and beside him waltzed a huge dog that seemed to be half an Airedale and half a Retriever, and the worst half of both.

"Oh, what a relief!" said Miss Lark, sighing loudly. "What a load off my mind!"

Mary Poppins and the children waited in the Lane outside Miss Lark's gate, Miss Lark herself and her two maids leant over the fence, Robertson Ay, resting from his labours, propped himself up with his broom-handle, and all of them watched in silence the return of Andrew.

He and his friend marched sedately up to the group, whisking their tails jauntily and keeping their ears well cocked, and you could tell by the look in Andrew's eye that, whatever he meant, he meant business.

"That dreadful dog!" said Miss Lark, looking at Andrew's companion.

"Shoo! Shoo! Go home!" she cried.

But the dog just sat down on the pavement and scratched his right ear with his left leg and yawned.

"Go away! Go home! Shoo, I say!" said Miss Lark, waving her arms angrily at the dog.

"And you, Andrew," she went on, "come indoors this minute! Going out like that—all alone and without your overcoat. I am very displeased with you!"

Andrew barked lazily, but did not move.

"What do you mean, Andrew? Come in at once!" said Miss Lark. Andrew barked again.

"He says," put in Mary Poppins, "that he's not coming in."

Miss Lark turned and regarded her haughtily.

"How do *you* know what my dog says, may I ask? Of course he will come in."

Andrew, however, merely shook his head and gave one or two low growls.

"He won't," said Mary Poppins. "Not unless his friend comes, too."

"Stuff and nonsense," said Miss Lark crossly. "That *can't* be what he says. As if I could have a great hulking mongrel like that inside my gate."

Andrew yapped three or four times.

"He says he means it," said Mary Poppins. "And what's more, he'll go and live with his friend unless his friend is allowed to come and live with him."

"Oh, Andrew, you can't—you can't, really,—after all I've done for you and everything!" Miss Lark was nearly weeping.

Andrew barked and turned away. The other dog got up.

"Oh, he *does* mean it!" cried Miss Lark. "I see he does. He is going away." She sobbed a moment into her handkerchief, then she blew her nose and said:

"Very well, then, Andrew. I give in. This—this common dog can stay. On condition, of course, that he sleeps in the coal-cellar."

Another yap from Andrew.

"He insists, ma'am, that that won't do. His friend must have a silk cushion just like his and sleep in your room too. Otherwise he will go and sleep in the coal-cellar with his friend," said Mary Poppins.

"Andrew, how could you?" moaned Miss Lark. "I shall never consent to such a thing."

Andrew looked as though he were preparing to depart. So did the other dog.

"Oh, he's leaving me!" shrieked Miss Lark. "Very well, then, Andrew. It will be as you wish. He *shall* sleep in my room. But I shall never be the same again, never, never. Such a common dog!"

She wiped her streaming eyes and went on:

"I should never have thought it of you, Andrew. But I'll say no more, no matter what I think. And this—er—creature—I shall call Waif or Stray or—"

At that the other dog looked at Miss Lark very indignantly, and Andrew barked loudly.

"They say you must call him Willoughby, and nothing else," said Mary Poppins. "Willoughby being his name."

"Willoughby! What a name! Worse and worse!" said Miss Lark despairingly. "What is he saying now?" For Andrew was barking again.

"He says that if he comes back you are never to make him wear overcoats or go to the Hairdresser's again—that's his last word," said Mary Poppins.

There was a pause.

"Very well," said Miss Lark at last. "But I warn you, Andrew, if you catch your death of cold—don't blame me!"

And with that she turned and walked haughtily up the steps, sniffing away at the last of her tears.

Andrew cocked his head towards Willoughby as if to say: "Come on!" and the two of them waltzed side by side slowly up the garden path, waving their tails like banners, and followed Miss Lark into the house.

"He isn't a ninkypoop after all, you see," said Jane as they went upstairs to the nursery and Tea.

"No," agreed Michael. "But how do you think Mary Poppins knew?"

"I don't know," said Jane. "And she'll never, never tell us. I am sure of that. . . ."

Elegy on the Death of a Mad Dog

OLIVER GOLDSMITH

Good people all, of every sort,
    Give ear unto my song;
And if you find it wondrous short,
    It cannot hold you long.

In Islington there was a man
    Of whom the world might say,
That still a godly race he ran—
    Whene'er he went to pray.

A kind and gentle heart he had,
    To comfort friends and foes:
The naked every day he clad—
    When he put on his clothes.

And in that town a dog was found,
    As many dogs there be,
Both mongrel, puppy, whelp, and hound,
    And curs of low degree.

This dog and man at first were friends;
    But when a pique began,
The dog, to gain his private ends,
    Went mad, and bit the man.

Around from all the neighboring streets
    The wondering neighbors ran,
And swore the dog had lost his wits,
    To bite so good a man!

The wound it seemed both sore and sad
　　To every Christian eye:
And while they swore the dog was mad,
　　They swore the man would die.

But soon a wonder came to light,
　　That showed the rogues they lied:—
The man recovered of the bite,
　　The dog it was that died!

"Rikki-tikki-tavi"

RUDYARD KIPLING

≈ ≈ ≈ *Animals and birds can't really talk like people. But for thousands of years people have told and written stories about imaginary animals who could. This is one of the best. —From* The Jungle Book

> At the hole where he went in
> Red-Eye called to Wrinkle-Skin,
> Hear what little Red-Eye saith:
> "Nag, come up and dance with death!"
>
> Eye to eye and head to head,
>   (*Keep the measure, Nag,*)
> This shall end when one is dead;
>   (*At thy pleasure, Nag.*)
> Turn for turn and twist for twist—
>   (*Run and hide thee, Nag.*)
> Hah! The hooded Death has missed!
>   (*Woe betide thee, Nag!*)

This is the story of the great war that Rikki-tikki-tavi fought single-handed, through the bathrooms of the big bungalow in Segowlee cantonment. Darzee, the tailor-bird, helped him, and Chuchundra, the muskrat, who never comes out into the middle of the floor, but always creeps round by the wall, gave him advice; but Rikki-tikki-tavi did the real fighting.

He was a mongoose, rather like a little cat in his fur and his tail, but quite like a weasel in his head and his habits. His eyes and the end of his restless nose were pink; he could scratch himself anywhere he pleased, with any leg, front or back, that he chose to use; he could fluff up his tail till it looked like a bottle-brush, and his war-cry as he scuttled through the long grass, was: "*Rikki-tikk-tikki-tikki-tchk!*"

One day, a high summer flood washed him out of the burrow where he lived with his father and mother, and carried him, kicking and clucking, down a roadside ditch. He found a little wisp of grass floating there, and clung to it till he lost his senses. When he revived, he was lying in the hot sun on the middle of a garden path, very draggled indeed, and a small boy was saying: "Here's a dead mongoose. Let's have a funeral."

"No," said his mother; "let's take him and dry him. Perhaps he isn't really dead."

They took him into the house, and a big man picked him up between his finger and thumb and said he was not dead but half choked; so they wrapped him in cotton-wool, and warmed him, and he opened his eyes, and sneezed.

"Now," said the big man (he was an Englishman who had just moved into the bungalow): "don't frighten him, and we'll see what he'll do."

It is the hardest thing in the world to frighten a mongoose, because he is eaten up from nose to tail with curiosity. The motto of all the mongoose family is, "Run and find out"; and Rikki-tikki was a true mongoose. He looked at the cotton-wool, decided that it was not good to eat, ran all round the table, sat up and put his fur in order, scratched himself, and jumped on the small boy's shoulder.

"Don't be frightened, Teddy," said his father. "That's his way of making friends."

"Ouch! He's tickling under my chin," said Teddy.

Rikki-tikki looked down between the boy's collar and neck, snuffed at his ear, and climbed down to the floor, where he sat rubbing his nose.

"Good gracious," said Teddy's mother, "and that's a wild creature! I suppose he's so tame because we've been kind to him."

"All mongooses are like that," said her husband. "If Teddy doesn't pick him up by the tail, or try to put him in a cage, he'll run in and out of the house all day long. Let's give him something to eat."

They gave him a little piece of raw meat. Rikki-tikki liked it immensely, and when it was finished he went out into the veranda and sat in the sunshine and fluffed up his fur to make it dry to the roots. Then he felt better.

"There are more things to find out about in this house," he said to himself, "than all my family could find out in all their lives. I shall certainly stay and find out."

He spent all that day roaming over the house. He nearly drowned himself in the bath-tubs, put his nose into the ink on a writing-table, and burned it on the end of the big man's cigar, for he climbed up in the big man's lap to see how writing was done. At nightfall he ran into Teddy's nursery to watch how kerosene lamps were lighted, and when Teddy went to bed Rikki-tikki climbed up too; but he was a restless companion, because he had to get up and attend to every noise all through the night, and find out what made it. Teddy's mother and father came in, the last thing, to look at their boy, and Rikki-tikki was awake on the pillow. "I don't like that," said Teddy's mother; "he may bite the child." "He'll do no such thing," said the father. "Teddy's safer with that little beast than if he had a bloodhound to watch him. If a snake came into the nursery now—"

But Teddy's mother wouldn't think of anything so awful.

Early in the morning Rikki-tikki came to early breakfast in the veranda riding on Teddy's shoulder, and they gave him banana and some boiled egg; and he sat on all their laps one after the other, because every well-brought-up mongoose always hopes to be a house-mongoose some day and have rooms to run about in, and Rikki-tikki's mother (she used to live in the General's house at Segowlee) had carefully told Rikki what to do if ever he came across white men.

Then Rikki-tikki went out into the garden to see what was to be seen. It was a large garden, only half cultivated, with bushes as big as summer-houses of Marshal Niel roses, lime and orange trees, clumps of bamboos, and thickets of high grass. Rikki-tikki licked his lips. "This is a splendid hunting-ground," he said, and his tail grew bottle-brushy at the thought of it, and he scuttled up and down the garden, snuffing here and there till he heard very sorrowful voices in a thorn-bush.

It was Darzee, the tailor-bird, and his wife. They had made a beautiful nest by pulling two big leaves together and stitching them up the edges with fibers, and had filled the hollow with cotton and downy fluff. The nest swayed to and fro, as they sat on the rim and cried.

"What is the matter?" asked Rikki-tikki.

"We are very miserable," said Darzee. "One of our babies fell out of the nest yesterday and Nag ate him."

"H'm!" said Rikki-tikki, "that is very sad—but I am a stranger here. Who is Nag?"

Darzee and his wife only cowered down in the nest without answering, for from the thick grass at the foot of the bush there came a low hiss—a horrid cold sound that made Rikki-tikki jump back two clear feet. Then inch by inch out of the grass rose up the head and spread hood of Nag, the big black cobra, and he was five feet long from tongue to tail. When he had lifted one-third of himself clear of the ground, he stayed balancing to and fro exactly as a dandelion-tuft balances in the wind, and he looked at Rikki-tikki with the wicked snake's eyes that never change their expression, whatever the snake may be thinking of.

"Who is Nag?" he said. "I am Nag. The great god Brahm put his mark upon all our people when the first cobra spread his hood to keep the sun off Brahm as he slept. Look, and be afraid!"

He spread out his hood more than ever, and Rikki-tikki saw the spectacle-mark on the back of it that looks exactly like the eye part of a hook-and-eye fastening. He was afraid for the minute; but it is impossible for a mongoose to stay frightened for any length of time, and though Rikki-tikki had never met a live cobra before, his mother had fed him on dead ones, and he knew that a grown mongoose's business in life was to fight and eat snakes. Nag knew that too, and at the bottom of his cold heart he was afraid.

"Well," said Rikki-tikki, and his tail began to fluff up again, "marks or no marks, do you think it is right for you to eat fledglings out of a nest?"

Nag was thinking to himself, and watching the least little movement in the grass behind Rikki-tikki. He knew that mongooses in the garden meant death sooner or later for him and his family; but he wanted to get Rikki-tikki off his guard. So he dropped his head a little, and put it on one side.

"Let us talk," he said. "You eat eggs. Why should not I eat birds?"

"Behind you! Look behind you!" sang Darzee.

Rikki-tikki knew better than to waste time in staring. He jumped up in the air as high as he could go, and just under him whizzed by the head of Nagaina, Nag's wicked wife. She had crept up behind him as he was talking, to make an end of him; and he heard her savage hiss as the stroke missed. He came down almost across her back, and if he had been an old mongoose he would have known that then was the time to break her back with one bite; but he was afraid of the terrible lashing return-stroke of the cobra. He bit, indeed, but did not bite long enough, and he jumped clear of the whisking tail, leaving Nagaina torn and angry.

"Wicked, wicked Darzee!" said Nag, lashing up as high as he could reach toward the nest in the thorn-bush; but Darzee had built it out of reach of snakes, and it only swayed to and fro.

Rikki-tikki felt his eyes growing red and hot (when a mongoose's eyes grow red, he is angry), and he sat back on his tail and hind legs like a little kangaroo, and looked all around him, and chattered with rage. But Nag and Nagaina had disappeared into the grass. When a snake misses its stroke, it never says anything or gives any sign of what it means to do next. Rikki-tikki did not dare to follow them, for he did not feel sure that he could manage two snakes at once. So he trotted off to the gravel path near the house, and sat down to think. It was a serious matter for him.

If you read the old books of natural history, you will find they say that when the mongoose fights the snake and happens to get bitten, he runs off and eats some herb that cures him. That is not true. The victory is only a matter of quickness of eye and quickness of foot,—snake's blow against mongoose's jump,—and as no eye can follow the motion of a snake's head when it strikes, that makes things much more wonderful than any magic herb. Rikki-tikki knew he was a young mongoose, and it made him all the more pleased to think that he had managed to escape a blow from behind. It gave him confidence in himself, and when Teddy came running down the path, Rikki-tikki was ready to be petted.

But just as Teddy was stopping, something flinched a little in the dust, and a tiny voice said: "Be careful. I am death!" It was Karait, the dusty brown snakeling that lies for choice on the dusty earth; and his bite is as dangerous as the cobra's. But he is so small that nobody thinks of him, and so he does more harm to people.

Rikki-tikki's eyes grew red again, and he danced up to Karait with the peculiar rocking, swaying motion that he had inherited from his family. It looks very funny, but it is so perfectly balanced a gait that you can fly off from it at any angle you please; and in dealing with snakes this is an advantage. If Rikki-tikki had only known, he was doing a much more dangerous thing than fighting Nag, for Karait is so small, and can turn so quickly, that unless Rikki bit him close to the back of the head, he would get the return-stroke in his eye or lip. But Rikki did not know: his eyes were all red, and he rocked back and forth, looking for a good place to hold. Karait struck out. Rikki jumped sideways and tried to run in, but the wicked little dusty gray head lashed within a fraction of his shoulder, and he had to jump over the body, and the head followed his heels close.

Teddy shouted to the house: "Oh, look here! Our mongoose is killing a snake"; and Rikki-tikki heard a scream from Teddy's mother. His father ran out with a stick, but by the time he came up, Karait had lunged out once too far, and Rikki-tikki had sprung, jumped on the snake's back, dropped his head far between his forelegs, bitten as high up the back as he could get hold, and rolled away. That bite paralyzed Karait, and Rikki-tikki was just going to eat him up from the tail, after the custom of his family at dinner, when he remembered that a full meal makes a slow mongoose, and if he wanted all his strength and quickness ready, he must keep himself thin.

He went away for a dust-bath under the castor-oil bushes, while Teddy's father beat the dead Karait. "What is the use of that?" thought Rikki-tikki. "I have settled it all"; and then Teddy's mother picked him up from the dust and hugged him, crying that he had saved Teddy from death, and Teddy's father said that he was a providence, and Teddy looked on with big scared eyes. Rikki-tikki was rather amused at all the fuss, which, of course, he did not understand. Teddy's mother might just as well have petted Teddy for playing in the dust. Rikki was thoroughly enjoying himself.

That night, at dinner, walking to and fro among the wine-glasses on the table, he could have stuffed himself three times over with nice things; but he remembered Nag and Nagaina, and though it was very pleasant to be patted and petted by Teddy's mother, and to sit on Teddy's shoulder, his eyes would get red from time to time, and he would go off into his long war-cry of *"Rikk-tikk-tikki-tikki-tchk!"*

Teddy carried him off to bed, and insisted on Rikki-tikki sleeping under his chin. Rikki-tikki was too well bred to bite or scratch, but as soon as Teddy was asleep he went off for his nightly walk round the house, and in the dark he ran up against Chuchundra, the muskrat, creeping round by the wall. Chuchundra is a broken-hearted little beast. He whimpers and cheeps all the night, trying to make up his mind to run into the middle of the room, but he never gets there.

"Don't kill me," said Chuchundra, almost weeping. "Rikki-tikki, don't kill me."

"Do you think a snake-killer kills muskrats?" said Rikki-tikki scornfully.

"Those who kill snakes get killed by snakes," said Chuchundra more sorrowfully than ever. "And how am I to be sure that Nag won't mistake me for you some dark night?"

"There's not the least danger," said Rikki-tikki; "but Nag is in the garden, and I know you don't go there."

"My cousin Chua, the rat, told me—" said Chuchundra, and then he stopped.

"Told you what?"

"H'sh! Nag is everywhere, Rikki-tikki. You should have talked to Chua in the garden."

"I didn't—so you must tell me. Quick, Chuchundra, or I'll bite you!"

Chuchundra sat down and cried till the tears rolled off his whiskers. "I am a very poor man," he sobbed. "I never had spirit enough to run out into the middle of the room. H'sh! I mustn't tell you anything. Can't you *hear*, Rikki-tikki?"

Rikki-tikki listened. The house was as still as still, but he thought he could just catch the faintest *scratch-scratch* in the world,—a noise as faint as that of a wasp walking on a window-pane,—the dry scratch of a snake's scales on brickwork.

"That's Nag or Nagaina," he said to himself; "and he is crawling into the bath-room sluice. You're right, Chuchundra; I should have talked to Chua."

He stole off to Teddy's bath-room, but there was nothing there, and then to Teddy's mother's bath-room. At the bottom of the smooth plaster wall there was a brick pulled out to make a sluice for the bath-water, and as Rikki-tikki stole in by the masonry curb where the bath is put, he heard Nag and Nagaina whispering together outside in the moonlight.

"When the house is emptied of people," said Nagaina to her husband, "*he* will have to go away, and then the garden will be our own again. Go in quietly, and remember that the big man who killed Karait is the first one to bite. Then come out and tell me, and we will hunt for Rikki-tikki together."

"But are you sure that there is anything to be gained by killing the people?" said Nag.

"Everything. When there were no people in the bungalow, did we have any mongoose in the garden? So long as the bungalow is empty, we are king and queen of the garden; and remember that as soon as our eggs in the melon-bed hatch (as they may tomorrow), our children will need room and quiet."

"I had not thought of that," said Nag. "I will go, but there is no need that we should hunt for Rikki-tikki afterward. I will kill the big man and his wife, and the child if I can, and come away quietly. Then the bungalow will be empty, and Rikki-tikki will go."

Rikki-tikki tingled all over with rage and hatred at this, and then Nag's head came through the sluice, and his five feet of cold body followed it. Angry as he was, Rikki-tikki was very frightened as he saw the size of the big cobra. Nag coiled himself up, raised his head, and looked into the bath-room in the dark, and Rikki could see his eyes glitter.

"Now, if I kill him here, Nagaina will know; and if I fight him on the open floor, the odds are in his favour. What am I to do?" said Rikki-tikki-tavi.

Nag waved to and fro, and then Rikki-tikki heard him drinking from the biggest water-jar that was used to fill the bath. "That is good," said the snake. "Now, when Karait was killed, the big man had a stick. He may have that stick still, but when he comes in to bathe in the morning he will not have a stick. I shall wait here till he comes. Nagaina—do you hear me?—I shall wait here in the cool till daytime."

There was no answer from outside, so Rikki-tikki knew Nagaina had gone away. Nag coiled himself down, coil by coil, round the bulge at the bottom of the water-jar, and Rikki-tikki stayed still as death. After an hour he began to move, muscle by muscle, toward the jar. Nag was asleep, and Rikki-tikki looked at his big back, wondering which would be the best place for a good hold. "If I don't break his back at the first jump," said Rikki, "he can still fight; and if he fights—O Rikki!" He looked at the thickness of the neck below the hood, but that was too much for him; and a bite near the tail would only make Nag savage.

"It must be the head, he said at last; "the head above the hood; and, when I am once there, I must not let go."

Then he jumped. The head was lying a little clear of the water-jar, under the curve of it; and, as his teeth met, Rikki braced his back against the bulge of the red earthenware to hold down the head. This gave him just one second's purchase, and he made the most of it. Then he was battered to and fro as a rat is shaken by a dog—to and fro on the floor, up and down, and round in great circles; but his eyes were red, and he held on as the body cartwhipped over the floor, upsetting the tin dipper and the soap-dish and the flesh-brush, and banged against the tin side of the bath. As he held he closed his jaws tighter and tighter, for he made sure he would be banged to death, and, for the honour of his family, he preferred to be found with his teeth locked. He was dizzy, aching, and felt shaken to pieces when something went off like a thunder-clap just behind him; a hot wind knocked him senseless and red fire singed his fur. The big man had been wakened by the noise, and had fired both barrels of a shot-gun into Nag just behind the hood.

Rikki-tikki held on with his eyes shut, for now he was quite sure he was dead; but the head did not move, and the big man picked him up, and said: "It's the mongoose again, Alice; the little chap has saved *our* lives now." Then Teddy's mother came in with a very white face, and saw what was left of Nag, and Rikki-tikki dragged himself to Teddy's bedroom and spent half the rest of the night shaking himself tenderly to find out whether he really was broken into forty pieces, as he fancied.

When morning came he was very stiff, but well pleased with his doings. "Now I have Nagaina to settle with, and she will be worse than five Nags, and there's no knowing when the eggs she spoke of will hatch. Goodness! I must go and see Darzee," he said.

Without waiting for breakfast, Rikki-tikki ran to the thorn-bush where Darzee was singing a song of triumph at the top of his voice. The news of Nag's death was all over the garden, for the sweeper had thrown the body on the rubbish-heap.

"Oh, you stupid tuft of feathers!" said Rikki-tikki angrily. "Is this the time to sing?"

"Nag is dead—is dead—is dead!" sang Darzee. "The valiant Rikki-tikki caught him by the head and held fast. The big man brought the bang-stick and Nag fell in two pieces! He will never eat my babies again."

"All that's true enough; but where's Nagaina?" said Rikki-tikki, looking carefully round him.

"Nagaina came to the bath-room sluice and called for Nag," Darzee went on; "and Nag came out on the end of a stick—the sweeper picked him up on the end of a stick, and threw him upon the rubbish-heap. Let us sing about the great, the red-eyed Rikki-tikki!" and Darzee filled his throat and sang.

"If I could get up to your nest, I'd roll all your babies out!" said

Rikki-tikki. "You don't know when to do the right thing at the right time. You're safe enough in your nest there, but it's war for me down here. Stop singing a minute, Darzee."

"For the great, the beautiful Rikki-tikki's sake I will stop," said Darzee. "What is it, O Killer of the terrible Nag?"

"Where is Nagaina, for the third time?"

"On the rubbish-heap by the stables, mourning for Nag. Great is Rikki-tikki with the white teeth."

"Bother my white teeth! Have you ever heard where she keeps her eggs?"

"In the melon-bed, on the end nearest the wall, where the sun strikes nearly all day. She had them there weeks ago."

"And you never thought it worth while to tell me? The end nearest the wall, you said?"

"Rikki-tikki, you are not going to eat her eggs?"

"Not eat exactly; no. Darzee, if you have a grain of sense you will fly off to the stables and pretend that your wing is broken, and let Nagaina chase you away to this bush! I must get to the melon-bed, and if I went there now she'd see me."

Darzee was a feather-brained little fellow who could never hold more than one idea at a time in his head; and just because he knew that Nagaina's children were born in eggs like his own, he didn't think at first that it was fair to kill them. But his wife was a sensible bird, and she knew that cobra's eggs meant young cobras later on; so she flew off from the nest, and left Darzee to keep the babies warm, and continue his song about the death of Nag. Darzee was very like a man in some ways.

She fluttered in front of Nagaina by the rubbish-heap, and cried out, "Oh, my wing is broken! The boy in the house threw a stone at me and broke it." Then she fluttered more desperately than ever.

Nagaina lifted up her head and hissed, "You warned Rikki-tikki when I would have killed him. Indeed and truly, you've chosen a bad place to be lame in." And she moved toward Darzee's wife, slipping along over the dust.

"The boy broke it with a stone!" shrieked Darzee's wife.

"Well! It may be some consolation to you when you're dead to know that I shall settle accounts with the boy. My husband lies on the rubbish-heap this morning, but before night the boy in the house will lie very still. What is the use of running away? I am sure to catch you. Little fool, look at me!"

Darzee's wife knew better than to do *that*, for a bird who looks at a snake's eyes gets so frightened that she cannot move. Darzee's wife fluttered on, piping sorrowfully, and never leaving the ground, and Nagaina quickened her pace.

Rikki-tikki heard them going up the path from the stables, and he raced for the end of the melon-patch near the wall. There, in the warm litter about the melons, very cunningly hidden, he found twenty-five eggs, about the size of a bantam's eggs, but with whitish skin instead of shell.

"I was not a day too soon," he said; for he could see the baby cobras curled up inside the skin, and he knew that the minute they were hatched they could each kill a man or a mongoose. He bit off the tops of the eggs as fast as he could, taking care to crush the young cobras, and turned over the litter from time to time to see whether he had missed any. At last there were only three eggs left, and Rikki-tikki began to chuckle to himself, when he heard Darzee's wife screaming:

"Rikki-tikki, I led Nagaina toward the house, and she has gone into the veranda, and—oh, come quickly—she means killing!"

Rikki-tikki smashed two eggs, and tumbled backward down the melon-bed with the third egg in his mouth, and scuttled to the veranda as hard as he could put foot to the ground. Teddy and his mother and father were there at early breakfast; but Rikki-tikki saw that they were not eating anything. They sat stone-still, and their faces were white. Nagaina was coiled up on the matting by Teddy's chair, within easy striking distance of Teddy's bare leg, and she was swaying to and fro singing a song of triumph.

"Son of the big man that killed Nag," she hissed, "stay still. I am not ready yet. Wait a little. Keep very still, all you three. If you move I strike, and if you do not move I strike. Oh, foolish people, who killed my Nag!"

Teddy's eyes were fixed on his father, and all his father could do was to whisper, "Sit still, Teddy. You mustn't move. Teddy, keep still."

Then Rikki-tikki came up and cried: "Turn round, Nagaina; turn and fight!"

"All in good time," said she, without moving her eyes. "I will settle my account with *you* presently. Look at your friends, Rikki-tikki. They are still and white; they are afraid. They dare not move, and if you come a step nearer I strike."

"Look at your eggs," said Rikki-tikki, "in the melon-bed near the wall. Go and look, Nagaina."

The big snake turned half round, and saw the egg on the veranda. "Ah-h! Give it to me," she said.

Rikki-tikki put his paws one on each side of the egg, and his eyes were blood-red. "What price for a snake's egg? For a young cobra? For a young king-cobra? For the last—the very last of the brood? The ants are eating all the others down by the melon-bed."

Nagaina spun clear round, forgetting everything for the sake of the one egg; and Rikki-tikki saw Teddy's father shoot out a big hand, catch Teddy by the shoulder, and drag him across the little table with the tea-cups, safe and out of reach of Nagaina.

"Tricked! Tricked! Tricked! *Rikk-tck-tck!*" chuckled Rikki-tikki. "The boy is safe, and it was I—I—I that caught Nag by the hood last night in the bath-room." Then he began to jump up and down, all four feet together, his head close to the floor. "He threw me to and fro, but he could not shake me off. He was dead before the big man blew him in two. I did it. *Rikki-tikki-tck-tck!* Come then, Nagaina. Come and fight with me. You shall not be a widow long."

Nagaina saw that she had lost her chance of killing Teddy, and the egg lay between Rikki-tikki's paws. "Give me the egg, Rikki-tikki. Give me the last of my eggs, and I will go away and never come back," she said, lowering her hood.

"Yes, you will go away, and you will never come back; for you will go to the rubbish-heap with Nag. Fight, widow! The big man has gone for his gun! Fight!"

Rikki-tikki was bounding all round Nagaina, keeping just out of the reach of her stroke, his little eyes like hot coals. Nagaina gathered herself together, and flung out at him. Rikki-tikki jumped up and backward. Again and again and again she struck, and each time her head came with a whack on the matting of the veranda and she gathered herself together like a watch-spring. Then Rikki-tikki danced in a circle to get behind her, and Nagaina spun round to keep her head to his head, so that the rustle of her tail on the matting sounded like dry leaves blown along by the wind.

He had forgotten the egg. It still lay on the veranda, and Nagaina came nearer and nearer to it, till at last, while Rikki-tikki was drawing breath, she caught it in her mouth, turned to the veranda steps, and flew like an arrow down the path, with Rikki-tikki behind her. When the cobra runs for her life, she goes like a whiplash flicked across a horse's neck.

Rikki-tikki knew that he must catch her, or all the trouble would begin again. She headed straight for the long grass by the thorn-bush, and as he was running Rikki-tikki heard Darzee still singing his foolish little song of triumph. But Darzee's wife was wiser. She flew off her nest as Nagaina came along, and flapped her wings about Nagaina's head. If Darzee had helped they might have turned her; but Nagaina only lowered her hood and went on. Still, the instant's delay brought Rikki-tikki up to her, and as she plunged into the rat-hole where she and Nag used to live, his little white teeth were clenched on her tail, and he went down with her—and very few mongooses, however wise and old they may be, care to follow a cobra into its hole. It was dark in the hole; and Rikki-tikki never knew when it might open out and give Nagaina room to turn and strike at him. He held on savagely, and struck out his feet to act as brakes on the dark slope of the hot, moist earth.

Then the grass by the mouth of the hole stopped waving, and Darzee said: "It is all over with Rikki-tikki! We must sing his death-song. Valiant Rikki-tikki is dead! For Nagaina will surely kill him underground."

So he sang a very mournful song that he made up all on the spur of the minute, and just as he got to the most touching part the grass quivered again, and Rikki-tikki, covered with dirt, dragged himself out of the hole leg by leg, licking his whiskers, Darzee stopped with a little shout. Rikki-tikki shook some of the dust out of his fur and sneezed. "It is all over," he said. "The widow will never come out again." And the red ants that live between the grass stems heard him, and began to troop down one after another to see if he had spoken the truth.

Rikki-tikki curled himself up in the grass and slept where he was—slept and slept till it was late in the afternoon, for he had done a hard day's work.

"Now," he said, when he awoke, "I will go back to the house. Tell the Coppersmith, Darzee, and he will tell the garden that Nagaina is dead."

The Coppersmith is a bird who makes a noise exactly like the beating of a little hammer on a copper pot; and the reason he is always making it is because he is the town-crier to every Indian garden, and tells all the news to everybody who cares to listen. As Rikki-tikki went up the path, he heard his "attention" notes like a tiny dinner-gong; and then the steady *"Ding-dong-tock!* Nag is dead—*dong!* Nagaina is dead! *Ding-dong-tock!"* That set all the birds in the garden singing, and the frogs croaking; for Nag and Nagaina used to eat frogs as well as little birds.

When Rikki got to the house, Teddy and Teddy's mother (she looked very white still, for she had been fainting) and Teddy's father came out and almost cried over him; and that night he ate all that was given him till he could eat no more, and went to bed on Teddy's shoulder, where Teddy's mother saw him when she came to look late at night.

"He saved our lives and Teddy's life," she said to her husband. "Just think, he saved all our lives."

Rikki-tikki woke up with a jump, for all the mongooses are light sleepers.

"Oh, it's you," said he. "What are you bothering for? All the cobras are dead; and if they weren't I'm here."

Rikki-tikki had a right to be proud of himself; but he did not grow too proud, and he kept that garden as a mongoose should keep it, with tooth and jump and spring and bite, till never a cobra dared show its head inside the walls.

Darzee's Chaunt

(Sung in Honour of Rikki-tikki-tavi)

Singer and tailor am I—
    Doubled the joys that I know—
Proud of my lilt through the sky,
    Proud of the house that I sew—
Over and under, so weave I my music—so weave I the house
    that I sew.

Sing to your fledglings again,
    Mother, oh lift up your head!
Evil that plagued us is slain,
    Death in the garden lies dead.

Terror that hid in the roses is impotent—flung on the
   dung-hill and dead!

Who hath delivered us, who?
   Tell me his nest and his name.
Rikki, the valiant and true,
   Tikki, with eyeballs of flame.
Rik-tikki-tikki, the ivory-fanged, the hunter with eyeballs
   of flame.

Give him the Thanks of the Birds,
   Bowing with tail-feathers spread!
Praise him with nightingale words—
   Nay, I will praise him instead
Hear! I will sing you the praise of the bottle-tailed Rikki,
   with eyeballs of red!

(Here Rikki-tikki interrupted, and the rest of the song is lost.)

Invictus

W. E. HENLEY

Out of the night that covers me,
　Black as the pit from pole to pole,
I thank whatever gods may be
　For my unconquerable soul.

In the fell clutch of circumstance
　I have not winced nor cried aloud.
Under the bludgeonings of chance
　My head is bloody, but unbow'd.

Beyond this place of wrath and tears
　Looms but the Horror of the shade,
And yet the menace of the years
　Finds and shall find me unafraid.

It matters not how strait the gate,
　How charged with punishments the scroll,
I am the master of my fate;
　I am the captain of my soul.

Bambi

FELIX SALTEN

≈ ≈ ≈ *Although animals also talk in these two stories from* Bambi, *the fear and danger described are part of the entire lives of many kinds of animals. Bambi was a fawn who lived with his mother and other deer in an Austrian forest.*

FEAR

Winter dragged on. Sometimes it was warmer, but then the snow would fall again and lie deeper and deeper, so that it became impossible to scrape it away. It was worst when the thaws came and the melted snow water froze again in the night. Then there was a slippery film of ice. Often it broke in pieces and the sharp splinters cut the deers' tender fetlocks till they bled.

A heavy frost had set in several days before. The air was purer and rarer than it had ever been, and full of energy. It began to hum in a very fine high tone. It hummed with the cold.

It was silent in the woods, but something horrible happened every day. Once the crows fell upon Friend Hare's small son who was lying sick, and killed him in a cruel way. He could be heard moaning pitifully for a long while. Friend Hare was not at home, and when he heard the sad news he was beside himself with grief.

Another time the squirrel raced about with a great wound in his neck where the ferret had caught him. By a miracle the squirrel had escaped. He could not talk because of the pain, but he ran up and down the branches. Everyone could see him. He ran like mad. From time to time he stopped, sat down, raised his forepaws desperately and clutched his head in terror and agony while the red blood oozed on his white chest. He ran about for an hour, then suddenly crumpled up, fell across a branch, and dropped dead in the snow. A couple of magpies flew down at once to begin their meal.

Another day a fox tore to pieces the strong and handsome pheasant who had enjoyed such general respect and popularity. His death

121

aroused the sympathies of a wide circle who tried to comfort his disconsolate widow.

The fox had dragged the pheasant out of the snow, where he was
buried, thinking himself well hidden. No one could have felt safer than
the pheasant for it all happened in broad daylight. The terrible hardship that seemed to have no end spread bitterness and brutality. It
destroyed all their memories of the past, their faith in each other, and
ruined every good custom they had. There was no longer either peace
or mercy in the forest.

"It's hard to believe that it will ever be better," Bambi's mother
sighed.

Aunt Ena sighed too. "It's hard to believe that it was ever any
better," she said.

"And yet," Marena said, looking in front of her, "I always think how
beautiful it was before."

"Look," old Nettla said to Aunt Ena, "your little one is trembling."
She pointed to Gobo. "Does he always tremble like that?"

"Yes," Aunt Ena answered gravely, "he's shivered that way for the
last few days."

"Well," said old Nettla in her frank way, "I'm glad that I have no
more children. If that little one were mine I'd wonder if he'd last out
the winter."

The future really didn't look very bright for Gobo. He was weak. He
had always been much more delicate than Bambi or Faline and remained smaller than either of them. He was growing worse from day
to day. He could not eat even the little food there was. It made his
stomach ache. And he was quite exhausted by the cold, and by the
horrors around him. He shivered more and more and could hardly
stand up. Everyone looked at him sympathetically.

Old Nettla went up to him and nudged him good-naturedly. "Don't
be so sad," she said encouragingly, "that's no way for a little prince to
act, and besides it's unhealthy." She turned away so that no one should
see how moved she was.

Ronno who had settled himself a little to one side in the snow
suddenly sprang up. "I don't know what it is," he mumbled and gazed
around.

Everyone grew watchful. "What is it?" they asked.

"I don't know," Ronno repeated. "But I'm restless. I suddenly felt
restless as if something were wrong."

Karus was snuffing the air. "I don't smell anything strange," he declared.

They all stood still, listening and snuffing the air. "It's nothing, there's absolutely nothing to smell," they agreed one after another.

"Nevertheless," Ronno insisted, "you can say what you like, something is wrong."

Marena said, "The crows are calling."

"There they go calling again," Faline added quickly, but the others had already heard them.

"They are flying," said Karus and the others.

Everybody looked up. High above the tree-tops a flock of crows flapped by. They came from the farthest edge of the forest, the direction from which danger always came, and they were complaining to one another. Apparently something unusual had happened.

"Wasn't I right?" asked Ronno. "You can see that something is happening."

"What shall we do?" Bambi's mother whispered anxiously.

"Let's get away," Aunt Ena urged in alarm.

"Wait," Ronno commanded.

"But the children," Aunt Ena replied, "the children. Gobo can't run."

"Go ahead," Ronno agreed, "go off with your children. I don't think there's any need for it, but I don't blame you for going." He was alert and serious.

"Come, Gobo. Come, Faline. Softly now, go slowly. And keep behind me," Aunt Ena warned them. She slipped away with the children.

Time passed. They stood still, listening and trembling.

"As if we hadn't suffered enough already," old Nettla began. "We still have this to go through . . ." She was very angry. Bambi looked at her, and he felt that she was thinking of something horrible.

Three or four magpies had already begun to chatter on the side of the thicket from which the crows had come. "Look out! Look out, out, out!" they cried. The deer could not see them, but could hear them calling and warning each other. Sometimes one of them, and sometimes all of them together, would cry, "Look out, out, out!" Then they came nearer. They fluttered in terror from tree to tree, peered back and fluttered away again in fear and alarm.

"Akh!" cried the jays. They screamed their warning loudly.

Suddenly all the deer shrank together at once as though a blow had struck them. Then they stood still snuffing the air.

It was He.

A heavy wave of scent blew past. There was nothing they could do. The scent filled their nostrils, it numbed their senses and made their hearts stop beating.

The magpies were still chattering. The jays were still screaming overhead. In the woods around them everything had sprung to life. The tit-mice flitted through the branches, like tiny feathered balls, chirping, "Run! run!"

The blackbirds fled swiftly and darkly above them with long-drawn twittering cries. Through the dark tangle of bare bushes, they saw on the white snow a wild aimless scurrying of smaller, shadowy creatures. These were the pheasants. Then a flash of red streaked by. That was the fox. But no one was afraid of him now. For that fearful scent kept streaming on in a wide wave, sending terror into their hearts and uniting them all in one mad fear, in a single feverish impulse to flee, to save themselves.

That mysterious overpowering scent filled the woods with such strength that they knew that this time He was not alone, but had come with many others, and there would be no end to the killing.

They did not move. They looked at the tit-mice, whisking away in a sudden flutter, at the blackbirds and the squirrels who dashed from tree-top to tree-top in mad bounds. They knew that all the little creatures on the grounds had nothing to fear. But they understood their flight when they smelt Him, for no forest creature could bear His presence.

Presently Friend Hare hopped up. He hesitated, sat still and then hopped on again.

"What is it?" said Ronno gloomily.

Friend Hare gasped for breath. "We are surrounded," he said in a lifeless voice. "We can't escape on any side. He is everywhere."

At the same instant they heard His voice. Twenty or thirty strong, He cried, "Ho! ho! ha! ha!" It roared like the sound of winds and storms. He beat on the tree trunks as though they were drums. It was wracking and terrifying. A distant twisting and rending of parted bushes rang out. There was a snapping and cracking of broken boughs.

He was coming.

He was coming into the heart of the thicket.

Then short whistling flute-like trills sounded together with the loud flap of soaring wings. A pheasant rose from under His very feet. The deer heard the wing-beats of the pheasant grow fainter as he mounted into the air. There was a loud crash like thunder. Then silence. Then a dull thud on the ground.

"He is dead," said Bambi's mother, trembling.

"The first," Ronno added.

The young doe, Marena, said, "In this very hour many of us are going to die. Perhaps I shall be one of them." No one listened to her, for a mad terror had seized them all.

Bambi tried to think. But His savage noises grew louder and louder and paralyzed Bambi's senses. He heard nothing but those noises. They numbed him while amidst the howling, shouting and crashing, he could hear his own heart pounding. He felt nothing but curiosity and did not even realize that he was trembling in every limb. From time to time his mother whispered in his ear, "Stay close to me." She was shouting, but in the uproar it sounded to Bambi as if she were whispering. Her "Stay close to me," encouraged him. It was like a chain holding him. Without it he would have rushed off senselessly, and he heard it at the very moment when his wits were wandering and he wanted to dash away.

He looked around. All sorts of creatures were swarming past, scampering blindly over one another. A pair of weasels ran by like thin snake-like streaks. The eye could scarcely follow them. A ferret listened as though bewitched to every shriek that desperate Friend Hare let out.

A fox was standing in a whole flurry of fluttering pheasants. They paid no attention to him. They ran right under his nose and he paid no attention to them. Motionless, with his head thrust forward, he listened to the onrushing tumult, lifting his pointed ears and snuffed the air with his nose. Only his tail moved, slowly wagging with his intense concentration.

A pheasant dashed up. He had come from where the danger was worst, and was beside himself with fear.

"Don't try to fly," he shouted to the others.

"Don't fly, just run! Don't lose your head! Don't try to fly! Just run, run, run!"

He kept repeating the same thing over and over again as though to encourage himself. But he no longer knew what he was saying.

"Ho! ho! ha! ha!" came the death cry from quite near apparently.

"Don't lose your head," screamed the pheasant. And at the same time his voice broke in a whistling gasp and, spreading his wings, he flew up with a loud whir. Bambi watched how he flew straight up, directly between the trees, beating his wings. The dark metallic blue and greenish-brown markings on his body gleamed like gold. His long tail feathers swept proudly behind him. A short crash like thunder sounded sharply. The pheasant suddenly crumpled up in mid-flight. He turned head over tail as though he wanted to catch his claws with his beak, and then dropped violently to earth. He fell among the others and did not move again.

Then everyone lost his senses. They all rushed toward one another. Five or six pheasants rose at one time with a loud whir. "Don't fly," cried the rest and ran. The thunder cracked five or six times and more of the flying birds dropped lifeless to the ground.

"Come," said Bambi's mother. Bambi looked around. Ronno and Karus had already fled. Old Nettla was disappearing. Only Marena was still beside them. Bambi went with his mother, Marena following them timidly. All around them was a roaring and shouting, and the thunder was crashing. Bambi's mother was calm. She trembled quietly but she kept her wits together.

"Bambi, my child," she said, "keep behind me all the time. We'll have to get out of here and across the open place. But now we'll go slowly."

The din was maddening. The thunder crashed ten, twelve times as He hurled it from His hands.

"Watch out," said Bambi's mother. "Don't run. But when we have to cross the open place, run as fast as you can. And don't forget, Bambi, my child, don't pay any attention to me when we get out there. Even if I fall, don't pay any attention to me, just keep running. Do you understand, Bambi?"

His mother walked carefully step by step amidst the uproar. The pheasants were running up and down, burying themselves in the snow. Suddenly, they would spring out and begin to run again. The whole Hare family was hopping to and fro, squatting down and then hopping again. No one said a word. They were all spent with terror and numbed by the din and thunderclaps.

It grew lighter in front of Bambi and his mother. The clearing showed through the bushes. Behind them the terrifying drumming on the tree trunks came crashing nearer and nearer. The breaking branches snapped. There was a roaring of "Ha, ha! Ho, ho!"

Then Friend Hare and two of his cousins rushed past them across the clearing. Bing! Ping! Bang! roared the thunder. Bambi saw how Friend Hare struck an elder in the middle of his flight and lay with his white belly turned upward. He quivered a little and then was still. Bambi stood petrified. But from behind him came the cry, "Here they are! Run! Run!"

There was a loud clapping of wings suddenly opened. There were gasps, sobs, showers of feathers, flutterings. The pheasants took wing and the whole flock rose almost at one instant. The air was throbbing with repeated thunderclaps and the dull thuds of the fallen and the high, piercing shrieks of those who had escaped.

Bambi heard steps and looked behind him. He was there. He came bursting through the bushes on all sides. He sprang up everywhere, struck about Him, beat the bushes, drummed on the tree trunks and shouted with a fiendish voice.

"Now," said Bambi's mother. "Get away from here. And don't stay too close to me." She was off with a bound that barely skimmed the snow. Bambi rushed out after her. The thunder crashed around them on all sides. It seemed as if the earth would split in half. Bambi saw nothing. He kept running. A growing desire to get away from the tumult and out of reach of that scent which seemed to strangle him, the growing impulse to flee, the longing to save himself were loosed in him at last. He ran. It seemed to him as if he saw his mother hit but he did not know if it was really she or not. He felt a film come over his eyes from fear of the thunder crashing behind him. It had gripped him completely at last. He could think of nothing or see nothing around him. He kept running.

The open space was crossed. Another thicket took him in. The hue and cry still rang behind him. The sharp reports still thundered. And in the branches above him there was a light pattering like the first fall of hail. Then it grew quieter. Bambi kept running.

A dying pheasant, with its neck twisted, lay on the snow, beating feebly with its wings. When he heard Bambi coming he ceased his convulsive movements and whispered: "It's all over with me." Bambi paid no attention to him and ran on.

A tangle of bushes he blundered into forced him to slacken his pace and look for a path. He pawed the ground impatiently with his hoofs. "This way!" called someone with a gasping voice. Bambi obeyed involuntarily and found an opening at once. Someone moved feebly in front of him. It was Friend Hare's wife who had called.

"Can you help me a little?" she said. Bambi looked at her and shuddered. Her hind leg dangled lifelessly in the snow, dyeing it red and melting it with warm, oozing blood. "Can you help me a little?" she repeated. She spoke as if she were well and whole, almost as if she were happy. "I don't know what can have happened to me," she went on. "There's really no sense to it, but I just can't seem to walk . . ."

In the middle of her words she rolled over on her side and died. Bambi was seized with horror again and ran.

"Bambi!"

He stopped with a jolt. A deer was calling him. Again he heard the cry. "Is that you, Bambi?"

Bambi saw Gobo floundering helplessly in the snow. All his strength was gone; he could no longer stand on his feet. He lay there half buried and lifted his head feebly. Bambi went up to him excitedly.

"Where's your mother, Gobo?" he asked, gasping for breath. "Where's Faline?" Bambi spoke quickly and impatiently. Terror still gripped his heart.

"Mother and Faline had to go on," Gobo answered resignedly. He spoke softly, but as seriously and as well as a grown deer. "They had to leave me here. I fell down. You must go on, too, Bambi."

"Get up," cried Bambi. "Get up, Gobo! You've rested long enough. There's not a minute to lose now. Get up and come with me!"

"No, leave me," Gobo answered quietly. "I can't stand up. It's impossible. I'd like to, but I'm too weak."

"What will happen to you?" Bambi persisted.

"I don't know. Probably I'll die," said Gobo simply.

The uproar began again and re-echoed. New crashes of thunder followed. Bambi shrank together. Suddenly a branch snapped. Young Karus pounded swiftly through the snow, galloping ahead of the din.

"Run," he called when he saw Bambi. "Don't stand there if you can run!" He was gone in a flash and his headlong flight carried Bambi along with it. Bambi was hardly aware that he had begun to run again and only after an interval did he say, "Good-bye, Gobo." But he was already too far away. Gobo could no longer hear him.

He ran until nightfall through the woods that were filled with shouting and thunder. As darkness closed in, it grew quiet. Soon a light wind carried away the horrible scent that spread everywhere. But the excitement remained.

The first friend whom Bambi saw again was Ronno. He was limping more than ever.

"Over in the oak grove the fox has a burning fever from his wound," Ronno said. "I just passed him. He's suffering terribly. He keeps biting the snow and the ground."

"Have you seen my mother?" asked Bambi.

"No," answered Ronno evasively, and walked quickly away.

Later during the night Bambi met old Nettla with Faline. All three were delighted to meet.

"Have you seen my mother?" asked Bambi.

"No," Faline answered. "I don't even know where my own mother is."

"Well," said old Nettla cheerfully. "Here's a nice mess. I was so glad that I didn't have to bother with children any more and now I have to look after two at once. I'm heartily grateful."

Bambi and Faline laughed.

They talked about Gobo. Bambi told how he had found him, and they grew so sad they began to cry. But old Nettla would not have them crying. "Before everything else you have got to get something to eat. I never heard of such a thing. You haven't had a bite to eat this livelong day!"

She led them to places where there were still a few leaves that had not completely withered. Old Nettla was wonderfully gentle. She ate nothing herself, but made Bambi and Faline eat heartily. She pawed away the snow from the grassy spots and ordered them to eat with "The grass is good here." Or else she would say, "No, wait. We'll find something better farther on." But between whiles she would grumble. "It's perfectly ridiculous the trouble children give you."

Suddenly they saw Aunt Ena coming and rushed toward her. "Aunt Ena," cried Bambi. He had seen her first. Faline was beside herself with joy and bounded around her. "Mother," she cried. But Ena was weeping and nearly dead from exhaustion.

"Gobo is gone," she cried. "I've looked for him. I went to the little place where he lay down when he broke down in the snow . . . there was nothing there . . . he is gone . . . my poor Gobo . . ."

Old Nettla grumbled. "If you had looked for his tracks it would have been more sensible than crying," she said.

"There weren't any tracks," said Aunt Ena. "But . . . His tracks were there. He found Gobo."

She was silent. Then Bambi asked despondently, "Aunt Ena, have you seen my mother?"

"No," answered Aunt Ena gently.

Bambi never saw his mother again.

≈ ≈ ≈

THE TRAITOR

The forest was again under snow, lying silent beneath its deep white mantle. Only the crows' calls could be heard. Now and then came a magpie's noisy chattering. The soft twittering of the tit-mice sounded timidly. Then the frost hardened and everything grew still. The air began to hum with the cold.

One morning a dog's baying broke the silence.

It was a continuous hurrying bay that pressed on quickly through the woods, eager and clear and harrying with loud yelps.

Bambi raised his head in the hollow under the fallen tree, and looked at the old stag who was lying beside him.

"That's nothing," said the old stag in answer to Bambi's glance, "nothing that need bother us."

Still they both listened.

They lay in their hollow with the old beech trunk like a sheltering roof above them. The deep snow kept the icy draught from them, and the tangled bushes hid them from curious eyes.

The baying grew nearer. It was angry and panting and relentless. It sounded like the bark of a small hound. It came constantly closer.

Then they heard panting of another kind. They heard a low labored snarling under the angry barking. Bambi grew uneasy, but the old stag quieted him again. "We don't need to worry about it," he said. They lay silent in their warm hollow and peered out.

The footsteps drew nearer and nearer through the branches. The snow dropped from the shaken boughs and clouds of it rose from the earth.

Through the snow and over the roots and branches, the fox came springing, crouching and slinking. They were right; a little, short-legged hound was after him.

One of the fox's forelegs was crushed and the fur torn around it. He held his shattered paw in front of him, and blood poured from his wound. He was gasping for breath. His eyes were staring with terror and exertion. He was beside himself with rage and fear. He was desperate and exhausted.

Once in a while he would face around and snarl so that the dog was startled and would fall back a few steps.

Presently the fox sat down on his haunches. He could go no farther. Raising his mangled forepaw pitifully, with his jaws open and his lips drawn back, he snarled at the dog.

But the dog was never silent for a minute. His high, rasping bark only grew fuller and deeper. "Here," he yapped, "here he is! Here! Here! Here!" He was not abusing the fox. He was not even speaking to him, but was urging on someone else who was still far behind.

Bambi knew as well as the old stag did that it was He the dog was calling.

The fox knew it too. The blood was streaming down from him and fell from his breast into the snow, making a fiery spot on the icy white surface, and steaming slowly.

A weakness overcame the fox. His crushed foot sank down helpless, but a burning pain shot through it when it touched the snow. He lifted it again with an effort and held it quivering in front of him.

"Let me go," said the fox beginning to speak, "let me go." He spoke softly and beseechingly. He was quite weak and despondent.

"No! No! No!" the dog howled.

The fox pleaded still more insistently. "We're relations," he pleaded, "we're brothers almost. Let me go home. Let me die with my family at least. We're brothers almost, you and I."

"No! No! No!" the dog raged.

Then the fox rose so that he was sitting perfectly erect. He dropped his handsome pointed muzzle on his bleeding breast, raised his eyes and looked the dog straight in the face. In a completely altered voice, restrained and embittered, he growled, "Aren't you ashamed, you traitor!"

"No! No! No!" yelped the dog.

But the fox went on, "You turncoat, you renegade!" His maimed body was taut with contempt and hatred. "You spy," he hissed, "you blackguard, you track us where He could never find us. You betray us, your own relations, me who am almost your brother. And you stand there and aren't ashamed!"

Instantly many other voices sounded loudly round about.

"Traitor!" cried the magpie from the tree.

"Spy!" shrieked the jay.

"Blackguard!" the weasel hissed.

"Renegade!" snarled the ferret.

From every tree and bush came chirpings, peepings, shrill cries, while overhead the crows cawed, "Spy! Spy!" Everyone had rushed up, and from the trees or from safe hiding places on the ground, they watched the contest. The fury that had burst from the fox released an embittered anger in them all. And the blood spilt on the snow, that steamed before their eyes, maddened them and made them forget all caution.

The dog stared around him. "Who are you?" he yelped. "What do you want? What do you know about it? What are you talking about? Everything belongs to Him, just as I do. But I, I love Him. I worship Him, I serve Him. Do you think you can oppose Him, poor creatures like you? He's all-powerful. He's above all of you. Everything we have comes from Him. Everything that lives or grows comes from Him." The dog was quivering with exultation.

"Traitor!" cried the squirrel shrilly.

"Yes, traitor!" hissed the fox. "Nobody is a traitor but you, only you."

The dog was dancing about in a frenzy of devotion. "Only me?" he cried, "you lie. Aren't there many many others on His side? The horse, the cow, the sheep, the chickens, many, many of you and your kind are on His side and worship Him and serve Him."

"They're rabble!" snarled the fox, full of a boundless contempt.

Then the dog could contain himself no longer and sprang for the fox's throat. Growling, spitting, and yelping, they rolled in the snow, a writhing, savagely snapping mass from which fur flew. The snow rose in clouds and was spattered with fine drops of blood. At last the fox could not fight any more. In a few seconds he was lying on his back, his white belly uppermost. He twitched and stiffened and died.

The dog shook him a few times, then let him fall on the trampled snow. He stood beside him, his legs planted, calling in a deep, loud voice, "Here! Here! He's here!"

The others were horrorstruck and fled in all directions.

"Dreadful," said Bambi softly to the old stag in the hollow.

"The most dreadful part of all," the old stag answered, "is that the dogs believe what the hound just said. They believe it, they pass their lives in fear, they hate Him and themselves and yet they'd die for His sake."

The Tyger

WILLIAM BLAKE

Tyger, Tyger, burning bright
In the forests of the night
What immortal hand or eye
Could frame thy fearful symmetry?

In what distant deeps or skies
Burnt the fire of thine eyes?
On what wings dare he aspire?
What the hand dare seize the fire?

And what shoulder, and what art,
Could twist the sinews of thy heart?
And when thy heart began to beat,
What dread hand? and what dread feet?

What the hammer? what the chain,
In what furnace was thy brain?
What the anvil? what dread grasp
Dare its deadly terrors clasp?

When the stars threw down their spears,
And water'd heaven with their tears,
Did he smile his work to see?
Did he who made the Lamb make thee?

Tyger, Tyger, burning bright
In the forests of the night,
What immortal hand or eye
Dare frame thy fearful symmetry?

David and Goliath

≈ ≈ ≈ *The Bible is full of marvelous stories that do not need to be simplified for young readers. The archaic words and splendid rhythms of the King James translation contribute to the charm and wonder of the old tales. Saul, of course, was the first King of the Jews. David was a shepherd boy. A "target" was a small shield and "greaves" were armor worn to protect the shins.*

Now the Philistines gathered together their armies to battle, and were gathered together at Shochoh, which belongeth to Judah, and pitched between Shochoh and Azekah, in Ephes-dammim. And Saul and the men of Israel were gathered together, and pitched by the valley of Elah, and set the battle in array against the Philistines. And the Philistines stood on a mountain on the one side, and Israel stood on a mountain on the other side: and there was a valley between them.

And there went out a champion out of the camp of the Philistines, named Goliath, of Gath, whose height was six cubits and a span. And he had an helmet of brass upon his head, and he was armed with a coat of mail; and the weight of the coat was five thousand shekels of brass. And he had greaves of brass upon his legs, and a target of brass between his shoulders. And the staff of his spear was like a weaver's beam; and his spear's head weighed six hundred shekels of iron: and one bearing a shield went before him. And he stood and cried unto the armies of Israel, and said unto them, Why are ye come out to set your battle in array? am not I a Philistine, and ye servants to Saul? choose you a man for you, and let him come down to me. If he be able to fight with me, and to kill me, then will we be your servants: but if I prevail against him, and kill him, then shall ye be our servants, and serve us. And the Philistine said, I defy the armies of Israel this day; give me a man, that we may fight together. When Saul and all Israel heard those words of the Philistine, they were dismayed, and greatly afraid.

Now David was the son of that Ephrathite of Beth-lehem-judah, whose name was Jesse; and he had eight sons: and the man went among men for an old man in the days of Saul. And the three eldest sons of Jesse went and followed Saul to the battle: and the names of his three sons that went to the battle were Eliab the firstborn, and next unto him Abinadab, and the third Shammah. And David was the youngest: and the three eldest followed Saul. But David went and returned from Saul to feed his father's sheep at Beth-lehem. And the Philistine drew near morning and evening, and presented himself forty days. And Jesse said unto David his son, Take now for thy brethren an ephah of this parched corn, and these ten loaves, and run to the camp to thy brethren; and carry these ten cheeses unto the captain of their thousand, and look how thy brethren fare, and take their pledge. Now Saul, and they, and all the men of Israel, were in the valley of Elah, fighting with the Philistines.

And David rose up early in the morning, and left the sheep with a keeper, and took, and went, as Jesse had commanded him; and he came to the trench, as the host was going forth to the fight, and shouted for the battle. For Israel and the Philistines had put the battle in array, army against army. And David left his carriage in the hand of the keeper of the carriage, and ran into the army, and came and saluted his brethren. And as he talked with them, behold, there came up the champion, the Philistine of Gath, Goliath by name, out of the armies of the Philistines, and spake according to the same words: and David heard them. And all the men of Israel, when they saw the man, fled from him, and were sore afraid. And the men of Israel said, Have ye seen this man that is come up? surely to defy Israel is he come up: and it shall be, that the man who killeth him, the king will enrich him with great riches, and will give him his daughter, and make his father's house free in Israel. And David spake to the men that stood by him, saying, What shall be done to the man that killeth this Philistine, and taketh away the reproach from Israel? for who is this uncircumcised Philistine, that he should defy the armies of the living God? And the people answered him after this manner, saying, So shall it be done to the man that killeth him.

And Eliab his eldest brother heard when he spake unto the men; and Eliab's anger was kindled against David, and he said, Why camest thou down hither? and with whom has thou left those few sheep in the wilderness? I know thy pride, and the naughtiness of thine heart; for thou art come down that thou mightest see the battle. And David said, What have I now done? Is there not a cause?

And he turned from him toward another, and spake after the same manner: and the people answered him again after the former manner. And when the words were heard which David spake, they rehearsed them before Saul: and he sent for him.

And David said to Saul, Let no man's heart fail because of him; thy servant will go and fight with this Philistine. And Saul said to David, Thou art not able to go against this Philistine to fight with him: for thou art but a youth, and he a man of war from his youth. And David said unto Saul, Thy servant kept his father's sheep, and there came a lion, and a bear, and took a lamb out of the flock: and I went out after him, and smote him, and delivered it out of his mouth: and when he arose against me, I caught him by his beard, and smote him, and slew him. Thy servant slew both the lion and the bear: and this uncircumcised Philistine shall be as one of them, seeing he hath defied the armies of the living God. David said moreover, The LORD that delivered me out of the paw of the lion, and out of the paw of the bear, he will deliver me out of the hand of this Philistine. And Saul said unto David, Go, and the LORD be with thee.

And Saul armed David with his armour, and he put an helmet of brass upon his head; also he armed him with a coat of mail. And David girded his sword upon his armour, and he assayed to go; for he had not proved it. And David said unto Saul, I cannot go with these; for I have not proved them. And David put them off him. And he took his staff in his hand, and chose him five smooth stones out of the brook, and put them in a shepherd's bag which he had, even in a scrip; and his sling was in his hand: and he drew near to the Philistine. And the Philistine came on and drew near unto David; and the man that bare the shield went before him. And when the Philistine looked about, and saw David, he disdained him: for he was but a youth, and ruddy, and of a fair countenance. And the Philistine said unto David, Am I a dog, that thous comest to me with staves? And the Philistine cursed David by his gods. And the Philistine said to David, Come to me, and I will give thy flesh unto the fowls of the air, and to the beasts of the field. Then said David to the Philistine, Thou comest to me with a sword, and with a spear, and with a shield: but I come to thee in the name of the LORD of hosts, the God of the armies of Israel, whom thou hast defied. This day will the LORD deliver thee into mine hand; and I will smite thee, and take thine head from thee; and I will give the carcases of the host of the Philistines this day unto the fowls of the air, and to the wild beasts of the earth; that all the earth may know that there is a God in Israel. And all this assembly shall know that the LORD saveth not with sword and spear: for the battle is the LORD's, and he will give you into our hands. And it came to pass, when the Philistine arose, and came and drew nigh to meet David, that David hasted, and ran toward the army to meet the Philistine. And David put his hand in his bag, and took thence a stone, and slang it, and smote the Philistine in his forehead, that the stone sunk into his forehead; and he fell upon his face to the earth. So David prevailed over the Philistine with a sling and with a stone, and smote the Philistine, and slew him; but there was no sword in the hand of David. Therefore David ran, and stood upon the Philistine, and took his sword, and drew it out of the sheath thereof, and slew him, and cut off his head therewith. And when the Philistines saw their champion was dead, they fled. And the men of Israel and of Judah arose, and shouted, and pursued the Philistines, until thou come to the valley, and to the gates of Ekron. And the wounded of the Philistines fell down by the way to Shaaraim, even unto Gath, and unto Ekron. And the children of Israel returned from chasing after the Philistines, and they spoiled their tents. And David took the head of the Philistine, and brought it to Jerusalem; but he put his armour in his tent.

And when Saul saw David go forth against the Philistine he said unto Abner, the captain of the host, Abner, whose son is this youth? And Abner said, As thy soul liveth, O king, I cannot tell. And the king said, Enquire thou whose son the stripling is. And as David returned from the slaughter of the Philistine, Abner took him, and brought him before Saul with the head of the Philistine in his hand. And Saul said to him, Whose son art thou, thou young man? And David answered, I am the son of thy servant Jesse the Beth-lehemite.

Saint Crispin's Day

WILLIAM SHAKESPEARE

≋ ≋ ≋ *Love of honor and glory, which throughout history has inspired many deeds of courage and self-sacrifice, has never been expressed more eloquently than in this speech by Henry V, England's heroic warrior-king, before the Battle of Agincourt.*

Westmoreland: O that we now had here
   But one ten thousand of those men in England
   That do no work to-day!

King Henry: What's he that wishes so?
   My cousin Westmoreland? No, my fair cousin:
   If we are marked to die, we are enow
   To do our country loss; and if to live,
   The fewer men, the greater share of honour.
   God's will! I pray thee, wish not one man more.
   By Jove, I am not covetous for gold,
   Nor care I who doth feed upon my cost;
   It yearns me not if men my garments wear:
   Such outward things dwell not in my desires:
   But if it be a sin to covet honour,
   I am the most offending soul alive.
   No, faith, my coz, wish not a man from England.
   God's peace! I would not lose so great an honour
   As one man more, methinks, would share from me
   For the best hope I have. O, do not wish one more!
   Rather proclaim it, Westmoreland, through my host,
   That he which hath no stomach to this fight,
   Let him depart: his passport shall be made
   And crowns for convoy put into his purse.
   We would not die in that man's company

That fears his fellowship to die with us.
This day is called the feast of Crispian:
He that outlives this day, and comes safe home,
Will stand a tip-toe when this day is named,
And rouse him at the name of Crispian.
He that shall see this day, and live old age,
Will yearly on the vigil feast his neighbours,
And say, 'To-morrow is Saint Crispian.'
Then will he strip his sleeve and show his scars,
And say 'These wounds I had on Crispin's day.'
Old men forget; yet all shall be forgot,
But he'll remember with advantages
What feats he did that day. Then shall our names,
Familiar in his mouth as household words,
Harry the King, Bedford and Exeter,
Warwick and Talbot, Salisbury and Gloucester,
Be in their flowing cups freshly remembered.
This story shall the good man teach his son;
And Crispin Crispian shall ne'er go by,
From this day to the ending of the world,
But we in it shall be remembered:
We few, we happy few, we band of brothers;
For he to-day that sheds his blood with me
Shall be my brother; be he ne'er so vile,
This day shall gentle his condition:
And gentlemen in England now abed
Shall think themselves accursed they were not here,
And hold their manhoods cheap whiles any speaks
That fought with us upon Saint Crispin's day.

Education in the Forest Sauvage

T . H . WHITE

≈ ≈ ≈ *Long ago when knights and even dragons roamed the forests of England, an orphan boy called the Wart lived in Sir Ector's castle in the Forest Sauvage. No boy ever enjoyed so grand an education, because the Wart's tutor was Merlyn the magician, who performed several great magics so the Wart could learn about power and courage.* —*From* The Once and Future King

POWER

They were staring down into the moat. It was the season of water-lilies. If Sir Ector had not kept one section free of them for the boys' bathing, all the water would have been covered. As it was, about twenty yards on each side of the bridge were cut each year, and one could dive in from the bridge itself. The moat was deep. It was used as a stew, so that the inhabitants of the castle could have fish on Fridays, and for this reason the architects had been careful not to let the drains and sewers run into it. It was stocked with fish every year.

"I wish I was a fish," said the Wart.

"What sort of fish?"

It was almost too hot to think about this, but the Wart stared down into the cool amber depths where a school of small perch were aimlessly hanging about.

"I think I should like to be a perch," he said. "They are braver than the silly roach, and not quite so slaughterous as the pike are."

Merlyn took off his hat, raised his staff of lignum vitæ politely in the air, and said slowly, "Snylrem stnemilpmoc ot enutpen dna lliw eh yldnik tpecca siht yob sa a hsif?"

Immediately there was a loud blowing of sea-shells, conches and so forth, and a stout, jolly-looking gentleman appeared seated on a well-blown-up cloud above the battlements. He had an anchor tattooed on his stomach and a handsome mermaid with Mabel written under her on his chest. He ejected a quid of tobacco, nodded affably to Merlyn

140

and pointed his trident at the Wart. The Wart found he had no clothes on. He found that he had tumbled off the drawbridge, landing with a smack on his side in the water. He found that the moat and the bridge had grown hundreds of times bigger. He knew that he was turning into a fish.

"Oh, Merlyn," he cried, "please come too."

"For this once," said a large and solemn tench beside his ear, "I will come. But in future you will have to go by yourself. Education is experience, and the essence of experience is self-reliance."

The Wart found it difficult to be a new kind of creature. It was no good trying to swim like a human being, for it made him go corkscrew and much too slowly. He did not know how to swim like a fish.

"Not like that," said the tench in ponderous tones. "Put your chin on your left shoulder and do jack-knives. Never mind about the fins to begin with."

The Wart's legs had fused together into his backbone and his feet and toes had become a tail fin. His arms had become two more fins—of a delicate pink—and he had sprouted some more somewhere about his stomach. His head faced over his shoulder, so that when he bent in the middle his toes were moving toward his ear instead of toward his forehead. He was a beautiful olive-green, with rather scratchy plate-armour all over him, and dark bands down his sides. He was not sure which were his sides and which were his back and front, but what now appeared to be his belly had an attractive whitish colour, while his back was armed with a splendid great fin that could be erected for war and had spikes in it. He did jack-knives as the tench directed and found that he was swimming vertically downward into the mud.

"Use your feet to turn to left or right," said the tench, "and spread those fins on your tummy to keep level. You are living in two planes now, not one."

The Wart found that he could keep more or less level by altering the inclination of his arm fins and the ones on his stomach. He swam feebly off, enjoying himself very much.

"Come back," said the tench. "You must learn to swim before you can dart."

The Wart returned to his tutor in a series of zig-zags and remarked, "I do not seem to keep quite straight."

"The trouble with you is that you do not swim from the shoulder. You swim as if you were a boy, bending at the hips. Try doing your jack-knives right from the neck downward, and move your body exactly the same amount to the right as you are going to move it to the left. Put your back into it."

Wart gave two terrific kicks and vanished altogether in a clump of mare's tail several yards away.

"That's better," said the tench, now out of sight in the murky olive water, and the Wart backed himself out of his tangle with infinite trouble, by wriggling his arm fins. He undulated back toward the voice in one terrific shove, to show off.

"Good," said the tench, as they collided end to end. "But direction is the better part of valour."

"Try if you can do this one," it added.

Without apparent exertion of any kind it swam off backward under a water-lily. Without apparent exertion—but the Wart, who was an enterprising learner, had been watching the slightest movement of its fins. He moved his own fins anti-clockwise, gave the tip of his tail a cunning flick, and was lying alongside the tench.

"Splendid," said Merlyn. "Let us go for a little swim."

The Wart was on an even keel now, and reasonably able to move about. He had leisure to look at the extraordinary universe into which the tattooed gentleman's trident had plunged him. It was different from the universe to which he had been accustomed. For one thing, the heaven or sky above him was now a perfect circle. The horizon had closed to this. In order to imagine yourself into the Wart's position, you would have to picture a round horizon, a few inches about your head, instead of the flat horizon which you usually see. Under this horizon of air you would have to imagine another horizon of under water, spherical and practically upside down—for the surface of the water acted partly as a mirror to what was below it. It is difficult to imagine. What makes it a great deal more difficult to imagine is that everything which human beings would consider to be above the water level was fringed with all the colours of the spectrum. For instance, if you had happened to be fishing for the Wart, he would have seen you, at the rim of the tea saucer which was the upper air to him, not as one person waving a fishing-rod, but as seven people, whose outlines were red, orange, yellow, green, blue, indigo, and violet, all waving the same rod whose colours were as varied. In fact, you would have been a rainbow man to him, a beacon of flashing and radiating colours, which ran into one another and had rays all about. You would have burned upon the water like Cleopatra in the poem.

The next most lovely thing was that the Wart had no weight. He was not earth-bound any more and did not have to plod along on a flat surface, pressed down by gravity and the weight of the atmosphere. He could do what men have always wanted to do, that is, fly. There is practically no difference between flying in the water and flying in the air. The best of it was that he did not have to fly in a machine, by pulling levers and sitting still, but could do it with his own body. It was like the dreams people have.

Just as they were going to swim off on their tour of inspection, a timid young roach appeared from between two waving bottle bushes of mare's tail and hung about, looking pale with agitation. It looked at them with big, apprehensive eyes and evidently wanted something, but could not make up its mind.

"Approach," said Merlyn gravely.

At this the roach rushed up like a hen, burst into tears, and began stammering its message.

"If you p-p-p-please, doctor," stammered the poor creature, gabbling so that they could scarcely understand what it said, "we have such a d-dretful case of s-s-s-something or other in our family, and we w-w-w-wondered if you could s-s-s-spare the time? It's our d-d-d-dear Mamma, who w-w-w-will swim a-a-all the time upside d-d-d-down, and she d-d-d-does look so horrible and s-s-s-speaks so strange, that we r-r-r-really thought she ought to have a doctor, if it w-w-w-wouldn't be too much? C-C-C-Clara says to say so, Sir, if you s-s-s-see w-w-w-what I m-m-m-mean?"

Here the poor roach began fizzing so much, what with its stammer and its tearful disposition, that it became quite inarticulate and could only stare at Merlyn with mournful eyes.

"Never mind, my little man," said Merlyn. "There, there, lead me to your dear Mamma, and we shall see what we can do."

They all three swam off into the murk under the drawbridge, upon their errand of mercy.

"Neurotic, these roach," whispered Merlyn, behind his fin. "It is probably a case of nervous hysteria, a matter for the psychologist rather than the physician."

The roach's Mamma was lying on her back as he had described. She was squinting, had folded her fins on her chest, and every now and then she blew a bubble. All her children were gathered round her in a circle, and every time she blew they nudged each other and gasped. She had a seraphic smile on her face.

"Well, well, well," said Merlyn, putting on his best bed-side manner, "and how is Mrs. Roach today?"

He patted the young roaches on the head and advanced with stately motions toward his patient. It should perhaps be mentioned that Merlyn was a ponderous, deep-beamed fish of about five pounds, leather coloured, with small scales, adipose in his fins, rather slimy, and having a bright marigold eye—a respectable figure.

Mrs. Roach held out a languid fin, sighed emphatically and said, "Ah, doctor, so you've come at last?"

"Hum," said the physician, in his deepest tone.

Then he told everybody to close their eyes—the Wart peeped—and began to swim around the invalid in a slow and stately dance. As he danced he sang. His song was this:

> Therapeutic,
> Elephantic,
> Diagnosis,
> Boom!
> Pancreatic,
> Microstatic,
> Anti-toxic,
> Doom!

> With a normal catabolism,
> Gabbleism and babbleism,
> Snip Snap, Snorum,
> Cut out his abdonorum.
> Dyspepsia,
> Anaemia,
> Toxaemia.
> One, two, three,
> And out goes He,
> With a fol-de-rol-derido for the Five Guinea Fee.

At the end of the song he was swimming round his patient so close that he actually touched her, stroking his brown smooth-scaled flanks against her more rattly pale ones. Perhaps he was healing her with his slime—for all the fishes are said to go to the Tench for medicine—or perhaps it was by touch or massage or hypnotism. In any case, Mrs.

Roach suddenly stopped squinting, turned the right way up, and said, "Oh, doctor, dear doctor, I feel I could eat a little lob-worm now."

"No lob-worm," said Merlyn, "not for two days. I shall give you a prescription for a strong broth of algae every two hours, Mrs. Roach. We must build up your strength, you know. After all, Rome was not built in a day."

Then he patted all the little roaches once more, told them to grow up into brave little fish, and swam off with an air of importance into the gloom. As he swam, he puffed his mouth in and out.

"What did you mean by that about Rome?" asked the Wart, when they were out of earshot.

"Heaven knows."

They swam along, Merlyn occasionally advising him to put his back into it when he forgot, and the strange under-water world began to dawn about them, deliciously cool after the heat of the upper air. The great forests of weed were delicately traced, and in them there hung motionless many schools of sticklebacks learning to do their physical exercises in strict unison. On the word One they all lay still; at Two they faced about; at Three they all shot together into a cone, whose apex was a bit of something to eat. Water snails slowly ambled about on the stems of the lilies or under their leaves, while fresh-water mussels lay on the bottom doing nothing in particular. Their flesh was salmon pink, like a very good strawberry cream ice. The small congregations of perch—it was a strange thing, but all the bigger fish seemed to have hidden themselves—had delicate circulations, so that they blushed or grew pale as easily as a lady in a Victorian novel. Only their blush was a deep olive colour, and it was the blush of rage. Whenever Merlyn and his companion swam past them, they raised their spiky dorsal fins in menace, and only lowered them when they saw that Merlyn was a tench. The black bars on their sides made them look as if they had been grilled, and these also could become darker or lighter. Once the two travellers passed under a swan. The white creature floated above like a Zeppelin, all indistinct except what was under the water. The latter part was quite clear and showed that the swan was floating slightly on one side with one leg cocked over its back.

"Look," said the Wart, "it is the poor swan with the deformed leg. It can only paddle with one leg, and the other side of it is hunched."

"Nonsense," said the swan snappily, putting its head into the water and giving them a frown with its black nares. "Swans like to rest in this position, and you can keep your fishy sympathy to yourself, so there." It continued to glare at them from up above, like a white snake suddenly let down through the ceiling, until they were out of sight.

"You swim along," said the tench, "as if there was nothing to be afraid of in the world. Don't you see that this place is exactly like the forest which you had to come through to find me?"

"Is it?"

"Look over there."

The Wart looked, and at first saw nothing. Then he saw a small translucent shape hanging motionless near the surface. It was just outside the shadow of a water-lily and was evidently enjoying the sun. It was a baby pike, absolutely rigid and probably asleep, and it looked like a pipe stem or a sea-horse stretched out flat. It would be a brigand when it grew up.

"I am taking you to see one of those," said the tench, "the Emperor of these purlieus. As a doctor I have immunity, and I dare say he will respect you as my companion as well—but you had better keep your tail bent in case he is feeling tyrannical."

"Is he the King of the Moat?"

"He is. Old Jack they call him, and some call him Black Peter, but for the most part they do not mention him by name at all. They just call him Mr. P. You will see what it is to be a king."

The Wart began to hang behind his conductor a little, and perhaps it was as well that he did, for they were almost on top of their destination before he noticed it. When he did see the old despot he started back in horror, for Mr. P. was four feet long, his weight incalculable. The great body, shadowy and almost invisible among the stems, ended in a face which had been ravaged by all the passions of an absolute monarch— by cruelty, sorrow, age, pride, selfishness, loneliness and thoughts too strong for individual brains. There he hung or hoved, his vast ironic mouth permanently drawn downward in a kind of melancholy, his lean clean-shaven chops giving him an American expression, like that of Uncle Sam. He was remorseless, disillusioned, logical, predatory, fierce, pitiless—but his great jewel of an eye was that of a stricken deer, large, fearful, sensitive and full of griefs. He made no movement, but looked upon them with his bitter eye.

The Wart thought to himself that he did not care for Mr. P.

"Lord," said Merlyn, not paying attention to his nervousness, "I have brought a young professor who would learn to profess."

"To profess what?" asked the King of the Moat slowly, hardly opening his jaws and speaking through his nose.

"Power," said the tench.

"Let him speak for himself."

"Please," said the Wart, "I don't know what I ought to ask."

"There is nothing, said the monarch, "except the power which you pretend to seek: power to grind and power to digest, power to seek and power to find, power to await and power to claim, all power and pitilessness springing from the nape of the neck."

"Thank you."

"Love is a trick played on us by the forces of evolution. Pleasure is the bait laid down by the same. There is only power. Power is of the individual mind, but the mind's power is not enough. Power of the body decides everything in the end, and only Might is Right.

"Now I think it is time that you should go away, young master, for I find this conversation uninteresting and exhausting. I think you ought to go away really almost at once, in case my disillusioned mouth should suddenly determine to introduce you to my great gills, which have teeth in them also. Yes, I really think you might be wise to go away this moment. Indeed, I think you ought to put your back into it. And so, a long farewell to all my greatness."

The Wart had found himself almost hypnotized by the big words, and had hardly noticed that the tight mouth was coming closer and closer to him. It came imperceptibly, as the lecture distracted his attention, and suddenly it was looming within an inch of his nose. On the last sentence it opened, horrible and vast, the skin stretching ravenously from bone to bone and tooth to tooth. Inside there seemed to be nothing but teeth, sharp teeth like thorns in rows and ridges everywhere, like the nails in labourers' boots, and it was only at the last second that he was able to regain his own will, to pull himself together, to recollect his instructions and to escape. All those teeth clashed behind him at the tip of his tail, as he gave the heartiest jack-knife he had ever given.

In a second he was on dry land once again, standing beside Merlyn on the piping drawbridge, panting in his stuffy clothes.

〜 〜 〜 *Peregrine falcons, merlins, kestrels and spar-hawks are all varieties of hawks. For many centuries training them to catch and kill other birds has been an aristocratic sport. "Timor Mortis Conturbat Me" means "Fear of death frightens me." "Bruckle" means frail and "slee" means crafty.*

COURAGE

Wart draggled off to the tower room, where Merlyn was busy knitting himself a woollen night-cap for the winter.

"I cast off two together at every other line," said the magician, "but for some reason it seems to end too sharply. Like an onion. It is the turning of the heel that does one, every time."

"I think I ought to have some eddication," said the Wart. "I can't think of anything to do."

"You think that education is something which ought to be done when all else fails?" inquired Merlyn nastily, for he was in a bad mood too.

"Well," said the Wart, "some sorts of education."

"Mine?" asked the magician with flashing eyes.

"Oh, Merlyn," exclaimed the Wart without answering, "please give me something to do, because I feel so miserable. Nobody wants me for anything today, and I just don't know how to be sensible. It rains so."

"You should learn to knit."

"Could I go out and be something, a fish or anything like that?"

"You have been a fish," said Merlyn. "Nobody with any go needs to do their education twice."

"Well, could I be a bird?"

"If you knew anything at all," said Merlyn, "which you do not, you would know that a bird does not like to fly in the rain because it wets its feathers and makes them stick together. They get bedraggled."

"I could be a hawk in Hob's mews," said the Wart stoutly. "Then I should be indoors and not get wet."

"That is pretty ambitious," said the old man, "to want to be a hawk."

"You know you will turn me into a hawk when you want to," shouted the Wart, "but you like to plague me because it is wet. I won't have it."

"Hoity-toity!"

"Please," said the Wart, "dear Merlyn, turn me into a hawk. If you don't do that I shall do something. I don't know what."

Merlyn put down his knitting and looked at his pupil over the top of his spectacles. "My boy," he said, "you shall be everything in the world, animal, vegetable, mineral, protista or virus, for all I care—before I have done with you—but you will have to trust to my superior back-sight. The time is not yet ripe for you to be a hawk—for one thing Hob is still in the mews feeding them—so you may as well sit down for the moment and learn to be a human being."

"Very well," said the Wart, "if that's a go." And he sat down.

After several minutes he said, "Is one allowed to speak as a human being, or does the thing about being seen and not heard have to apply?"

"Everybody can speak."

"That's good, because I wanted to mention that you have been knitting your beard into the night-cap for three rows now."

"Well, I'll be . . ."

"I should think the best thing would be to cut off the end of your beard. Shall I fetch some scissors?"

"Why didn't you tell me before?"

"I wanted to see what would happen."

"You run a grave risk, my boy," said the magician, "of being turned into a piece of bread, and toasted."

With this he slowly began to unpick his beard, muttering to himself meanwhile and taking the greatest precautions not to drop a stitch.

"Will it be as difficult to fly," asked the Wart when he thought his tutor had calmed down, "as it was to swim?"

"You will not need to fly. I don't mean to turn you into a loose hawk, but only to set you in the mews for the night, so that you can talk to the others. That is the way to learn, by listening to the experts."

"Will they talk?"

"They talk every night, deep into the darkness. They say about how they were taken, about what they can remember of their homes: about their lineage and the great deeds of their ancestors, about their training and what they have learned and will learn. It is military conversation really, like you might have in the mess of a crack cavalry regiment:

tactics, small arms, maintenance, betting, famous hunts, wine, women and song."

"Another subject they have," he continued, "is food. It is a depressing thought, but of course they are mainly trained by hunger. They are a hungry lot, poor chaps, thinking of the best restaurants where they used to go, and how they had champagne and caviare and gypsy music. Of course, they all come of noble blood."

"What a shame that they should be kept prisoners and be hungry."

"Well, they do not really understand that they are prisoners, any more than the cavalry officers do. They look on themselves as being dedicated to their profession, like an order of knighthood or something of that sort. You see, the membership of the mews is, after all, restricted to the raptors—and that does help a lot. They know that none of the lower classes can get in. Their screen perches don't carry blackbirds or such trash as that. And then, as to the hungry part, they are far from starving or that kind of hunger. They are in training, you know, and like everybody in strict training, they think about food."

"How soon can I begin?"

"You can begin right now, if you want to. My insight tells me that Hob has this minute finished for the night. But first of all you must choose what kind of hawk you would prefer to be."

"I should like to be a merlin," said the Wart politely.

This answer flattered the magician. "A very good choice," he said, "and if you please we will proceed at once."

The Wart got up from his stool and stood in front of his tutor. Merlyn put down his knitting.

"First you go small," said he, pressing him on the top of his head until he was a bit smaller than a pigeon. "Then you stand on the ball of your toes, bend at the knees, hold your elbows to your sides, lift your hands to the level of your shoulders, and press your first and second fingers together, as also your third and fourth. Look, it is like this."

With these words the ancient nigromant stood upon tiptoe and did as he had explained.

The Wart copied him carefully and wondered what would happen next. What did happen was that Merlyn, who had been saying the final spells under his breath, suddenly turned himself into a condor, leaving the Wart standing on tiptoe unchanged. He stood there as if he were drying himself in the sun, with a wingspread of about eleven feet, a bright orange head and a magenta carbuncle. He looked very surprised and rather funny.

"Come back," said the Wart. "You have changed the wrong one."

"It is this by-our-lady spring cleaning," exclaimed Merlyn, turning back into himself. "Once you let a woman into your study for half an hour, you do not know where to lay your hands on the right spell, not if it was ever so. Stand up and we will try again."

This time the now tiny Wart felt his toes shooting out and scratching on the floor. He felt his heels rise and stick out behind and his knees draw into his stomach. His thighs became quite short. A web of skin grew from his wrists to his shoulders, while his primary feathers burst out in soft blue quills from the ends of his fingers and quickly grew. His secondaries sprouted along his forearms, and a charming little false primary sprang from the end of each thumb.

The dozen feathers of his tail, with the double deck-feathers in the middle, grew out in the twinkling of an eye, and all the covert feathers of his back and breast and shoulders slipped out of the skin to hide the roots of the more important plumes. Wart looked quickly at Merlyn, ducked his head between his legs and had a look through there, rattled the feathers into place, and began to scratch his chin with the sharp talon of one toe.

"Good," said Merlyn. "Now hop on my hand—ah, be careful and don't gripe—and listen to what I have to tell you. I shall take you into the mews now that Hob has locked up for the night, and I shall put you loose and unhooded beside Balin and Balan. Now pay attention. Don't go close to anybody without speaking first. You must remember that most of them are hooded and might be startled into doing something rash. You can trust Balin and Balan, also the kestrel and the spar-hawk. Don't go within reach of the falcon unless she invites you to. On no account must you stand beside Cully's special enclosure, for he is unhooded and will go for you through the mesh if he gets half a chance. He is not quite right in his brains, poor chap, and if he once grips you, you will never leave his grip alive. Remember that you are visiting a kind of Spartan military mess. These fellows are regulars. As the junior subaltern your only business is to keep your mouth shut, speak when you are spoken to, and not to interrupt."

"I bet I am more than a subaltern," said the Wart, "if I am a merlin."

"Well, as a matter of fact, you are. You will find that both the kestrel and the spar-hawk will be polite to you, but for all sake's sake don't interrupt the senior merlins or the falcon. She is the honorary colonel of the regiment. And as for Cully, well, he is a colonel too, even if he is infantry, so you must mind your p's and q's."

"I will be careful," said the Wart, who was beginning to feel rather scared.

"Good. I shall come for you in the morning, before Hob is up."

All the hawks were silent as Merlyn carried their new companion into the mews, and silent for some time afterward when they had been left in the dark. The rain had given place to a full August moonlight, so clear that you could see a woolly bear caterpillar fifteen yards away out of doors, as it climbed up and up the knobbly sandstone of the great keep, and it took the Wart only a few moments for his eyes to become accustomed to the diffused brightness inside the mews. The darkness became watered with light, with silver radiance, and then it was an eerie sight which dawned upon his vision. Each hawk or falcon stood in the silver upon one leg, the other tucked up inside the apron of its panel, and each was a motionless statue of a knight in armour. They stood gravely in their plumed helmets, spurred and armed. The canvas or sacking screens of their perches moved heavily in a breath of wind, like banners in a chapel, and the rapt nobility of the air kept their knight's vigil in knightly patience. In those days they used to hood everything they could, even the goshawk and the merlin, which are no longer hooded according to modern practice.

Wart drew his breath at the sight of all these stately figures, standing so still that they might have been cut of stone. He was overwhelmed by their magnificence, and felt no need of Merlyn's warning that he was to be humble and behave himself.

Presently there was a gentle ringing of a bell. The great peregrine falcon had bestirred herself and now said, in a high nasal voice which came from her aristocratic nose, "Gentlemen you may converse."

There was dead silence.

Only, in the far corner of the room, which had been netted off for Cully—loose there, unhooded and deep in moult—they could hear a faint muttering from the choleric infantry colonel. "Damned niggers," he was mumbling. "Damned administration. Damned politicians. Damned bolsheviks. Is this a damned dagger that I see before me, the handle toward my hand? Damned spot. Now, Cully, hast thou but one brief hour to live, and then thou must be damned perpetually."

"Colonel" said the peregrine coldly, "not before the younger officers."

"I beg your pardon, Mam," said the poor colonel at once. "It is something that gets into my head, you know. Some deep demnation."

There was silence again, formal, terrible and calm.

"Who is the new officer?" inquired the first fierce and beautiful voice.

Nobody answered.

"Speak for yourself, sir," commanded the peregrine, looking straight before her as if she were talking in her sleep.

They could not see him through their hoods.

"Please," began the Wart, "I am a merlin. . . ."

And he stopped, scared in the stillness.

Balan, who was one of the real merlins standing beside him, leaned over and whispered quite kindly in his ear, "Don't be afraid. Call her Madam."

"I am a merlin, Madam, an it please you."

"A Merlin. That is good. And what branch of the Merlins do you stoop from?"

The Wart did not know in the least what branch he stooped from, but he dared not be found out now in his lie.

"Madam," he said, "I am one of the Merlins of the Forest Sauvage."

There was silence at this again, the silver silence which he had begun to fear.

"There are the Yorkshire Merlins," said the honorary colonel in her slow voice at last, "and the Welsh Merlins, and the McMerlins of the North. Then there are the Salisbury ones, and several from the neighbourhood of Exmoor, and the O'Merlins of Connaught. I do not think I have heard of any family in the Forest Sauvage."

"It would be a cadet branch, Madam," said Balan, "I dare say."

"Bless him," thought the Wart. "I shall catch him a special sparrow tomorrow and give it to him behind Hob's back."

"That will be the solution, Captain Balan, no doubt."

The silence fell again.

At last the peregrine rang her bell. She said, "We will proceed with the catechism, prior to swearing him in."

The Wart heard the spar-hawk on his left giving several nervous coughs at this, but the peregrine paid no attention.

"Merlin of the Forest Sauvage," said the peregrine, "what is a Beast of the Foot?"

"A Beast of the Foot," replied the Wart, blessing his stars that Sir Ector had chosen to give him a First Rate Eddication, "is a horse, or a hound, or a hawk."

"Why are these called beasts of the foot?"

"Because these beasts depend upon the powers of their feet, so that, by law, any damage to the feet of a hawk, hound or horse, is reckoned as damage to its life. A lamed horse is a murdered horse."

"Good," said the peregrine. "What are your most important members?"

"My wings," said the Wart after a moment, guessing because he did not know.

At this there was a simultaneous tintinnabulation of all the bells, as each graven image lowered its raised foot in distress. They stood on both feet now, disturbed.

"Your what?" called the peregrine sharply.

"He said his damned wings," said Colonel Cully from his private enclosure. "And damned be he who first cries Hold, enough!"

"But even a thrush has wings!" cried the kestrel, speaking for the first time in his sharp-beaked alarm.

"Think!" whispered Balan, under his breath.

The Wart thought feverishly.

A thrush had wings, tail, eyes, legs—apparently everything.

"My talons!"

"It will do," said the peregrine kindly, after one of her dreadful pauses. "The answer ought to be Feet, just as it is to all the other questions, but Talons will do."

All the hawks, and of course we are using the term loosely, for some were hawks and some were falcons, raised their belled feet again and sat at ease.

"What is the first law of the foot?"

("Think," said friendly little Balan, behind his false primary.)

The Wart thought, and thought right.

"Never to let go," he said.

"Last question," said the peregrine. "How would you, as a Merlin, kill a pigeon bigger than yourself?"

Wart was lucky in this one, for he had heard Hob giving a description of how Balan did it one afternoon, and he answered warily, "I should strangle her with my foot."

"Good!" said the peregrine.

"Bravo!" cried the others, raising their feathers.

"Ninety per cent," said the spar-hawk after a quick sum. "That is, if you give him a half for the talons."

"The devil damn me black!"

"Colonel, please!"

Balan whispered to the Wart, "Colonel Cully is not quite right in his wits. It is his liver, we believe, but the kestrel says it is the constant strain of living up to her ladyship's standard. He says that her ladyship spoke to him from her full social station once, cavalry to infantry, you know, and that he just closed his eyes and got the vertigo. He has never been the same since."

"Captain Balan," said the peregrine, "it is rude to whisper. We will proceed to swear the new officer in. Now, padre, if you please."

The poor spar-hawk, who had been getting more and more nervous for some time, blushed deeply and began faltering out a complicated oath about varvels, jesses and hoods. "With this varvel," the Wart heard, "I thee endow . . . love, honour and obey . . . till jess us do part."

But before the padre had got to the end of it, he broke down altogether and sobbed out, "Oh, please your ladyship. I beg your pardon, but I have forgotten to keep my tirings."

("Tirings are bones and things," explained Balan, "and of course you have to swear on bones.")

"Forgotten to keep any tirings? But it is your duty to keep tirings."

"I—I know."

"What have you done with them?"

The spar-hawk's voice broke at the enormity of his confession. "I—I ate 'em," wept the unfortunate priest.

Nobody said anything. The dereliction of duty was too terrible for words. All stood on two feet and turned their blind heads toward the culprit. Not a word of reproach was spoken. Only, during an utter silence of five minutes, they could hear the incontinent priest snivelling and hiccoughing to himself.

"Well," said the peregrine at last, "the initiation will have to be put off till tomorrow."

"If you will excuse me, Madam," said Balin, "perhaps we could manage the ordeal tonight? I believe the candidate is loose, for I did not hear him being tied up."

At the mention of an ordeal the Wart trembled within himself and privately determined that Balin should have not one feather of Balan's sparrow next day.

"Thank you, Captain Balin. I was reflecting upon that subject myself."

Balin shut up.

"Are you loose, candidate?"

"Oh, Madam, yes, I am, if you please: but I do not think I want an ordeal."

"The ordeal is customary."

"Let me see," continued the honorary colonel reflectively. "What was the last ordeal we had? Can you remember, Captain Balan?"

"My ordeal, Mam," said the friendly merlin, "was to hang by my jesses during the third watch."

"If he is loose he cannot do that."

"You could strike him yourself, Mam," said the Kestrel, "judiciously, you know."

"Send him over to stand by Colonel Cully while we ring three times," said the other merlin.

"Oh, no!" cried the crazy colonel in an agony out of his remoter darkness. "Oh no, your ladyship. I beg of you not to do that. I am such a damned villain, your ladyship, that I do not answer for the consequences. Spare the poor boy, your ladyship, and lead us not into temptation."

"Colonel, control yourself. That ordeal will do very well."

"Oh, Madam, I was warned not to stand by Colonel Cully."

"Warned? And by whom?"

The poor Wart realised that now he must choose between confessing himself a human, and learning no more of their secrets, or going through with this ordeal to earn his education. He did not want to be a coward.

"I will stand by the Colonel, Madam," he said, immediately noticing that his voice sounded insulting.

The peregrine falcon paid no attention to the tone.

"It is well," she said. "But first we must have the hymn. Now, padre, if you have not eaten your hymns as well as your tirings, will you be so kind as to lead us in Ancient but not Modern No. 23? The Ordeal Hymn.

"And you, Mr. Kee," she added to the kestrel, "you had better keep quiet, for you are always too high."

The hawks stood still in the moonlight, while the spar-hawk counted "One, Two, Three." Then all those curved or toothed beaks opened in their hoods to a brazen unison, and this is what they chanted:

Life is blood, shed and offered,
    The eagle's eye can face this dree.
To beasts of chase the lie is proffered:
    Timor Mortis Conturbat Me.

The beast of foot sings Holdfast only,
    For flesh is bruckle and foot is slee.
Strength to the strong and the lordly and lonely.
    Timor Mortis Exultat Me.

Shame to the slothful and woe to the weak one.
    Death to the dreadful who turn to flee.
Blood to the tearing, the talon'd, the beaked one.
    Timor Mortis are We.

"Very nice," said the peregrine. "Captain Balan, I think you were a little off on the top C. And now, candidate, you will go over and stand next to Colonel Cully's enclosure, while we ring our bells thrice. On the third ring you may move as quickly as you like."

"Very good, Madam," said the Wart, quite fearless with resentment. He flipped his wings and was sitting on the extreme end of the screen perch, next to Cully's enclosure of string netting.

"Boy!" cried the Colonel in an unearthly voice, "don't come near me, don't come near. Ah, tempt not the foul fiend to his damnation."

"I do not fear you, sir," said the Wart. "Do not vex yourself, for no harm will come to either of us."

"No harm, quotha! Ah, go, before it is too late. I feel eternal longings in me."

"Never fear, sir. They have only to ring three times."

At this the knights lowered their raised legs and gave them a solemn shake. The first sweet tinkling filled the room.

"Madam, Madam!" cried the Colonel in torture. "Have pity, have pity on a damned man of blood. Ring out the old, ring in the new. I can't hold off much longer."

"Be brave, sir," said the Wart softly.

"Be brave, sir! Why, but two nights since, one met the duke 'bout midnight in a lane behind Saint Mark's Church, with the leg of a man upon his shoulder: and he howled fearfully."

"It is nothing," said the Wart.

"Nothing! Said he was a wolf, only the difference was a wolf's skin was hairy on the outside, his on the inside. Rip up my flesh and try. Ah, for quietus, with a bare bodkin!"

The bells rang for the second time.

The Wart's heart was thumping, and now the Colonel was sidling toward him along the perch. Stamp, stamp, he went, striking the wood he trod on with a convulsive grip at every pace. His poor, mad, brooding eyes glared in the moonlight, shone against the persecuted darkness of his scowling brow. There was nothing cruel about him, no ignoble passion. He was terrified of the Wart, not triumphing, and he must slay.

"If it were done when 'tis done," whispered the Colonel, "then 'twere well it were done quickly. Who would have thought the young man had so much blood in him?"

"Colonel!" said the Wart, but held himself there.

"Boy!" cried the Colonel. "Speak, stop me, mercy!"

"There is a cat behind you," said the Wart calmly, "or a pine-marten. Look."

The Colonel turned, swift as a wasp's sting, and menaced into the gloom. There was nothing. He swung his wild eyes again upon the Wart, guessing the trick. Then, in the cold voice of an adder, "The bell invites me. Hear it not, Merlin, for it is a knell that summons thee to heaven or to hell."

The third bells were indeed ringing as he spoke, and honour was allowed to move. The ordeal was over and the Wart might fly. But as he moved, but as he flew, quicker than any movement or flight in the world, the terrible sickles had shot from the Colonel's plated legs—not flashed out, for they moved too quick for sight—and with a thump, with a clutch, with an apprehension, like being arrested by a big policeman, the great scimitars had fixed themselves in his retreating thumb.

They fixed themselves, and fixed irrevocably. Gripe, gripe, the enormous thigh muscles tautened in two convulsions. Then the Wart was two yards further down the screen, and Colonel Cully was standing on one foot with a few meshes of string netting and the Wart's false primary, with its covert-feathers, vice-fisted in the other. Two or three minor feathers drifted softly in a moonbeam toward the floor.

"Well stood!" cried Balan, delighted.

"A very gentlemanly exhibition," said the peregrine, not minding that Captain Balan had spoken before her.

"Amen!" said the spar-hawk.

"Brave heart!" said the kestrel.

"Might we give him the Triumph Song?" asked Balin, relenting.

"Certainly," said the peregrine.

And they all sang together, led by Colonel Cully at the top of his voice, all belling triumphantly in the terrible moonlight.

> The mountain birds are sweeter
>   But the valley birds are fatter,
> And so we deem it meeter
>   To carry off the latter.
> We met a cowering coney
>   And struck him through the vitals.
> The coney was like honey
>   And squealed our requitals.
> Some struck the lark in feathers
>   Whose puffing clouds were shed off.
> Some plucked the partridge's nethers,
>   While others pulled his head off.
> But Wart the King of Merlins
>   Struck foot most far before us.
>   His birds and beasts
>   Supply our feasts,
> And his feats our glorious chorus!

"Mark my words," cried the beautiful Balan, "we shall have a regular king in that young candidate. Now, birds, chorus altogether for the last time:"

> But Wart the King of Merlins
>   Struck foot most far before us.
>   His birds and beasts
>   Supply our feasts,
> And his feats our glorious chorus!

"Well!" said the Wart, as he woke up in his own bed next morning, "What a horrible, grand crew!"

Kubla Khan

SAMUEL TAYLOR COLERIDGE

≈ ≈ ≈

In Xanadu did Kubla Khan
   A stately pleasure-dome decree:
Where Alph, the sacred river, ran
Through caverns measureless to man
   Down to a sunless sea.
So twice five miles of fertile ground
   With walls and towers were girdled round:
And here were gardens bright with sinuous rills
Where blossom'd many an incense-bearing tree:
And here were forests ancient as the hills,
Enfolding sunny spots of greenery.

But O, that deep romantic chasm which slanted
Down the green hill athwart a cedarn cover!
A savage place! as holy and enchanted
As e'er beneath a waning moon was haunted
By woman wailing for her demon-lover!
And from this chasm, with ceaseless turmoil seething,
As if this mighty earth in fast thick pants were breathing,
A mighty fountain momently was forced;
Amid whose swift half-intermitted burst
Huge fragments vaulted like rebounding hail,
Or chaffy grain beneath the thresher's flail:
And 'mid these dancing rocks at once and ever
It flung up momently the sacred river.
Five miles meandering with a mazy motion
Through wood and dale the sacred river ran,
Then reach'd the caverns measureless to man,
And sank in tumult to a lifeless ocean:

And 'mid this tumult Kubla heard from far
Ancestral voices prophesying war!

    The shadow of the dome of pleasure
      Floated midway on the waves;
    Where was heard the mingled measure
      From the fountain and the caves.
It was a miracle of rare device,
A sunny pleasure-dome with caves of ice!

    A damsel with a dulcimer
      In a vision once I saw:
    It was an Abyssinian maid,
      And on her dulcimer she play'd,
    Singing of Mount Abora.
    Could I revive within me,
      Her symphony and song,
To such a deep delight 'twould win me,
That with music loud and long,
I would build that dome in air,
That sunny dome! those caves of ice!
And all who heard should see them there,
And all should cry, Beware! Beware!
His flashing eyes, his floating hair!
Weave a circle round him thrice,
    And close your eyes with holy dread
    For he on honey-dew hath fed,
And drunk the milk of Paradise.

The Wrastling Match Between Lord Goldry Bluszco and Gorice XI, King of Witchland

E. R. EDDISON

≋ ≋ ≋ *In the marvelous world of E. R. Eddison's romantic imagination a great war was waged by two semibarbarous peoples called Demons and Witches. The war began when the King of the Witches and a champion of the Demons wrestled in the strange wrestling match described here.* — *From* The Worm Ouroboros

Now began a great company to come forth from the palace and take their stand on either side of the wrastling ground. The Red Foliot sate in his car of polished ebony, drawn by six black horses with flowing manes and tails; before him went his musicians, pipers and minstrels doing their craft, and behind him fifty spearmen, weighed down with armour and ponderous shields that covered them from chin to toe. Their armour was stained with madder, in such wise that they seemed bathed in blood. Mild to look on was the Red Foliot, yet kingly. His skin was scarlet like the head of the green woodpecker. He wore a diadem of silver, and robes of scarlet trimmed with black fur.

So when the Foliots were assembled, one stood forth with a horn at the command of the Red Foliot and blew three blasts. Therewith came forth from their booths the lords of Demonland and their men-at-arms, Juss, Goldry, Spitfire, and Brandoch Daha, all armed as for battle save Goldry, who was muffled in a cloak of cloth of gold with great hearts worked thereon in red silk thread. And from their booths in turn came the lords of Witchland all armed, and their fighting men, and little love there was in the glances they and the Demons cast upon each other. In the midst stalked the King, his great limbs muffled, like Goldry's, in a cloak: and it was black silk lined with black bearskin, and orna-

162

mented with crabs worked in diamonds. The crown of Witchland, fashioned like a hideous crab and encrusted with jewels so thickly that none might discern the iron whereof it was framed, weighed on his beetling brow. His beard was black and bristly, spade-shaped and thick: his hair close cropped. His upper lip was shaved, displaying his sneering mouth, and from the darkness below his eyebrows looked forth eyes that showed a green light, like those of a wolf. Corund walked at the King's left elbow, his giant frame an inch less in stature than the King. Corinius went on the right, wearing a rich cloak of sky-blue tissue over his shining armour. Tall and soldier-like was Corinius, and young and goodly to look upon, with swaggering gait and insolent eye, thick-lipped withal and somewhat heavy of feature, and the sun shone brightly on his shaven jowl.

Now the Red Foliot let sound the horn again, and standing in his ebony car he read out the conditions, as thus:

"O Gorice XI, most glorious King of Witchland, and O Lord Goldry Bluszco, captain of the hosts of Demonland, it is compact betwixt you, and made fast by mighty oaths whereof I, the Red Foliot, am keeper, that ye shall wrastle three falls together on these conditions, namely, that if Gorice the King be victorious, then hath he that glory and withal full liberty to enforce with the sword his claims of lordship over many-mountained Demonland: but if victory fall to the Lord Goldry Bluszco, then shall the Demons let the Witches abide in peace, and they them, and the Witches shall forswear for ever their claims of lordship over the Demons. And you, O King, and you, O Goldry Bluszco, are likewise bound by oath to wrastle fairly and to abide by the ruling of me, the Red Foliot, whom ye are content to choose as your umpire. And I do swear to judge justly between you. And the laws of your wrastling are that neither shall strangle his adversary with his hands, nor bite him, nor claw nor scratch his flesh, nor poach out his eyes, nor smite him with his fists, nor do any other unfair thing against him, but in all other respects ye shall wrastle freely together. And he that shall be brought to earth with hip or shoulder shall be accounted fallen."

The Red Foliot said, "Have I spoken well, O King, and do you swear to these conditions?"

The King said, "I swear."

The Red Foliot asked in like manner, "Dost thou swear to these conditions, O Lord Goldry Bluszco?"

And Goldry answered him, "I swear."

Without more ado the King stepped into the wrastling ground on his side, and Goldry Bluszco on his, and they cast aside their rich mantles and stood forth naked for the wrastling. And folk stood silent for admiration of the thews and sinews of those twain, doubting which were mightier of build and likelier to gain the victory. The King stood taller by a little, and was longer in the arm than Goldry. But the great frame of Goldry showed excellent proportions, each part wedded to each as in the body of a God, and if either were brawnier of chest it was he, and he was thicker of neck than the King.

Now the King mocked Goldry, saying, "Rebellious hound, it is fit that I make demonstration unto thee, and unto these Foliots and Demons that witness our meeting, that I am thy King and Lord not by virtue only of this my crown of Witchland, which I thus put by for an hour, but even by the power of my body over thine and by my might and main. Be satisfied that I will not have done with thee until I have taken away thy life, and sent thy soul squealing bodiless into the unknown. And thy skull and thy marrow-bones will I have away to Carcë, to my palace, to be a token unto all the world that I have been the bane of an hundredth great champion by my wrastling, and thou not least among them that I have slain in that exercise. Thereafter, when I have eaten and drunken and made merry in my royal palace at Carcë, I will sail with my armies over the teeming deep to many-mountained Demonland. And it shall be my footstool, and these other Demons the slaves of me, yea, and the slaves of my slaves."

But the Lord Goldry Bluszco laughed lightly and said to the Red Foliot, "O Red Foliot, I am not come hither to contend with the King of Witchland in windy railing, but to match my strength against his, sinew against sinew."

Now they stood ready, and the Red Foliot made a sign with his hand, and the cymbals clashed for the first bout.

At the clash the two champions advanced and clasped one another with their strong arms, each with his right arm below and left arm above the other's shoulder, until the flesh shrank beneath the might of their arms that were as brazen bands. They swayed a little this way and that, as great trees swaying in a storm, their legs planted firmly so that they seemed to grow out of the ground like the trunks of oak trees. Nor did either yield ground to other, nor might either win a master hold upon his enemy. So swayed they back and forth for a long time, breathing heavily. And now Goldry, gathering his strength, gat the King lifted a little from the ground, and was minded to swing him round and so dash him to earth. But the King, in that moment when he found himself lifted, leaned forward mightily and smote his heel swiftly round Goldry's leg on the outside, striking him behind and a little above the ankle, in such wise that Goldry was fain to loosen his hold on the King; and greatly folk marvelled that he was able in that plight to save himself from being thrown backward by the King. So they gripped again until red wheals rose on their backs and shoulders by reason of the grievous clasping of their arms. And the King on a sudden twisted his body sideways, with his left side turned from Goldry; and catching with his leg Goldry's leg on the inside below the great muscle of the calf, and hugging him yet closer, he lurched mightily against him, striving to pull Goldry backward and so fall upon him and crush him as they fell to earth. But Goldry leaned violently forward, ever tightening his hold on the King, and so violently bare he forward in his strength that the King was baulked of his design; and clutched together they both fell to earth side by side with a heavy crash, and lay bemused while one might count half a score.

The Red Foliot proclaimed them even in this bout, and each returned to his fellows to take breath and rest for a space.

Now while they rested, a flittermouse flew forth from the Witchland booths and went widdershins round the wrastling ground and so returned silently whence she came. Lord Gro saw her, and his heart waxed heavy within him. He spake to Corund and said, "Needs must that I make trial even at this late hour if there be not any means to turn the King from further adventuring of himself, ere all be lost."

Corund said, "Be it as thou wilt, but it will be in vain."

So Gro stood by the King and said, "Lord, give over this wrastling. Great of growth and mightier of limb than any that you did overcome aforetime is this Demon, yet have you vanquished him. For you did throw him, as we plainly saw, and wrongfully hath the Red Foliot judged you evenly matched because in the throwing of him your majesty's self did fall to earth. Tempt not the fates by another bout. Yours is the victory in this wrastling: and now we, your servants, wait but your nod to make a sudden onslaught on these Demons and slay them, as we may lightly overcome them taken at unawares. And for the Foliots, they be peaceful and sheep-like folk, and will be held in awe when we have smitten the Demons with the edge of the sword. So may you depart, O King, with pleasure and great honour, and afterward fare to Demonland and bring it into subjection."

The King looked sourly upon Lord Gro, and said, "Thy counsel is unacceptable and unseasonable. What lieth behind it?"

Gro answered, "There have been omens, O King."

And the King said, "What omens?"

Gro answered and said. "I will not hide it from you, O my Lord the King, that in my sleep about the darkest hour a dream of the night came to my bed and beheld me with a glance so fell that the hairs of my head stood up and pale terror gat hold upon me. And methought the dream smote up the roof above my bed, and the roof yawned to the naked air of the midnight, that laboured with fiery signs, and a bearded star travelling in the houseless dark. And I beheld the roof and the walls one gore of blood. And the dream screeched like the screech-owl, crying, *Witchland from thy hand, O King!* And therewith the whole world seemed lighted in one flame, and with a shout I awoke sweating from the dream."

But the King rolled his eyes in anger upon Lord Gro and said, "Well am I served and faithfully by such false scheming foxes as thou. It ill fits your turn that I should carry this deed to the end with mine own hand only, and in the blindness of your impudent folly ye come to me with tales made for scaring of babes, praying me gently to forgo my glory that thou and thy fellows may make yourselves big in the world's eyes by deeds of arms."

Gro said, "Lord, it is not so."

But the King would not hear him, but said, "Methinks it is for loyal subjects to seek greatness of their King, nor desire to shine of their own brightness. As for this Demon, when thou sayest that I have over-come him thou speakest a gross and impudent lie. In this bout I did but measure myself with him. But thereby know I of a surety that when I put forth my might he will not be able to withstand me; and all ye shall shortly behold how, as one shattereth a stalk of angelica, I will break and shatter the limbs of this Goldry Bluszco. As for thee, false friend, subtle fox, unfaithful servant, this long time am I grown weary of thee slinking up and down my palace devising darkly things I know not: thou, that art nought akin to Witchland, but an outlander, a Goblin exile, a serpent warmed in my bosom to my hurt. But these things shall have an end. When I have put down this Goldry Bluszco, then shall I have leisure to put down thee also."

And Gro bowed in sorrow of heart before the anger of the King, and held his peace.

Now was the horn blown for the second bout, and they stepped into the wrastling ground. At the clashing of the cymbals the King sprang at Goldry as the panther springeth, and with the rush bare him backward and well nigh forth of the wrastling ground. But when they were carried almost among the Demons where they stood to behold the contest, Goldry swung to the left and strove as before to get the King lifted off his feet; but the King foiled him and bent his ponderous weight upon him, so that Goldry's spine was like to have been crushed beneath the murthering violence of the King's arms. Then did the Lord Goldry Bluszco show forth his great power as a wrastler, for, even under the murthering clasp of the King, he by the might that was in the muscles of his brawny chest shook the King first to the right and then to the left; and the King's hold was loosened, and all his skill and mastery but narrowly saved him from a grievous fall. Nor did Goldry delay nor ponder how next to make trial of the King, but sudden as the lightning he slackened his hold and turned, and with his back under the King's belly gave a mighty lift; and they that witnessed it stood amazed in expectancy to see the King thrown over Goldry's head. Yet for all his striving might not Goldry get the King lifted clean off the ground. Twice and three times he strove, and at each trial he seemed further from his aim, and the King bettered his hold. And at the fourth essay that Goldry made to lift the King over his back and fling him headlong, the King thrust him forward and tripped him from behind, so that Goldry was crawled on his hands and knees. And the King clung to him from behind and passed his arms round his body beneath the armpits and so back over the shoulders, being minded to clasp his two hands at the back of Goldry's neck.

Then said Corund, "The Demon is sped already. By this hold hath the King brought to their bane more than three score famous champions. He delayeth only till his fingers be knit together behind the neck of the accursed Demon to draw the head of him forward until the bones of the neck or the breastbone be bursten asunder."

"He delayeth over long for my peace," said Gro.

The King's breath came out of him in great puffs and grunts as he strained to bring his fingers to meet behind Goldry's neck. Nor was it aught else than the hugeness of his neck and burly chest that saved the Lord Goldry Bluszco in that hour of utter destruction. Crawled on his hands and knees he could nowise escape from the hold of the King, neither lay hold on him in turn; howbeit because of the bigness of Goldry's neck and chest it was impossible for the King to fasten that hold upon him, for all his striving.

When the King perceived that this was so, and that he but wasted his strength, he said, "I will loose my hold on thee and let thee up, and we will stand again face to face. For I deem it unworthy to grapple on the ground like dogs."

So they stood up, and wrastled another while in silence. Soon the King made trial once again of the fall whereby he had sought to throw him in the first bout, twisting suddenly his right side against Goldry, and catching with his leg Goldry's leg, and therewith leaning against him with main force. And when as before, Goldry bare forward with great violence, tightening his grip, the King lurched mightily against him, and, being still ill content to have missed his hold that never heretofore had failed him, he thrust his fingers up Goldry's nose in his cruel anger, scratching and clawing at the delicate inner parts of the nostrils in such wise that Goldry was fain to draw back his head. Therewith the King, lurching against him yet more heavily, gat him thrown a grievous fall on his back, and himself fell atop of him, crushing him and stunning him on the earth.

And the Red Foliot proclaimed Gorice the King victorious in this bout.

Therewithal the King turned him back to his Witches, that loudly acclaimed his mastery over Goldry. He said unto Lord Gro, "It is as I have spoken: the testing first, next the bruising, and in the last bout the breaking and killing." And the King looked evilly on Gro. Gro answered him not a word, for his soul was grieved to see blood on the nails and fingers of the King's left hand, and he thought he knew that the King must have been sore bested in this bout, seeing that he must do this beastly deed or ever he might overcome the might of his adversary.

But the Lord Goldry Bluszco when he was come to his senses and had gotten him up from that great fall, spake to the Red Foliot in mickle wrath, saying, "This devil hath overcome me by craft, doing that which it is a shame to do, in that he clawed me with his fingers up my nose."

The sons of Corund raised an uproar at the words of Goldry, loudly crying that he was the greatest liar and dastard; and all they of Witchland shouted and cursed in like manner. But Goldry shouted in a voice like a brazen trumpet that was plain to hear above the clamour of the Witches, "O Red Foliot, judge now fairly betwixt me and King Gorice, as thou art sworn to do. Let him show his finger nails, if there be not blood on them. This fall is void, and I claim that we wrastle it anew." And the lords of Demonland in like manner shouted that this fall should be wrastled anew.

Now the Red Foliot had seen somewhat of what was done, and well was he minded to call the bout void. Yet had he forborne to do this out of fear of King Gorice that had looked upon him with a basilisk's eye, threatening him. And now, while the Red Foliot was troubled in his mind, uncertain between the angry shouts of the Witches and the Demons whether safety lay rather with his honour or with truckling to King Gorice, the King spake a word to Corinius, who went straightway and standing by the Red Foliot spake privily in his ear. And Corinius menaced the Red Foliot, and said, "Beware lest thy mind be swayed by the brow-beating of the Demons. Rightfully hast thou adjudged the victory in this bout unto our Lord the King, and this talk of thrusting of fingers in the nose is but a pretext and a vile imagination of this Goldry Bluszco, who, being thrown fairly before thine eyes and before us all, and perceiving himself unable to stand against the King, now thinketh with his swaggering he can bear it away, and thinketh by cheats and subtleties to avoid defeat. If, against thine own beholding and the witness of us and the plighted word of the King, thou art so hardy as to harken to the guileful persuading of these Demons, yet bethink thee that the King hath overborne ninety and nine great champions in this exercise, and this shall be the hundredth; and bethink thee, too, that Witchland lieth nearer to thine Isles than Demonland by many days' sailing. Hard shall it be for thee to abide the avenging sword of Witchland if thou do him despite, and against thy sworn oath as umpire incline wrongfully to his enemies in this dispute."

So spake Corinius; and the Red Foliot was cowed. Albeit he believed in his heart that the King had done that whereof Goldry accused him, yet for terror of the King and of Corinius that stood by and threatened him he durst not speak his thought, but in sore perplexity gave order for the horn to be blown for the third bout.

And it came to pass at the blowing of the horn that the flittermouse fared forth again from the booths of the Witches, and going widder-shins round about the wrastling ground returned on silent wing whence she came.

When the Lord Goldry Bluszco understood that the Red Foliot would pay no heed to his accusation, he grew red as blood. A fearsome sight it was to behold how he swelled in his wrath, and his eyes blazed like disastrous stars at midnight, and being wood with anger he gnashed his teeth till the froth stood at his lips and slavered down his chin. Now the cymbals clashed for the onset. Therewith ran Goldry upon the King as one straught of his wits, bellowing as he ran, and gripped him by the right arm with both his hands, one at the wrist and one near the shoulder. And so it was that, before the King might move, Goldry spun round with his back to the King and by his mickle strength and the strength of the anger that was in him he heaved the King over his head, hurling him as one hurleth a ponderous spear, head-foremost to the earth. And the King smote the ground with his head, and the bones of his head and his spine were driven together and smashed, and blood flowed from his ears and nose. With the might of that throw Goldry's wrath departed from him and left him strengthless, in such sort that he reeled as he went from the wrastling ground. His brethren, Juss and Spitfire, bare him up on either side, and put his cloak of cloth of gold worked with red hearts about his mighty limbs.

Meanwhile dismay was fallen upon the Witches to behold their King so caught up on a sudden and dashed upon the ground, where he lay crumpled in an heap, shattered like the stalk of an hemlock that one breaketh and shattereth. In great agitation the Red Foliot came down from his car of ebony and made haste thither where the King was fallen; and the lords of Witchland came likewise thither stricken at heart, and Corund lifted the King in his burly arms. But the King was stone dead. So those sons of Corund made a litter with their spears and laid the King on the litter, and spread over him his royal mantle of black silk lined with bearskin, and set the crown of Witchland on his head, and without word spoken bare him away to the Witches' booths. And the other lords of Witchland without word spoken followed after.

The Listeners

WALTER DE LA MARE

≈ ≈ ≈

"Is there anybody there?" said the Traveller,
    Knocking on the moonlit door;
And his horse in the silence champed the grasses
    Of the forest's ferny floor:
And a bird flew up out of the turret,
    Above the Traveller's head:
And he smote upon the door again a second time;
    "Is there anybody there?" he said.
But no one descended to the Traveller;
    No head from the leaf-fringed sill
Leaned over and looked into his grey eyes,
    Where he stood perplexed and still.
But only a host of phantom listeners
    That dwelt in the lone house then
Stood listening in the quiet of the moonlight
    To that voice from the world of men:
Stood thronging the faint moonbeams on the dark stair,
    That goes down to the empty hall,
Hearkening in an air stirred and shaken
    By the lonely Traveller's call.
And he felt in his heart their strangeness,
    Their stillness answering his cry,
While his horse moved, cropping the dark turf,
    'Neath the starred and leafy sky;
For he suddenly smote on the door, even
    Louder, and lifted his head:—
"Tell them I came, and no one answered,
    That I kept my word," he said.

Never the least stir made the listeners,
  Though every word he spake
Fell echoing through the shadowiness of the still house
  From the one man left awake:
Ay, they heard his foot upon the stirrup,
  And the sound of iron on stone,
And how the silence surged softly backward,
  When the plunging hoofs were gone.

A Call on Miss Havisham

CHARLES DICKENS

≈ ≈ ≈ *The boy, Pip, was an orphan. He lived with his married sister, who was cruel, and with his sister's husband, Joe the blacksmith, who was kind. One day Pip's uncle, Mr. Pumblechook, said that Miss Havisham, a rich and eccentric recluse, wanted Pip to come and play at her house. This is the story of Pip's first visit to Miss Havisham's and of the lies Pip told about it. —From* Great Expectations

Mr. Pumblechook and I breakfasted at eight o'clock in the parlour behind the shop, while the shopman took his mug of tea and hunch of bread-and-butter on a sack of peas in the front premises. I considered Mr. Pumblechook wretched company. Besides being possessed by my sister's idea that a mortifying and penitential character ought to be imparted to my diet—besides giving me as much crumb as possible in combination with as little butter, and putting such a quantity of warm water into my milk that it would have been more candid to have left the milk out altogether—his conversation consisted of nothing but arithmetic. On my politely bidding him Good morning, he said, pompously, "Seven times nine, boy?" And how should I be able to answer, dodged in that way, in a strange place, on an empty stomach! I was hungry, but before I had swallowed a morsel, he began a running sum that lasted all through breakfast. "Seven?" "And four?" "And eight?" "And six?" "And two?" "And ten?" And so on. And after each figure was disposed of, it was as much as I could do to get a bite or a sup, before the next came; while he sat at his ease guessing nothing, and eating bacon and hot roll, in (if I may be allowed the expression) a gorging and gormandizing manner.

For such reasons I was very glad when ten o'clock came and we started for Miss Havisham's; though I was not at all at my ease regarding that lady's roof. Within a quarter of an hour we came to Miss Havisham's house, which was of old brick, and dismal, and had a great many iron bars to it. Some of the windows had been walled up; of those that remained, all of the lower were rustily barred. There was a court-yard in front, and that was barred; so, we had to wait, after ringing the bell, until some one should come to open it. While we waited at the gate, I peeped in (even then Mr. Pumblechook said, "And fourteen?" but I pretended not to hear him), and saw that at the side of the house there was a large brewery. No brewing was going on in it, and none seemed to have gone on for a long time.

A window was raised, and a clear voice demanded "What name?" To which my conductor replied, "Pumblechook." The voice returned, "Quite right," and the window was shut again, and a young lady came across the court-yard, with keys in her hand.

"This," said Mr. Pumblechook, "is Pip."

"This is Pip, is it?" returned the young lady, who was very pretty and seemed very proud; "come in, Pip."

Mr. Pumblechook was coming in also, when she stopped him with the gate.

"Oh!" she said. "Do you wish to see Miss Havisham?"

"If Miss Havisham wished to see me," returned Mr. Pumblechook, discomfited.

"Ah!" said the girl; "but you see she don't."

She said it so finally, and in such an indiscussible way, that Mr. Pumblechook, though in a condition of ruffled dignity, could not protest. But he eyed me severely—as if *I* had done anything to him!—and departed with the words reproachfully delivered: "Boy! Let your behaviour here be a credit unto them which brought you up by hand!" I was not free from apprehension that he would come back to propound through the gate, "And Sixteen?" But he didn't.

My young conductress locked the gate, and we went across the court-yard. It was paved and clean, but grass was growing in every crevice. The brewery buildings had a little lane of communication with it; and the wooden gates of that lane stood open, and all the brewery beyond stood open, away to the high enclosing wall; and all was empty and disused. The cold wind seemed to blow colder there, than outside the gate; and it made a shrill noise in howling in and out at the open sides of the brewery, like the noise of wind in the rigging of a ship at sea.

She saw me looking at it, and she said, "You could drink without hurt all the strong beer that's brewed there now, boy."

"I should think I could, miss," said I, in a shy way.

"Better not try to brew beer there now, or it would turn out sour, boy; don't you think so?"

"It looks like it, miss."

"Not that anybody means to try," she added, "for that's all done with, and the place will stand as idle as it is, till it falls. As to strong beer, there's enough of it in the cellars already, to drown the Manor House."

"Is that the name of this house, miss?"

"One of its names, boy."

"It has more than one, then, miss?"

"One more. Its other name was Satis; which is Greek, or Latin, or Hebrew, or all three—or all one to me—for enough."

"Enough House!" said I: "that's a curious name, miss."

"Yes," she replied; "but it meant more than it said. It meant, when it was given, that whoever had this house, could want nothing else. They must have been easily satisfied in those days, I should think. But don't loiter, boy."

Though she called me "boy" so often, and with a carelessness that was far from complimentary, she was of about my own age. She seemed much older than I, of course, being a girl, and beautiful and self-possessed; and she was as scornful of me as if she had been one-and-twenty, and a queen.

We went into the house by a side door—the great front entrance had two chains across it outside—and the first thing I noticed was, that the passages were all dark, and that she had left a candle burning there. She took it up, and we went through more passages and up a staircase, and still it was all dark, and only the candle lighted us.

At last we came to the door of a room, and she said, "Go in."

I answered, more in shyness than politeness, "After you, miss."

To this, she returned: "Don't be ridiculous, boy; I am not going in." And scornfully walked away, and—what was worse,—took the candle with her.

This was very uncomfortable, and I was half afraid. However, the only thing to be done being to knock at the door, I knocked, and was told from within to enter. I entered, therefore, and found myself in a pretty large room, well lighted with six wax candles. No glimpse of daylight was to be seen in it. It was a dressing-room, as I supposed from the furniture, though much of it was of forms and uses then quite unknown to me. But prominent in it was a draped table with a gilded looking-glass, and that I made out at first sight to be a fine lady's dressing-table.

Whether I should have made out this object so soon, if there had been no fine lady sitting at it, I cannot say. In an arm-chair, with an elbow resting on the table and her head leaning on that hand, sat the strangest lady I have ever seen, or shall ever see.

She was dressed in rich materials—satins, and lace, and silks—all of white. Her shoes were white. And she had a long white veil dependent from her hair, and she had bridal flowers in her hair, but her hair was white. Some bright jewels sparkled on her neck and on her hands, and some other jewels lay sparkling on the table. Dresses, less splendid than the dress she wore, and half-packed trunks, were scattered about. She had not quite finished dressing, for she had but one shoe on—the other was on the table near her hand—her veil was but half arranged, her watch and chain were not put on, and some lace for her bosom lay with those trinkets, and with her handkerchief, and gloves, and some flowers, and a Prayer-book, all confusedly heaped about the looking-glass.

It was not in the first few moments that I saw all these things, though I saw more of them in the first moments than might be supposed. But, I saw that everything within my view which ought to be white, had been white long ago, and had lost its lustre, and was faded and yellow. I saw that the bride within the bridal dress had withered like the dress, and like the flowers, and had no brightness left but the brightness of her sunken eyes. I saw that the dress had been put upon the rounded figure of a young woman, and that the figure upon which it now hung loose, had shrunk to skin and bone. Once, I had been taken to see some ghastly waxwork at the Fair, representing I know not what impossible personage lying in state. Once, I had been taken to one of our old marsh churches to see a skeleton in the ashes of a rich dress, that had been dug out of a vault under the church pavement. Now, waxwork and skeleton seemed to have dark eyes that moved and looked at me. I should have cried out, if I could.

"Who is it?" said the lady at the table.

"Pip, ma'am."

"Pip?"

"Mr. Pumblechook's boy, ma'am. Come—to play."

"Come nearer; let me look at you. Come close."

It was when I stood before her, avoiding her eyes, that I took note of the surrounding objects in detail, and saw that her watch had stopped at twenty minutes to nine, and that a clock in the room had stopped at twenty minutes to nine.

"Look at me," said Miss Havisham. "You are not afraid of a woman who has never seen the sun since you were born?"

I regret to state that I was not afraid of telling the enormous lie comprehended in the answer "No."

"Do you know what I touch here?" she said, laying her hands, one upon the other, on her left side.

"Yes, ma'am," (It made me think of the young man.)

"What do I touch?"

"Your heart."

"Broken!"

She uttered the word with an eager look, and with strong emphasis, and with a weird smile that had a kind of boast in it. Afterwards, she kept her hands there for a little while, and slowly took them away as if they were heavy.

"I am tired," said Miss Havisham. "I want diversion, and I have done with men and women. Play."

I think it will be conceded by my most disputatious reader, that she could hardly have directed an unfortunate boy to do anything in the wide world more difficult to be done under the circumstances.

"I sometimes have sick fancies," she went on, "and I have a sick fancy that I want to see someone play. There, there!" with an impatient movement of the fingers of her right hand; "play, play, play!"

For a moment, with the fear of my sister's working me before my eyes, I had a desperate idea of starting round the room in the assumed character of Mr. Pumblechook's chaise-cart. But, I felt myself so unequal to the performance that I gave it up, and stood looking at Miss Havisham in what I suppose she took for a dogged manner, inasmuch as she said, when we had taken a good look at each other:

"Are you sullen and obstinate?"

"No, ma'am, I am very sorry for you, and very sorry I can't play just now. If you complain of me I shall get into trouble with my sister, so I would do it if I could; but it's so new here, and so strange, and so fine—and melancholy—" I stopped, fearing I might say too much, or had already said it, and we took another look at each other.

Before she spoke again, she turned her eyes from me, and looked at the dress she wore, and at the dressing-table, and finally at herself in the looking-glass.

"So new to him," she muttered, "so old to me; so strange to him, so familiar to me; so melancholy to both of us! Call Estella."

As she was still looking at the reflection of herself, I thought she was still talking to herself, and kept quiet.

"Call Estella," she repeated, flashing a look at me. "You can do that. Call Estella. At the door."

To stand in the dark in a mysterious passage of an unknown house, bawling Estella to a scornful young lady neither visible nor responsive, and feeling it a dreadful liberty so to roar out her name, was almost as bad as playing to order. But, she answered at last, and her light came along the dark passage like a star.

Miss Havisham beckoned her to come close, and took up a jewel from the table, and tried its effect upon her fair young bosom and against her pretty brown hair. "Your own, one day, my dear, and you will use it well. Let me see you play cards with this boy."

"With this boy! Why, he is a common labouring-boy!"

I thought I overheard Miss Havisham answer—only it seemed so unlikely—"Well? You can break his heart."

"What do you play, boy?" asked Estella of myself, with the greatest disdain.

"Nothing but beggar my neighbour, Miss."

"Beggar him," said Miss Havisham to Estella. So we sat down to cards.

It was then I began to understand that everything in the room had stopped, like the watch and the clock, a long time ago. I noticed that Miss Havisham put down the jewel exactly on the spot from which she had taken it up. As Estella dealt the cards, I glanced at the dressing-table again, and saw that the shoe upon it, once white, now yellow, had never been worn. I glanced down at the foot from which the shoe was absent, and saw that the silk stocking on it, once white, now yellow, had been trodden ragged. Without this arrest of everything, this standing still of all the pale decayed objects, not even the withered bridal dress on the collapsed form could have looked so like grave-clothes, or the long veil like a shroud.

So she sat, corpse-like, as we played at cards; the frillings and trimmings on her bridal dress, looking like earthy paper. I knew nothing then of the discoveries that are occasionally made of bodies buried in ancient times, which fall to powder in the moment of being distinctly seen; but, I have often thought since, that she must have looked as if the admission of the natural light of day would have struck her to dust.

"He calls the knaves, Jacks, this boy!" said Estella with disdain, before our first game was out. "And what coarse hands he has! And what thick boots!"

I had never thought of being ashamed of my hands before; but I began to consider them a very indifferent pair. Her contempt for me was so strong, that it became infectious, and I caught it.

She won the game, and I dealt. I misdealt, as was only natural, when I knew she was lying in wait for me to do wrong; and she denounced me for a stupid, clumsy labouring-boy.

"You say nothing of her," remarked Miss Havisham to me, as she looked on. "She says many hard things of you, yet you say nothing of her. What do you think of her?"

"I don't like to say," I stammered.

"Tell me in my ear," said Miss Havisham, bending down.

"I think she is very proud," I replied, in a whisper.

"Anything else?"

"I think she is very pretty."

"Anything else?

"I think she is very insulting." (She was looking at me then with a look of supreme aversion.)

"Anything else?"

"I think I should like to go home."

"And never see her again, though she is so pretty?"

"I'm not sure that I wouldn't like to see her again, but I should like to go home now."

"You shall go soon," said Miss Havisham aloud. "Play the game out."

Saving for the one weird smile at first, I should have felt almost sure that Miss Havisham's face could not smile. It had dropped into a watchful and brooding expression—most likely when all the things about her had become transfixed—and it looked as if nothing could ever lift it up again. Her chest had dropped, so that she stooped; and her voice had dropped so that she spoke low, and with a dead lull upon her; altogether, she had the appearance of having dropped, body and soul, within and without, under the weight of a crushing blow.

I played the game to an end with Estella, and she beggared me. She threw the cards down on the table when she had won them all, as if she despised them for having been won of me.

"When shall I have you here again?" said Miss Havisham. "Let me think."

I was beginning to remind her that to-day was Wednesday, when she checked me with her former impatient movement of the fingers of her right hand.

"There! there! I know nothing of the days of the week; I know nothing of weeks of the year. Come again after six days. You hear?"

"Yes, ma'am."

"Estella, take him down. Let him have something to eat, and let him roam and look about him while he eats. Go, Pip."

I followed the candle down, as I had followed the candle up, and she stood it in the place where we had found it. Until she opened the side entrance, I had fancied, without thinking about it, that it must necessarily be night-time. The rush of the daylight quite confounded me, and made me feel as if I had been in the candlelight of the strange room many hours.

"You are to wait here, you boy," said Estella; and disappeared and closed the door.

I took the opportunity of being alone in the court-yard, to look at my coarse hands and my common boots. My opinion of those accessories was not favourable. They had never troubled me before, but they troubled me now, as vulgar appendages. I determined to ask Joe why he had ever taught me to call those picture-cards, Jacks, which ought to be knaves. I wished Joe had been rather more genteelly brought up, and then I should have been so too.

She came back, with some bread and meat and a little mug of beer. She put the mug down on the stones of the yard, and gave me the bread and meat without looking at me, as insolently as if I were a dog in disgrace. I was so humiliated, hurt, spurned, offended, angry, sorry —I cannot hit upon the right name for the smart—God knows what its name was—that tears started to my eyes. The moment they sprang there, the girl looked at me with a quick delight in having been the cause of them. This gave me power to keep them back and to look at her: so, she gave a contemptuous toss—but with a sense, I thought, of having made too sure that I was so wounded—and left me.

But, when she was gone, I looked about me for a place to hide my face in, and got behind one of the gates in the brewery-lane, and leaned my sleeve against the wall there, and leaned my forehead on it and cried. As I cried, I kicked the wall, and took a hard twist at my hair; so bitter were my feelings, and so sharp was the smart without a name, that needed counteraction.

My sister's bringing up had made me sensitive. In the little world in which children have their existence, whosoever brings them up, there is nothing so finely perceived and so finely felt, as injustice. It may be only small injustice that the child can be exposed to; but the child is small, and its world is small, and its rocking-horse stands as many hands high, according to scale, as a big-boned Irish hunter. Within myself, I had sustained, from my babyhood, a perpetual conflict with injustice. I had known, from the time when I could speak, that my sister, in her capricious and violent coercion, was unjust to me. I had cherished a profound conviction that her bringing me up by hand, gave her no right to bring me up by jerks. Through all my punishments, disgraces, fasts and vigils, and other penitential performances, I had nursed this assurance; and to my communing so much with it, in a solitary and unprotected way, I in great part refer the fact that I was morally timid and very sensitive.

I got rid of my injured feelings for the time, by kicking them into the brewery wall, and twisting them out of my hair, and then I smoothed my face with my sleeve, and came from behind the gate. The bread and meat were acceptable, and the beer warming and tingling, and I was soon in spirits to look about me.

To be sure, it was a deserted place, down to the pigeon-house in the brewery-yard, which had been blown crooked on its pole by some high wind, and would have made the pigeons think themselves at sea, if there had been any pigeons there to be rocked by it. But, there were no pigeons in the dove-cote, no horses in the stable, no pigs in the sty, no malt in the store-house, no smells of grains and beer in the copper or the vat. All the uses and scents of the brewery might have evaporated with its last reek of smoke. In a by-yard, there was a wilderness of empty casks, which had a certain sour remembrance of better days lingering about them; but it was too sour to be accepted as a sample of the beer that was gone—and in this respect I remember those recluses as being like most others.

Behind the furthest end of the brewery, was a rank garden with an old wall: not so high but that I could struggle up and hold on long enough to look over it, and see that the rank garden was the garden of the house, and that it was overgrown with tangled weeds, but that there was track upon the green and yellow paths, as if some one sometimes walked there, and that Estella was walking away from me even then. But she seemed to be everywhere. For, when I yielded to the temptation presented by the casks, and began to walk on them, I saw *her* walking on them at the end of the yard of casks. She had her back towards me, and held her pretty brown hair spread out in her two hands, and never looked round, and passed out of my view directly. So, in the brewery itself—by which I mean the large paved lofty space in which they used to make the beer, and where the brewing utensils still were. When I first went into it, and, rather oppressed by its gloom, stood near the door looking about me, I saw her pass among the extinguished fires, and ascend some light iron stairs, and go out by a gallery high overhead, as if she were going out into the sky.

It was in this place, and at this moment, that a strange thing happened to my fancy. I thought it a strange thing then, and I thought it a stranger thing long afterwards. I turned my eyes—a little dimmed by looking up at the frosty light—towards a great wooden beam in a low nook of the building near me on my right hand, and I saw a figure hanging there by the neck. A figure all in yellow white, with but one shoe to the feet; and it hung so, that I could see that the faded trimmings of the dress were like earthy paper, and that the face was Miss Havisham's, with a movement going over the whole countenance as if she were trying to call to me. In the terror of seeing the figure, and in the terror of being certain that it had not been there a moment before, I at first ran from it, and then ran towards it. And my terror was greatest of all when I found no figure there.

Nothing less than the frosty light of the cheerful sky, the sight of people passing beyond the bars of the court-yard gate, and the reviving influence of the rest of the bread and meat and beer, could have brought me round. Even with those aids, I might not have come to myself as soon as I did, but that I saw Estella approaching with the keys, to let me out. She would have some fair reason for looking down upon me, I thought, if she saw me frightened; and she should have no fair reason.

She gave me a triumphant glance in passing me, as if she rejoiced that my hands were so coarse and my boots were so thick, and she opened the gate, and stood holding it. I was passing out without looking at her, when she touched me with a taunting hand.

"Why don't you cry?"

"Because I don't want to."

"You do," said she. "You have been crying till you are half blind, and you are near crying again now."

She laughed contemptuously, pushed me out, and locked the gate upon me. I went straight to Mr. Pumblechook's, and was immensely relieved to find him not at home. So, leaving word with the shopman on what day I was wanted at Miss Havisham's again, I set off on the four-mile walk to our forge; pondering, as I went along, on all I had seen, and deeply revolving that I was a common labouring-boy; that my hands were coarse; that my boots were thick; that I had fallen into a despicable habit of calling knaves Jacks; that I was much more ignorant than I had considered myself last night, and generally that I was in a low-lived bad way.

When I reached home, my sister was very curious to know all about Miss Havisham's, and asked a number of questions. And I soon found myself getting heavily bumped from behind in the nape of the neck and the small of the back, and having my face ignominiously shoved against the kitchen wall, because I did not answer those questions at sufficient length.

If a dread of not being understood be hidden in the breasts of other young people to anything like the extent to which it used to be hidden in mine—which I consider probable, as I have no particular reason to suspect myself of having been a monstrosity—it is the key to many reservations. I felt convinced that if I described Miss Havisham's as my eyes had seen it, I should not be understood. Not only that, but I felt convinced that Miss Havisham too would not be understood; and although she was perfectly incomprehensible to me, I entertained an impression that there would be something coarse and treacherous in my dragging her as she really was (to say nothing of Miss Estella) before the contemplation of Mrs. Joe. Consequently, I said as little as I could, and had my face shoved against the kitchen wall.

The worst of it was that that bullying old Pumblechook, preyed upon by a devouring curiosity to be informed of all I had seen and heard, came gaping over in his chaise-cart at tea-time, to have the details divulged to him. And the mere sight of the torment, with his fishy eyes and mouth open, his sandy hair inquisitively on end, and his waistcoat heaving with windy arithmetic, made me vicious in my reticence.

"Well, boy," Uncle Pumblechook began, as soon as he was seated in the chair of honour by the fire. "How did you get on up town?"

I answered, "Pretty well, sir," and my sister shook her fist at me.

"Pretty well?" Mr. Pumblechook repeated. "Pretty well is no answer. Tell us what you mean by pretty well, boy?"

Whitewash on the forehead hardens the brain into a state of obstinacy perhaps. Anyhow, with whitewash from the wall on my forehead, my obstinacy was adamantine. I reflected for some time, and then answered as if I had discovered a new idea. "I mean pretty well."

My sister with an exclamation of impatience was going to fly at me—I had no shadow of defence, for Joe was busy in the forge—when Mr. Pumblechook interposed with "No! Don't lose your temper. Leave this lad to me, ma'am; leave this lad to me." Mr. Pumblechook then turned me towards him, as if he were going to cut my hair, and said:

"First (to get our thoughts in order): Forty-three pence?"

I calculated the consequence of replying "Four Hundred Pound," and finding them against me, went as near the answer as I could— which was somewhere about eight-pence off. Mr. Pumblechook then put me through my pence-table from "twelve pence make one shilling," and then triumphantly demanded, as if he had done for me, "Now! How much is forty-three pence?" To which I replied, after a long interval of reflection, "I don't know." And I was so aggravated that I almost doubt if I did know.

Mr. Pumblechook worked his head like a screw to screw it out of me, and said, "Is forty-three pence seven and six-pence three fardens, for instance?"

"Yes!" I said. And although my sister instantly boxed my ears, it was highly gratifying to me to see that the answer spoilt his joke, and brought him to a dead stop.

"Boy! What like is Miss Havisham?" Mr. Pumblechook began again when he had recovered; folding his arms tight on his chest and applying the screw.

"Very tall and dark," I told him.

"Is she, uncle?" asked my sister.

Mr. Pumblechook winked an assent; from which I at once inferred that he had never seen Miss Havisham, for she was nothing of the kind.

"Good!" said Mr. Pumblechook, conceitedly. ("This is the way to have him! We are beginning to hold our own, I think, Mum?")

"I am sure, uncle," returned Mrs. Joe, "I wish you had him always: you know so well how to deal with him."

"Now, boy! What was she a-doing of, when you went in today?" asked Mr. Pumblechook.

"She was sitting," I answered, "in a black velvet coach."

Mr. Pumblechook and Mrs. Joe stared at one another—as they well might—and both repeated, "In a black velvet coach?"

"Yes," said I. "And Miss Estella—that's her niece, I think—handed her in cake and wine at the coach-window, on a gold plate. And we all had cake and wine on gold plates. And I got up behind the coach to eat mine, because she told me to."

"Was anybody else there?" asked Mr. Pumblechook.

"Four dogs," said I.

"Large or small?"

"Immense," said I. "And they fought for veal-cutlets out of a silver basket."

Mr. Pumblechook and Mrs. Joe stared at one another again, in utter amazement. I was perfectly frantic—a reckless witness under the torture—and would have told them anything.

"Where *was* this coach, in the name of gracious?" asked my sister.

"In Miss Havisham's room." They stared again. "But there weren't any horses to it." I added this saving clause, in the moment of rejecting four richly caparisoned coursers, which I had had wild thoughts of harnessing.

"Can this be possible, uncle?" asked Mrs. Joe. "What can the boy mean?"

"I'll tell you, Mum," said Mr. Pumblechook. "My opinion is, it's a sedan-chair. She's flighty, you know—very flighty—quite flighty enough to pass her days in a sedan-chair."

"Did you ever see her in it, uncle?" asked Mrs. Joe.

"How could I," he returned, forced to the admission, "When I never see her in my life? Never clapped eyes upon her!"

"Goodness, uncle! And yet you have spoke to her?"

"Why, don't you know," said Mr. Pumblechook, testily, "That when I have been there, I have been took up to the outside of her door, and the door has stood ajar, and she has spoken to me that way. Don't say you don't know *that,* Mum. Howsever, the boy went there to play. What did you play at, boy?"

"We played with flags," I said. (I beg to observe that I think of myself with amazement, when I recall the lies I told on this occasion.)

"Flags!" echoed my sister.

"Yes," said I. "Estella waved a blue flag, and I waved a red one, and Miss Havisham waved one sprinkled all over with little gold stars, out at the coach-window. And then we all waved our swords and hurrahed."

"Swords!" repeated my sister. "Where did you get swords from?"

"Out of a cupboard," said I. "And I saw pistols in it—and jam—and pills. And there was no daylight in the room, but it was all lighted up with candles."

"That's true, Mum," said Mr. Pumblechook, with a grave nod. "That's the state of the case, for that much I've seen myself." And then they both stared at me, and I, with an obtrusive show of artlessness on my countenance, stared at them, and plaited the right leg of my trousers with my right hand.

If they had asked me any more questions I should undoubtedly have betrayed myself, for I was even then on the point of mentioning that there was a balloon in the yard, and should have hazarded the statement but for my invention being divided between that phenomenon and a bear in the brewery. They were so much occupied, however, in discussing the marvels I had already presented for their consideration, that I escaped. The subject still held them when Joe came in from his work to have a cup of tea. To whom my sister, more for the relief of her own mind than for the gratification of his, related my pretended experiences.

Now, when I saw Joe open his blue eyes and roll them all round the kitchen in helpless amazement, I was overtaken by penitence; but only as regarded him—not in the least as regarded the other two. Towards Joe, and Joe only, I considered myself a young monster, while they sat debating what results would come to me from Miss Havisham's acquaintance and favour. They had no doubt that Miss Havisham would "do something" for me; their doubts related to the form that something would take. My sister stood out for "property." Mr. Pumblechook was in favour of a handsome premium for binding me apprentice to some genteel trade—say, the corn and seed trade, for instance. Joe fell into the deepest disgrace with both, for offering the bright suggestion that I might only be presented with one of the dogs who had fought for the veal-cutlets. "If a fool's head can't express better opinions than that," said my sister, "and you have got any work to do, you had better go and do it." So he went.

After Mr. Pumblechook had driven off, and when my sister was washing up, I stole into the forge to Joe, and remained by him until he had done for the night. Then I said, "Before the fire goes out, Joe, I should like to tell you something."

"Should you, Pip?" said Joe, drawing his shoeing-stool near the forge. "Then tell us. What is it, Pip?"

"Joe," said I, taking hold of his rolled-up shirt sleeve, and twisting it between my finger and thumb, "you remember all that about Miss Havisham's?"

"Remember?" said Joe. "I believe you! Wonderful!"

"It's a terrible thing, Joe; it ain't true."

"What are you telling of, Pip?" cried Joe, falling back in the greatest amazement. "You don't mean to say it's—"

"Yes, I do; it's lies, Joe."

"But not all of it? Why sure you don't mean to say, Pip, that there was no black welwet co—ch?" For I stood shaking my head. "But at least there was dogs, Pip? Come, Pip," said Joe, persuasively, "If there warn't no weal-cutlets, at least there was dogs?"

"No, Joe."

"A dog?" said Joe. "A puppy? Come!"

"No, Joe, there was nothing at all of the kind."

As I fixed my eyes hopelessly on Joe, Joe contemplated me in dismay. "Pip, old chap! This won't do, old fellow! I say! Where do you expect to go to?"

"It's terrible, Joe; ain't it?"

"Terrible?" cried Joe. "Awful! What possessed you?"

"I don't know what possessed me, Joe," I replied, letting his shirt sleeve go, and sitting down in the ashes at his feet, hanging my head; "but I wish you hadn't taught me to call Knaves at cards, Jacks; and I wish my boots weren't so thick nor my hands so coarse."

And then I told Joe that I felt very miserable, and that I hadn't been able to explain myself to Mrs. Joe and Pumblechook, who were so rude to me, and that there had been a beautiful young lady at Miss Havisham's who was dreadfully proud, and that she had said I was common, and that I knew I was common, and that I wished I was not common, and that the lies had come of it somehow, though I didn't know how.

This was a case of metaphysics, at least as difficult for Joe to deal with, as for me. But Joe took the case altogether out of the region of metaphysics, and by that means vanquished it.

"There's one thing you may be sure of, Pip," said Joe, after some rumination, "namely, that lies is lies. Howsever they come, they didn't ought to come, and they come from the father of lies, and work round to the same. Don't you tell no more of 'em, Pip. *That* ain't the way to get out of being common, old chap. And as to being common, I don't make it out at all clear. You are oncommon in some things. You're oncommon small. Likewise you're a oncommon scholar."

"No, I am ignorant and backward, Joe."

"Why, see what a letter you wrote last night! Wrote in print even! I've seen letters—Ah! and from gentlefolks!—that I'll swear weren't wrote in print," said Joe.

"I have learnt next to nothing, Joe. You think much of me. It's only that."

"Well, Pip," said Joe, "be it so, or be it son't, you must be a common scholar afore you can be a oncommon one, I should hope! The king upon his throne, with his crown upon his 'ed, can't sit and write his acts of Parliament in print, without having begun, when he were a unpromoted Prince, with the alphabet—Ah!" added Joe, with a shake of the head that was full of meaning, "and begun at A too, and worked his way to Z. And *I* know what that is to do, though I can't say exactly I've done it."

There was some hope in this piece of wisdom, and it rather encouraged me.

"Whether common ones as to callings and earning," pursued Joe, reflectively, "mightn't be the better of continuing for to keep company with common ones, instead of going out to play with oncommon ones—which reminds me to hope that there were a flag, perhaps?"

"No, Joe."

"(I'm sorry there weren't a flag, Pip.) Whether that might be, or mightn't be, is a thing as can't be looked into now, without putting your sister on the Rampage; and that's a thing not to be thought of, as being done intentional. Lookee here, Pip, at what is said to you by a true friend. Which this to you the true friend say. If you can't get to be oncommon through going straight, you'll never get to do it through going crooked. So don't tell no more on 'em, Pip, and live well and die happy."

"You are not angry with me, Joe?"

"No, old chap. But bearing in mind that them were which I meanter say of a stunning and outdacious sort—alluding to them which bordered on weal-cutlets and dog-fighting—a sincere well-wisher would adwise, Pip, their being dropped into your meditations, when you go upstairs to bed. That's all, old chap, and don't never do it no more."

When I got up to my little room and said my prayers, I did not forget Joe's recommendation, and yet my young mind was in that disturbed and unthankful state, that I thought long after I laid me down, how common Estella would consider Joe, a mere blacksmith: how thick his boots, and how coarse his hands. I thought how Joe and my sister were then sitting in the kitchen, and how I had come up to bed from the kitchen, and how Miss Havisham and Estella never sat in a kitchen, but were far above the level of such common things. I fell asleep recalling what I "used to do" when I was at Miss Havisham's; as though I had been there weeks or months, instead of hours: and as though it were quite an old subject of remembrance, instead of one that had risen only that day.

That was a memorable day to me, for it made great changes in me. But it is the same with any life. Imagine one selected day struck out of it, and think how different its course would have been. Pause you who read this, and think for a moment of the long chain of iron or gold, of thorns or flowers, that would never have bound you, but for the formation of the first link on one memorable day.

The Dong With a Luminous Nose

EDWARD LEAR

≈ ≈ ≈

When awful darkness and silence reign
Over the great Grombolian plain,
    Through the long, long wintry nights;
When the angry breakers roar,
As they beat on the rocky shore;
    When Storm-clouds brood on the towering
       heights
Of the Hills on the Chankly Bore:

Then, through the vast and gloomy dark,
There moves what seems a fiery spark,
    A lonely spark with silvery rays
    Piercing the coal-black night,
    A meteor strange and bright:
Hither and thither the vision strays,
    A single lurid light.

Slowly it wanders—pauses—creeps—
Anon it sparkles—flashes and leaps;
And ever as onward it gleaming goes
A light on the Bong-tree stems it throws.
And those who watch at that midnight hour
From Hall or Terrace, or lofty Tower,
Cry, as the wild light passes along,
    "The Dong!—the Dong!
  The wandering Dong through the forest goes!
    The Dong! the Dong!
  The Dong with a luminous Nose!"

    Long years ago
  The Dong was happy and gay,
Till he fell in love with a Jumbly Girl
    Who came to those shores one day.

For the Jumblies came in a Sieve, they did—
Landing at eve near the Zemmery Fidd
  Where the Oblong Oysters grow,
  And the rocks are smooth and gray.
And all the woods and the valleys rang
With the Chorus they daily and nightly sang—

  "Far and few, far and few,
   Are the lands where the Jumblies live;
  Their heads are green, and their hands are blue,
   And they went to sea in a Sieve."

Happily, happily passed those days!
  While the cheerful Jumblies staid;
  They danced in circlets all night long,
  To the plaintive pipe of the lively Dong,
  In moonlight, shine, or shade,
For day and night he was always there
By the side of the Jumbly Girl so fair,
With her sky-blue hands, and sea-green hair.
Till the morning came of that hateful day
When the Jumblies sailed in their Sieve away,
And the Dong was left on the cruel shore
Gazing—gazing for evermore—
Ever keeping his weary eyes on
That pea-green sail on the far horizon—
Singing the Jumbly Chorus still
As he sat all day on the grassy hill—

  "Far and few, far and few,
   Are the lands where the Jumblies live;
  Their heads are green, and their hands are blue,
   And they went to sea in a Sieve."

But when the sun was low in the West,
  The Dong arose and said,
  "What little sense I once possessed
  Has quite gone out of my head!"
And since that day he wanders still
By lake and forest, marsh and hill,

Singing—"O somewhere, in valley or plain
Might I find my Jumbly Girl again!
For ever I'll seek by lake and shore
Till I find my Jumbly Girl once more!"
        Playing a pipe with silvery squeaks,
        Since then his Jumbly Girl he seeks,
        And because by night he could not see,
        He gathered the bark of the Twangum Tree
            On the flowery plain that grows.
            And he wove him a wondrous Nose,
        A Nose as strange as a Nose could be!
Of vast proportions and painted red,
And tied with cords to the back of his head.
        —In a hollow rounded space it ended
        With a luminous lamp within suspended,
            All fenced about
            With a bandage stout
            To prevent the wind from blowing it out;
        And with holes all around to send the light,
        In gleaming rays on the dismal night.

 And now each night and all night long,
Over those plains still roams the Dong!
And above the wail of the Chimp and Snipe
You may hear the squeak of his plaintive pipe,
While ever he seeks, but seeks in vain,
To meet with his Jumbly Girl again;
Lonely and wild—all night he goes—
The Dong with a luminous Nose!
And all who watch at the midnight hour,
From Hall or Terrace, or lofty Tower,
Cry, as they trace the Meteor bright,
Moving along through the dreary night,
        "This is the hour when forth he goes,
        The Dong with a luminous Nose!
        Yonder—over the plain he goes;
            He goes;
            He goes!
        The Dong with a luminous Nose!"

A Miserable, Merry Christmas

LINCOLN STEFFENS

≈ ≈ ≈ *Ninety years ago, in the 1870's, a ten-year-old boy lived in the city of Sacramento in California. His name was Lincoln Steffens, and he grew up to be one of the most famous of all American reporters. This story is about a Christmas he never forgot. You won't either.* —*From* The Autobiography of Lincoln Steffens

What interested me in our new neighborhood was not the school, nor the room I was to have in the house all to myself, but the stable which was built back of the house. My father let me direct the making of a stall, a little smaller than the other stalls, for my pony, and I prayed and hoped and my sister Lou believed that that meant that I would get the pony, perhaps for Christmas. I pointed out to her that there were three other stalls and no horses at all. This I said in order that she should answer it. She could not. My father, sounded, said that some day we might have horses and a cow; meanwhile a stable added to the value of the house. "Some day" is a pain to a boy who lives in and knows only "now." My good little sisters, to comfort me, remarked that Christmas was coming, but Christmas was always coming and grown-ups were always talking about it, asking you what you wanted and then giving you what they wanted you to have. Though everybody knew what I wanted, I told them all again. My mother knew that I told God, too, every night. I wanted a pony, and to make sure that they understood, I declared that I wanted nothing else.

"Nothing but a pony?" my father asked.

"Nothing," I said.

"Not even a pair of high boots?"

That was hard. I did want boots, but I stuck to the pony. "No, not even boots."

"Nor candy? There ought to be something to fill your stocking with, and Santa Claus can't put a pony into a stocking."

That was true, and he couldn't lead a pony down the chimney either. But no. "All I want is a pony," I said. "If I can't have a pony, give me nothing, nothing."

Now I had been looking myself for the pony I wanted, going to sales stables, inquiring of horsemen, and I had seen several that would do. My father let me "try" them. I tried so many ponies that I was learning fast to sit a horse. I chose several, but my father always found some fault with them. I was in despair. When Christmas was at hand I had given up all hope of a pony, and on Christmas Eve I hung up my stocking along with my sisters', of whom, by the way, I now had three. I haven't mentioned them or their coming because, you understand, they were girls, and girls, young girls, counted for nothing in my manly life. They did not mind me either; they were so happy that Christmas Eve that I caught some of their merriment. I speculated on what I'd get; I hung up the biggest stocking I had, and we all went reluctantly to bed to wait till morning. Not to sleep; not right away. We were told that we must not only sleep promptly, we must not wake up till seven-thirty the next morning—or if we did, we must not go to the fireplace for our Christmas. Impossible.

We did sleep that night, but we woke up at six A.M. We lay in our beds and debated through the open doors whether to obey till, say, half-past six. Then we bolted. I don't know who started it, but there was a rush. We all disobeyed; we raced to disobey and get first to the fireplace in the front room downstairs. And there they were, the gifts, all sorts of wonderful things, mixed-up piles of presents; only, as I disentangled the mess, I saw that my stocking was empty; it hung limp; not a thing in it; and under and around it—nothing. My sisters had knelt down, each by her pile of gifts; they were squealing with delight, till they looked up and saw me standing there in my night-gown with nothing. They left their piles to come to me and look with me at my empty place. Nothing. They felt my stocking: nothing.

I don't remember whether I cried at that moment, but my sisters did. They ran with me back to my bed, and there we all cried till I became indignant. That helped some. I got up, dressed, and driving my sisters away, I went alone out into the yard, down to the stable, and there, all by myself, I wept. My mother came out to me by and by; she found me in my pony stall, sobbing on the floor, and she tried to comfort me. But I heard my father outside; he had come part way with her, and she was having some sort of angry quarrel with him. She tried to comfort me; besought me to come to breakfast. I could not; I wanted no comfort and no breakfast. She left me and went on into the house with sharp words for my father.

I don't know what kind of a breakfast the family had. My sisters said it was "awful." They were ashamed to enjoy their own toys. They came to me, and I was rude. I ran away from them. I went around to the front of the house, sat down on the steps, and, as the crying was over, I ached. I was wronged, I was hurt—I can feel now what I felt then, and I am sure that if one could see the wounds upon our hearts, there would be found still upon mine a scar from that terrible Christmas morning. And my father, the practical joker, he must have been hurt, too, a little. I saw him looking out of the window. He was watching me or something for an hour or two, drawing back the curtain never so little lest I catch him, but I saw his face, and I think I can see now the anxiety upon it, the worried impatience.

After—I don't know how long—surely an hour or two—I was brought to the climax of my agony by the sight of a man riding a pony down the street, a pony and a brand-new saddle; the most beautiful saddle I ever saw, and it was a boy's saddle; the man's feet were not in the stirrups; his legs were too long. The outfit was perfect; it was the realization of all my dreams, the answer to all my prayers. A fine new bridle, with a light curb bit. And the pony! As he drew near, I saw that the pony was really a small horse, what we called an Indian pony, a bay, with black mane and tail, and one white foot and a white star on his forehead. For such a horse as that l would have given, I could have forgiven, anything.

But the man, a disheveled fellow with a blackened eye and a fresh-cut face, came along, reading the numbers on the houses, and, as my hopes—my impossible hopes—rose, he looked at our door and passed by, he and the pony, and the saddle and the bridle. Too much. I fell upon the steps, and having wept before, I broke now into such a flood of tears that I was a floating wreck when I heard a voice.

"Say, kid," it said, "do you know a boy named Lennie Steffens?"

I looked up. It was the man on the pony, back again, at our horse block.

"Yes," I spluttered through my tears. "That's me."

"Well," he said, "then this is your horse. I've been looking all over for you and your house. Why don't you put your number where it can be seen?"

"Get down," I said, running out to him.

He went on saying something about "ought to have got here at seven o'clock; told me to bring the nag here and tie him to your post and leave him for you; But, hell, I got into a drunk—and a fight—and a hospital, and—"

"Get down," I said.

He got down, and he boosted me up to the saddle. He offered to fit the stirrups to me, but I didn't want him to. I wanted to ride.

"What's the matter with you?" he said, angrily. "What you crying for? Don't you like the horse? He's a dandy, this horse. I know him of old. He's fine at cattle; he'll drive 'em alone."

I hardly heard, I could scarcely wait, but he persisted. He adjusted the stirrups, and then, finally, off I rode, slowly, at a walk, so happy, so thrilled, that I did not know what I was doing. I did not look back at the house or the man, I rode off up the street, taking note of everything—of the reins, of the pony's long mane, of the carved leather saddle. I had never seen anything so beautiful. And mine! I was going to ride up past Miss Kay's house. But I noticed on the horn of the saddle some stains like rain-drops, so I turned and trotted home, not to the house but to the stable. There was the family, father, mother, sisters, all working for me, all happy. They had been putting in place the tools of my new business: blankets, currycomb, brush, pitchfork— everything, and there was hay in the loft.

"What did you come back so soon for?" somebody asked. "Why didn't you go on riding?"

I pointed to the stains. "I wasn't going to get my new saddle rained on," I said. And my father laughed. "It isn't raining," he said. "Those are not rain-drops."

"They are tears," my mother gasped, and she gave my father a look which sent him off to the house. Worse still, my mother offered to wipe away the tears still running out of my eyes. I gave her such a look as she had given him, and she went off after my father, drying her own tears. My sisters remained and we all unsaddled the pony, put on his halter, led him to his stall; tied and fed him. It began really to rain; so that the rest of that memorable day we curried and combed that pony. The girls plaited his mane, forelock, and tail, while I pitchforked hay to him and curried and brushed, curried and brushed. For a change we brought him out to drink; we led him up and down, blanketed like a racehorse; we took turns at that. But the best, the most inexhaustible fun, was to clean him. When we went reluctantly to our midday Christmas dinner, we all smelt of horse, and my sisters had to wash their faces and hands. I was asked to, but I wouldn't, till my mother bade me look in the mirror. Then I washed up—quick. My face was caked with the muddy lines of tears that had coursed over my cheeks to my mouth. Having washed away that shame, I ate my dinner, and as I ate I grew hungrier and hungrier. It was my first meal that day, and as I filled up on the turkey and the stuffing, the cranberries and the pies, the fruit and the nuts—as I swelled, I could laugh. My mother said I still choked and sobbed now and then, but I laughed, too; I saw and enjoyed my sisters' presents till—I had to go out and attend to my pony, who was there, really and truly there, the promise, the beginning, of a happy double life. And—I went and looked to make sure—there was the saddle, too, and the bridle.

But that Christmas, which my father had planned so carefully, was it the best or the worst I ever knew? He often asked me that; I never could answer as a boy. I think now that it was both. It covered the whole distance from broken-hearted misery to bursting happiness—too fast. A grown-up could hardly have stood it.

Say Not the Struggle Naught Availeth

ARTHUR HUGH CLOUGH

Say not the struggle naught availeth,
　　The labour and the wounds are vain,
The enemy faints not, nor faileth,
　　And as things have been they remain.

If hopes were dupes, fears may be liars;
　　It may be, in yon smoke conceal'd,
Your comrades chase e'en now the fliers,
　　And, but for you, possess the field.

For while the tired waves, vainly breaking,
　　Seem here no painful inch to gain,
Far back, through creeks and inlets making,
　　Comes silent, flooding in, the main.

And not by eastern windows only,
　　When daylight comes, comes in the light;
In front the sun climbs slow, how slowly!
　　But westward, look, the land is bright!

Old Slewfoot

MARJORIE KINNAN RAWLINGS

≈ ≈ ≈ *Many years ago in the backwoods of Florida a boy named Jody went bear hunting with his father. In the excitement he learned something about bears and dogs, and something about fathers, too.* —*From* The Yearling

Jody opened his eyes unwillingly. Sometime, he thought, he would slip away into the woods and sleep from Friday until Monday. Daylight was showing through the east window of his small bedroom. He could not be certain whether it was the pale light that had awakened him, or the stirring of the chickens in the peach trees. He heard them fluttering one by one from their roost in the branches. The daylight lay in orange streaks. The pines beyond the clearing were still black against it. Now in April the sun was rising earlier. It could not be very late. It was good to awaken by himself before his mother called him. He turned over luxuriously. The dry corn shucks of his mattress rustled under him. The Dominick rooster crowed boisterously under the window.

"You crow now," the boy said. "See kin you rout me out."

The bright streaks in the east thickened and blended. A golden flush spread as high as the pines, and as he watched, the sun itself lifted, like a vast copper skillet being drawn to hang among the branches. A light wind stirred, as though the growing light had pushed it out of the restless east. The sacking curtains eddied out into the room. The breeze reached the bed and brushed him with the cool softness of clean fur. He lay for a moment in torment between the luxury of his bed and the coming day. Then he was out of his nest and standing on the deerskin rug, and his breeches were hanging handily, and his shirt right side out by good fortune, and he was in them, and dressed, and there was not any need of sleep, or anything but the day, and the smell of hot cakes in the kitchen.

"Hey, ol' Ma," he said at the door. "I like you, Ma."

"You and them hounds and all the rest o' the stock," she said.

199

"Mighty lovin' on a empty belly and me with a dish in my hand."

"That's the way you're purtiest," he said, and grinned.

He went whistling to the water-shelf and dipped into the wooden bucket to fill the wash-basin. He sousled his hands and face in the water, deciding against the strong lye soap. He wet his hair and parted and smoothed it with his fingers. He took down the small mirror from the wall and studied himself a moment.

"I'm turrible ugly, Ma," he called.

"Well, there ain't been a purty Baxter since the name begun."

He wrinkled his nose at the mirror. The gesture made the freckles across the bridge blend together.

"I wish I was dark like the Forresters."

"You be proud you ain't. Them fellers is black as their hearts. You are a Baxter and all the Baxters is fair."

"You talk like I wasn't no kin to you."

"My folks runs to fairness, too. They ain't none of 'em puny, though. Iffen you'll learn yourself to work, you'll be your Pa all over."

The mirror showed a small face with high cheek bones. The face was freckled and pale, but healthy, like a fine sand. The hair grieved him on the occasions when he went to church or any doings at Volusia. It was straw-colored and shaggy, and no matter how carefully his father cut it, once a month on the Sunday morning nearest the full moon, it grew in tufts at the back. "Drakes' tails," his mother called them. His eyes were wide and blue. When he frowned, in close study over his reader, or watching something curious, they narrowed. It was then that his mother claimed him kin.

"He do favor the Alverses a mite," she said.

Jody turned the mirror to inspect his ears; not for cleanliness, but remembering the pain of the day when Lem Forrester had held his chin with one vast hand and pulled his ears with the other.

"Boy, your ears is set up on your head like a 'possum's," Lem said.

Jody made a leering grimace at himself and returned the mirror to the wall.

"Do we got to wait for Pa to eat breakfast?" he asked.

"We do. Set it all in front of you and there'd likely not be enough left for him."

He hesitated at the back door.

"And don't you slip off, neither. He ain't but to the corncrib."

From the south, beyond the black-jacks, he heard the bell-like voice of old Julia, giving tongue in great excitement. He thought he heard, too, his father, giving her a command. He bolted away before his mother's sharp voice could stop him. She, too, had heard the dog. She followed to the door and called after him.

"Don't you and your Pa be gone too long now, follerin' that fool hound. I'm o' no mind to set around waitin' breakfast and you two piddlin' around in the woods."

He could no longer hear either old Julia or his father. He was in a frenzy for fear the excitement was over; the intruder gone and perhaps dog and father with it. He crashed through the black-jacks in the direction from which the sounds had come. His father's voice spoke, close at hand.

"Easy, son. What's done'll wait for you."

He stopped short. Old Julia stood trembling, not in fear but in eagerness. His father stood looking down at the crushed and mangled carcass of black Betsy, the brood sow.

"He must of heered me darin' him," Penny said. "Look careful, boy. See do you see what I see."

The sight of the mutilated sow sickened him. His father was looking beyond the dead animal. Old Julia had her sharp nose turned in the same direction. Jody walked a few paces and examined the sand. The unmistakable tracks made his blood jump. They were the tracks of a giant bear. And from the print of the right front paw, as big as the crown of a hat, one toe was missing.

"Old Slewfoot!"

Penny nodded.

"I'm proud you remembered his track."

They bent together and studied the signs and the direction in which they had both come and gone.

"That's what I call," Penny said, "carryin' the war into the enemy's camp."

"None o' the dogs bayed him, Pa. Lessen I didn't hear, for sleepin'."

"None of 'em bayed him. He had the wind in his favor. Don't you think he didn't know what he was doin'. He slipped in like a shadow and done his meanness and slipped out afore day."

A chill ran along Jody's backbone. He could picture the shadow, big and black as a shed in motion, moving among the black-jacks and gathering in the tame and sleeping sow with one sweep of the great clawed paw. Then the white tusks followed into the backbone, crushing it, and into the warm and palpitating flesh. Betsy had had no chance even to squeal for help.

"He'd a'ready fed," Penny pointed out. "He ate no more'n a mouthful. A bear's stomach is shrunk when he first comes outen his winter bed. That's why I hate a bear. A creetur that kills and eats what he needs, why, he's jest like the rest of us, making out the best he kin. But an animal, or a person either, that'll do harm jest to be a-doin'—You look in a bear's face and you'll see he's got no remorse."

"You aim to carry in old Betsy?"

"The meat's bad tore up, but I reckon there's sausage left. And lard."

Jody knew that he should feel badly about old Betsy, but all that he could feel was excitement. The unwarranted kill, inside the sanctuary of the Baxter acres, had made a personal enemy of the big bear that had evaded all the stock owners for five years. He was wild to begin the hunt. He acknowledged to himself, as well, a trace of fear. Old Slewfoot had struck close to home.

He took one hind leg of the sow and Penny the other. They dragged it to the house with Julia reluctant at their heels. The old bear-dog could not understand why they did not set out at once on the chase.

"I'll swear," Penny said, "I'm daresome to break the news to your Ma."

"She'll rare for certain," Jody agreed.

"Betsy was sich a fine brood sow. My, she was fine."

Ma Baxter was waiting for them by the gate.

"I been a-callin' and I been a-callin'," she hailed them. "What you got there, piddlin' around so long? Oh dear goodness, oh dear goodness—my sow, my sow."

She threw her arms toward the sky. Penny and Jody passed through the gate and back of the house. She followed wailing.

"We'll hang the meat to the cross-piece, son," Penny said. "The dogs'll not reach it there."

"You might tell me," Ma Baxter said. "The least you kin do is tell me, how come her dead and tore to ribbons right under my nose."

"Old Slewfoot done it, Ma," Jody said. "His tracks was certain."

"And them dogs asleep right here in the clearin'?"

The three had already appeared, nosing about the fresh smell of the blood. She threw a stick in their direction.

"You no-account creeturs! Hornin' in on our rations and leavin' sich as this to happen."

"Ain't a dog borned as smart as that bear," Penny said.

"They could of barked."

She threw another stick and the dogs slunk away.

The family went to the house. In the confusion, Jody went first into the kitchen, where the smell of breakfast tortured him. His mother could not be too disturbed to notice what he was doing.

"You git right back here," she called, "and wash your dirty hands."

He joined his father at the water-shelf. Breakfast was on the table. Ma Baxter sat, swaying her body in distress, and did not eat. Jody heaped his plate. There were grits and gravy, hot cakes, and butter-milk.

"Anyway," he said, "we got meat to eat for a whiles now."

She turned on him.

"Meat now, and none this winter."

"I'll ask the Forresters out of a sow," Penny said.

"Yes, and be beholden to them rascals." She began to wail again. "That blasted bear—I'd like to git my hands on him."

"I'll tell him when I see him," Penny said mildly between mouthfuls.

Jody burst out laughing.

"That's right," she said. "Make a fun-box outen me."

Jody patted her big arm.

"Hit jest come to me, Ma, how you'd look—you and ol' Slewfoot mixin' it."

"I'd bet on your Ma," Penny said.

"Nobody but me don't take life serious," she lamented.

Penny pushed back his plate and stood up from the table.

"Well, son, we got our day's work laid out for us."

Jody's heart fell. Hoeing—

"We stand a right good chancet o' coming up with that bear today."

The sun was bright again.

"Fetch me my shot-bag and my powder horn. And the tinder horn."

Jody jumped to bring them.

"Look at him move," his mother said. "To see him hoe, you'd think he was a snail. Say 'huntin'' and he's quick as a otter."

She went to the kitchen safe and took out one of the few remaining glasses of jelly. She spread the jelly on the left-over stack of hot cakes and tied them in a piece of cloth and dropped them in Penny's knap-sack. She took the remains of the sweet potato pone and set aside a piece for herself, then added the pone, wrapped in a fragment of paper, to the knapsack. She looked again at the pone she had saved, and with a quick motion dropped it in the sack with the other.

"This ain't much dinner," she said. "Mebbe you'll be soon back."

"Don't look for us 'til you see us," Penny said. "Anyways, no man never starved to death in a day."

"To hear Jody tell it," she said, "he kin starve to death about a hour after breakfast."

Penny swung the knapsack and tinder horn over his shoulder.

"Jody, take the big knife and go cut a good strip offen that 'gator tail."

The meat, dry-cured for the feeding of the dogs, hung in the smoke-house. Jody ran to it and swung open the heavy timbered door. The smoke-house was dark and cool, odorous with the smell of hams, and bacons, dusty with the ash of hickory. The rafters, studded with square-headed nails for the hanging of meats, were now almost bare. Three shoulders of ham hung, lean and withered, and two bacon sides. A haunch of jerked venison swung beside the smoked alligator meat. Old Slewfoot had indeed done damage. Betsy the brood-sow would have filled the room with her plump progeny by the coming fall. Jody hacked away a piece of alligator. The meat was dry but tender. He touched his tongue to it. Its saltiness was not unpleasing. He joined his father in the yard.

At sight of the old muzzle-loading shotgun, Julia lifted her voice in a wail of delight. Rip shot from under the house to join her. Perk, the new feice, wagged his tail stupidly and without understanding. Penny patted the dogs in turn.

"You'll likely not be so merry, time the day be done," he told them. "Jody-boy, you best put on your shoes. Hit'll be rough goin', places."

It seemed to Jody that he would burst if there was further delay. He dashed in to his room and routed out his heavy cowhide brogans from under the bed. He slipped his feet into them and raced after his father as though the hunt would be done and over before he reached him. Old Julia was loping ahead, her long nose against the trail of the bear.

"The trail'll not be too cold, Pa? Reckon he won't be gone too fur yonder to ketch up with him?"

"He'll be fur yonder, but we got a heap better chancet o' ketchin' up with him, do we let him take it easy and give him time to lay up. A bear that knows he's follered moves a sight faster'n one that figgers the world's his own, to prowl and feed in."

The trail led south through the black-jacks. After the rain of the afternoon before, the great nubbed tracks made a plain pattern across the sand.

"He's got a foot like a Georgia nigger," Penny said.

The black-jacks ended as though they had been sown by hand and there had been no more seed in the sack. The land was lower and the growth was of large pines.

"Pa, how big you reckon he be?"

"He's big. He ain't full weight right now, account of his stomach bein' shrunk up from layin' up, and empty. But look at that track. Hit's sizable enough to prove him. And look at the way it's deeper at the back. A deer track'll prove the same. A deer or bear that's fat and heavy'll sink in that-a-way. A leetle ol' light doe or yearlin'll walk tippy-toed, and you'll not see more than the front of their hooves. Oh, he's big."

"You'll not be scairt when we come up with him, Pa?"

"Not lessen things goes mighty wrong. I'm fearful, always, for the pore dogs. They're the scapers gits the worst of it."

Penny's eyes twinkled.

"I don't reckon you'll be scairt, son?"

"Not me." He thought a moment. "But if I was to be scairt, must I climb a tree?"

Penny chuckled.

"Yes, son. Even if you ain't scairt, hit's a good place to watch the ruckus."

They walked in silence. Old Julia moved certainly. Rip the bulldog was content to follow at her heels, snuffing where she snuffed, stopping when she hesitated. She blew through her soft nose when the grasses tickled it. The feice made dashes to one side or another and once tore wildly after a rabbit that bolted from under his nose. Jody whistled after him.

"Leave him go, son," Penny told him. "He'll join up again when it comes to him he's lonesome."

Old Julia gave a thin high wail and looked over her shoulder.

"The wise old scaper's changin' his direction," Penny said. "Likely he's headin' for the saw-grass ponds. Iffen that's his notion, we kin mebbe slip around and surprise him."

Some understanding came to Jody of the secret of his father's hunting. The Forresters, he thought, would have plunged after old Slewfoot the moment they had found his kill. They would have shouted and bellowed, their pack of dogs would have bayed until the scrub echoed with it, for they encouraged them in it, and the wary old bear would have had full warning of their coming. His father got game, ten to their one. The little man was famous for it.

Jody said, "You shore figger what a creetur'll do."

"You belong to figger. A wild creetur's quicker'n a man and a heap stronger. What's a man got that a bear ain't got? A mite more sense. He cain't out-run a bear, but he's a sorry hunter if he cain't out-study him."

The pines were becoming scattering. There was suddenly a strip of hammock land, and a place of live oaks and scrub palmettos. The undergrowth was thick, laced with cat-briers. Then hammock, too, ended, and to the south and west lay a broad open expanse that looked at first sight like a meadow. This was the saw-grass. It grew knee-deep in water, its harsh saw-edged blades rising so thickly that it seemed a compact vegetation. Old Julia splashed into it. The rippling of the water showed the pond. A gust of air passed across the open area, the saw-grass waved and parted, and the shallow water of a dozen ponds showed clearly. Penny watched the hound intently. The treeless expanse seemed to Jody more stirring than the shadowy forest. At any moment the great black form might rear itself high.

He whispered, "Will we cut around?"

Penny shook his head. He answered in a low voice.

"Wind's wrong. Don't seem to me like he's heading acrost it, nohow."

The hound splashed in a zigzag trail where solid ground edged the saw-grass. Here and there the scent was lost in the water. Once she dipped her head to lap, not in thirst, but for the very taste of the trail. She moved confidently down the middle of the pond. Rip and Perk found their short legs too deep in muck for comfort. They retreated to higher ground and shook themselves, watching Julia anxiously. Perk barked shortly, and Penny slapped him, for quiet. Jody stepped cautiously behind his father. A blue heron flew low over him without warning, and he started. The pond water was cold an instant against his legs, his breeches were clammy, the muck sucked at his shoes. Then the water was comfortable, and it was good to walk in the wet coolness, leaving sandy whirlpools behind.

"He's feedin' on the fire-plant," Penny murmured.

He pointed to the flat arrow-shaped leaves. Edges showed jagged tooth-marks. Others were bitten clear of the stalk.

"Hit's his spring tonic. A bear'll make for it first thing, time he comes out in the spring." He leaned close and touched a leaf whose ragged edge was turning brown. "Dogged if he wa'n't here a night ago, too. That's how come him to have appetite for a nip o' pore old Betsy."

The hound too paused. The scent lay now, not underfoot, but on the reeds and grasses where the strong-smelling fur had brushed. She laid her long nose against a bulrush and stared into space, then, satisfied as to direction, splashed due south at a lively pace. Penny spoke now freely.

"He's done feedin'. Old Julia says he's clippin' it for home."

He moved to higher land, keeping the hound in sight. He walked briskly, chatting.

"Many's the time I've seed a bear feedin' on the fire-plant in the moonlight. He'll snort and shuffle, and splash and grunt. He'll rip them leaves offen the stems and cram 'em in his ugly ol' mouth like a person. Then he'll nose along and chaw, like a dog chawin' grass. And the night-birds cryin' over him, and the bull-frogs hollerin' like nigger-boys, and the Mallards callin' 'Snake! Snake! Snake!' and the drops o' water on the leaves o' the fire-plant shinin' bright and red as a bull-bat's eyes—"

It was as good as seeing it, to hear Penny tell of it.

"I'd shore love to see a bear feedin' on the fire-plant, Pa."

"Well, you live long as me, and you'll see that and a heap more things, is strange and curious."

"Did you shoot 'em, Pa, while they was feedin'?"

"Son, I've helt back my shot and contented myself with watchin' many a time when creeturs was feedin' harmless and innocent. It goes agin me to crack down at sich a time. Or when creeturs is matin'. Now and agin, when it was git meat or the Baxters go hongry, I've done what I've no likin' to do. And don't you grow up like the Forresters, killin' meat you got no use for, for the fun of it. That's evil as the bears. You hear me?"

"Yes, sir."

Old Julia gave a sharp cry. The trail cut at right angles, to the east.

"I feared it," Penny said. "The bay—"

The red bay thicket seemed impenetrable. This land of sudden changes gave good cover for the game. Old Slewfoot in his careless feeding had never been far from shelter. The bay saplings stood close together as the palings of a stockade. Jody wondered how the bear had managed to work his bulk among them. But here and there the saplings thinned, or were young and limber, and he could see, plainly marked, a common trail. Other creatures had used it. Tracks crossed and criss-crossed. Wild-cat had followed deer, lynx had followed wildcat, and all about were the paw-prints of the small things, 'coons and rabbits and 'possums and skunks, feeding cautiously aside from their predatory kin.

Penny said, "I reckon I best load."

He clucked to Julia to wait for him. She lay down knowingly to rest and Rip and Perk dropped willingly beside her. Jody had been carrying the powder horn over his shoulder. Penny opened it and shook a measure of powder down the muzzle. From his shot-bag he pulled a wisp of dried black Spanish moss, inserted it for wadding, and packed it with the ramrod. He dropped in a measure of low-mould shot, more wadding, and at the last, a cap, and used the ramrod lightly again.

"All right, Julia. Git him."

The morning's trailing had been a leisurely business; a pleasant jaunt rather than a hunt. Now the dark bay thicket closed in over their heads, jorees flew from the denseness with an alarming whirr of wings, the earth was soft and black, and there were scurryings and rustlings on either side in the bushes. On the trail, a bar of sunlight lay occasionally where the thicket parted. The scent, for all the comings and goings, was not confused, for the taint of bear hung heavy in the leafy tunnel. The short fur of the bulldog stood on end. Old Julia ran swiftly. Penny and Jody were forced to stoop to follow. Penny swung the muzzle-loader in his right hand, its barrel tipped at an angle, so that if he stumbled and the charge went off, he would not touch the running dogs before him. A branch crashed behind and Jody clutched at his father's shirt. A squirrel ran chattering away.

The thicket thinned. The ground dropped lower and became a swamp. The sunlight came through in patches as big as a basket. There were giant ferns here, taller than their heads. One lay crushed where the bear had moved across it. Its spiced sweetness lay heavy on the warm air. A young tendril sprang back into an upright position. Penny pointed to it. Slewfoot, Jody understood, had passed not many minutes before. Old Julia was feverish. The trail was food and drink. Her nose skimmed the damp ground. A scrub jay flew ahead, warning the game, and crying "*Plick-up-wha-a-a.*"

The swamp dipped to a running branch no broader than a fence post. The print of the nubbed foot spanned it. A water moccasin lifted a curious head, then spun down-stream in smooth brown spirals. Across the branch, palmettos grew. The great track continued across the swamp. Jody noticed that the back of his father's shirt was wet. He touched his own sleeve. It was dripping. Suddenly Julia bayed and Penny began to run.

"The Creek!" he shouted. "He's tryin' to make the Creek!"

Sound filled the swamp. Saplings crashed. The bear was a black hurricane, mowing down obstructions. The dogs barked and bayed. The roaring in Jody's ears was his heart pounding. A bamboo vine tripped him and he sprawled and was on his feet again. Penny's short legs churned in front of him like paddles. Slewfoot would make Juniper Creek before the dogs could halt him at bay.

A clear space opened at the creek's bank. Jody saw a vast black shapeless form break through. Penny halted and lifted his gun. On the instant, a small brown missile hurled itself at the shaggy head. Old Julia had caught up with her enemy. She leaped and retreated, and in the moment of retreat, was at him again. Pip darted in beside her. Slewfoot wheeled and slashed at him. Julia flashed at his flank. Penny held his fire. He could not shoot, for the dogs.

Old Slewfoot was suddenly, deceptively, indifferent. He seemed to stand baffled, slow and uncertain, weaving back and forth. He whined, like a child whimpering. The dogs backed off an instant. The moment was perfect for a shot and Penny swung his gun to his shoulder, drew a bead on the left cheek, and pulled the trigger. A harmless pop sounded. He cocked the hammer again and pulled the trigger once more. The sweat stood out on his forehead. Again the hammer clicked futilely. Then a black storm broke. It roared in on the dogs with incredible swiftness. White tusks and curved claws were streaks of lightning across it. It snarled and whirled and gnashed its teeth and slashed in every direction. The dogs were as quick. Julia made swift sorties from the rear, and when Slewfoot wheeled to rake at her, Rip leaped for the hairy throat.

Jody was in a paralysis of horror. He saw that his father had cocked the hammer again and stood, half-crouching, licking his lips, fingering the trigger. Old Julia bored in at the bear's right flank. He wheeled, not on her, but on the bulldog at his left. He caught him sideways and sent him sprawling into the bushes. Again Penny pulled the trigger. The explosion that followed had a sizzling sound, and Penny fell backward. The gun had back-fired.

Rip returned to his attempts for the bear's throat and Julia took up her worrying from the rear. The bear stood again at bay, weaving. Jody ran to his father. Penny was already on his feet. The right side of his face was black with powder. Slewfoot shook free of Rip, whirled to Julia and caught her to his chest with his cupped claws. She yelped sharply. Rip hurled himself at the back and buried his teeth in the hide.

Jody screamed, "He's killin' Julia!"

Penny ran desperately into the heart of the fracas. He jammed the gun-barrel in the bear's ribs. Even in her pain, Julia had taken a grip on the black throat above her. Slewfoot snarled and turned suddenly and plunged down the bank of the creek and into the deep water. Both dogs kept their hold. Slewfoot swam madly. Only Julia's head showed above water, below the bear's snout. Rip rode the broad back with bravado. Slewfoot made the far bank and scrambled up its side. Julia loosed her hold and dropped limply on the earth. The bear plunged toward the dense thicket. For a moment more Rip stayed with him. Then, confused, he too dropped away and turned back uncertainly to the creek. He snuffed at Julia and sat down on his haunches and howled across the water. There was a crashing in the distant under-growth, then silence.

Penny called, "Here, Rip! Here, Julia!"

Rip wagged his stumpy tail and did not stir. Penny lifted his hunting horn to his lips and blew caressingly. Jody saw Julia lift her head, then fall back again.

Penny said, "I got to go fetch her."

He slipped off his shoes and slid down the bank into the water. He struck out strongly. A few yards from shore the current laid hold of him as though he were a log and shot him down-stream at a fierce clip. He struggled against it, fighting for distance. Jody saw him stagger to his feet far down the run, wipe the water from his eyes and push his way back up the shore to his dogs. He leaned to examine the hound, then gathered her up under one arm. This time he went some distance up-stream before taking to the creek. When he dropped into the water, stroking with his free arm, the current picked him up and deposited him almost at Jody's feet. Rip paddled behind him, landed and shook himself. Penny laid the old hound down gently.

"She's bad hurt," he said.

He took off his shirt and trussed the dog in it. He tied the sleeves together to make a sling and hoisted it on his back.

"This settles it," he said. "I got to git me a new gun."

The powder burn on his cheek had already turned into a blister.

"What's wrong, Pa?"

"Near about ever'thing. The hammer's loose on the cylinder. I knowed that. I been havin' to cock it two-three times right along. But when it backfired, that belongs to mean the mainspring's got weak. Well, le's git goin'. You tote the blasted ol' gun."

The procession started homeward through the swamp. Penny cut north and west.

"Now I'll not rest 'til I git that bear," he said. "Jest give me a new gun—and time."

Suddenly Jody could not endure the sight of the limp bundle in front of him. There were tricklings of blood down his father's thin bare back.

"I want to go ahead, Pa."

Penny turned and eyed him.

"Don't go gittin' faintified on me."

"I kin break a trail for you."

"All right. Go ahead, Jody—take the knapsack. Git you some bread. Eat a bite, boy. You'll feel better."

Jody fumbled blindly in the sack and pulled out the parcel of pancakes. The brierberry jelly was tart and cool on his tongue. He was ashamed to have it taste so good. He bolted several of the cakes. He handed some to his father.

"Rations is mighty comfortin'." Penny said.

A whine sounded in the bushes. A small cringing form was following them. It was Perk, the feice. Jody kicked at him in a fury.

"Don't bother him," Penny said. "I suspected him all along. There's dogs is bear-dogs and there's dogs jest isn't bear-dogs."

The feice dropped in at the end of the line. Jody tried to break trail, but fallen trees lay, thicker than his body, and would not be stirred. Bull-briers, tougher than his father's muscles, snared him, and he could only push his way around them or crawl beneath. Penny with his burden had to shift for himself. The swamp was close and humid. Rip was panting. The pancakes lay soothingly in Jody's belly. He reached in the knapsack for the sweet potato pone. His father refused his share and Jody divided it with Rip. The little feice, he thought, deserved nothing.

It was good to clear the swamp at last and come into the open pine woods. Even the scrub that followed after for a mile or two, seemed light and penetrable. Pushing through the low scrub oaks, the scrub palmettos, the gallberry bushes and the tit-ti, was less laborious than crossing the swamp. It was late afternoon when the high pines of Baxter's Island showed ahead. The procession filed down the sand road from the east and into the clearing. Rip and Perk ran ahead to the hollowed cypress watering trough kept for the chickens. Ma Baxter sat rocking on the narrow veranda, a mound of mending in her lap.

"A dead dog and no bear, eh?" she called.

"Not dead yit. Git me water and rags and the big needle and thread."

She rose quickly to help. Jody was amazed at the capability of her great frame and hands when there was trouble. Penny laid old Julia down on the veranda floor. She whimpered. Jody bent to stroke her head and she bared her teeth at him. He trailed his mother disconsolately. She was tearing an old apron into strips.

"You kin fetch the water," she told him, and he scurried to the kettle.

Penny returned to the veranda with an armful of crocus sacks to make a bed for the hound. Ma Baxter brought the surgical equipment. Penny unwrapped his blood-soaked shirt from the dog and bathed the deep gashes. Old Julia made no protest. She had known claws before. He sewed the two deepest cuts and rubbed pine gum into all of them. She yelped once and then was silent as he worked. A rib, he said, was broken. He could do nothing for that, but if she lived, it would mend. She had lost much blood. Her breath came short. Penny gathered her up, bed and all.

Ma Baxter demanded, "Now where you carryin' her?"

"To the bedroom. I got to watch her tonight."

"Not to my bedroom, Ezra Baxter. I'll do for her what's got to be done, but I'll not have you poppin' in and outen the bed all night, wakin' me. I didn't half sleep, last night."

"Then I'll sleep with Jody and bed Julia there," he said. "I'll not leave her alone in no shed tonight. Fetch me cold water, Jody."

He carried her to Jody's room and laid her in the corner on the pile of sacking. She would not drink, or could not, and he opened her mouth and poured water down her dry throat.

"Leave her rest now. We'll go do our chores."

The clearing possessed this evening a strange coziness. Jody gathered the eggs from the hay-mow, milked the cow and turned the calf in to her, and cut wood for his mother. Penny, as always, went to the sink-hole with a wooden ox-yoke supporting two wooden buckets over his thin shoulders. Ma Baxter cooked supper of poke-greens and dried cow-peas. She fried a frugal slice of the fresh pork.

"A piece o' bear meat'd go mighty good tonight," she lamented.

Jody was hungry but Penny had little appetite. He left the table twice to offer Julia food, which she rejected. Ma Baxter rose heavily to clear the table and wash the dishes. She asked for no details of the hunt. Jody longed to talk of it, to cast away the spell of the tracking, and the fight, and the fear that had struck him. Penny was silent. No one noticed the boy and he dipped deeply into the dish of cow-peas.

The sun set red and clear. Shadows lay long and black in the Baxter kitchen.

Penny said, "I'm wore out. I could do with bed."

Jody's feet were raw and blistered from the cowhide shoes.

"Me, too," he said.

"I'll set up a whiles," Ma Baxter said. "I ain't done much today, excusin' fret and worry, and mess with the sausage."

Penny and Jody went to their room. They undressed on the side of the narrow bed.

"Now if you was big as your Ma," Penny said, "we couldn't lay in it without somebody fell on the floor."

There was room enough for the two thin bony bodies. The red faded from the west and the room was dusky. The hound slept and whimpered in her sleep. The moon rose, an hour past the full, and the small room lay in a silver brightness. Jody's feet burned. His knees twitched.

Penny said, "You wakeful, son?"

"I cain't stop walkin'."

"We went a fur piece. How you like bear-huntin', boy?"

"Well—" He rubbed his knees. "I like thinkin' about it."

"I know."

"I liked the trackin' and the trailin'. I liked seein' the saplin's broke down, and the ferns in the swamp."

"I know."

"I like old Julia bayin' now and again—"

"But the fightin's right fearsome, ain't it, son?"

"Hit's mighty fearsome."

"Hit's sickenin', the dogs gittin' bloodied and sich as that. And son, you ain't never seed a bear kilt. But mean as they be, hit's someway piteeful when they go down and the dogs tears their throats and they cry out jest like a person, and lay down and die before you."

Father and son lay in silence.

"If the wild creeturs'd only leave us be," Penny said.

"I wisht we could kill 'em all off," Jody said. "Them that steals offen us and does us harm."

" 'Tain't stealin', in a creetur. A creetur's got his livin' to make and he makes it the best way he kin. Same as us. Hit's panther nature and wolf nature and bear nature to kill their meat. County lines is nothin' to them, nor a man's fences. How's a creetur to know the land's mine and paid for? How's a bear to know I'm depending on my hogs for my own rations? All he knows is, he's hongry."

Jody lay staring into the brightness. Baxter's Island seemed to him a fortress ringed around with hunger. Now in the moonlight eyes were shining, red and green and yellow. The hungry would dart in to the clearing in swift forays, and kill and eat and slink away again. Pole-cats and 'possums would raid the hen-roost, wolf or panther might slay the calf before daylight, old Slewfoot might come again to murder and feed.

"A creetur's only doin' the same as me when I go huntin' us meat," Penny said. "Huntin' him where he lives and beds and raises his young uns. Hit's a hard law, but it's the law. 'Kill or go hongry.' "

Yet the clearing was safe. The creatures came, but they went away again. Jody began to shiver and could not tell why.

"You cold, son?"

"I reckon."

He saw old Slewfoot wheel, and slash and snarl. He saw old Julia leap, and be caught and crushed, and hold on, and then fall away, broken and bleeding. But the clearing was safe.

"Move close, son. I'll warm you."

He edged closer to his father's bones and sinews. Penny slipped an arm around him and he lay close against the lank thigh. His father was the core of safety. His father swam the swift creek to fetch back his wounded dog. The clearing was safe, and his father fought for it, and for his own. A sense of snugness came over him and he dropped asleep. He awakened once, disturbed. Penny was crouched in the corner in the moonlight, ministering to the hound.

The Highwayman

ALFRED NOYES

≈ ≈ ≈

Part One

I

The wind was a torrent of darkness among the gusty trees,
The moon was a ghostly galleon tossed upon cloudy seas,
The road was a ribbon of moonlight over the purple moor,
And the highwayman came riding—
      Riding—riding—
The highwayman came riding, up to the old inn-door.

II

He'd a French cocked-hat on his forehead, a bunch of lace at his
    chin,
A coat of claret velvet, and breeches of brown doeskin:
They fitted with never a wrinkle; his boots were up to the thigh!
And he rode with a jewelled twinkle,
      His pistol butts a-twinkle,
His rapier hilt a-twinkle, under the jewelled sky.

III

Over the cobbles he clattered and clashed in the dark inn-yard,
And he tapped with his whip on the shutters, but all was locked
    and barred:
He whistled a tune to the window, and who should be waiting
    there
But the landlord's black-eyed daughter,
      Bess, the landlord's daughter,
Plaiting a dark red love-knot into her long black hair.

IV

And dark in the dark old inn-yard a stable wicket creaked
Where Tim, the ostler, listened; his face was white and peaked,
His eyes were hollows of madness, his hair like moldy hay;
But he loved the landlord's daughter,
      The landlord's red-lipped daughter:
Dumb as a dog he listened, and he heard the robber say—

V

"One kiss, my bonny sweetheart, I'm after a prize tonight,
But I shall be back with the yellow gold before the morning light.
Yet if they press me sharply, and harry me through the day,
Then look for me by moonlight,
      Watch for me by moonlight:
I'll come to thee by moonlight, though Hell should bar the way."

VI

He rose upright in the stirrups, he scarce could reach her hand;
But she loosened her hair i' the casement! His face burnt like a
      brand
As the black cascade of perfume came tumbling over his breast;
And he kissed its waves in the moonlight,
      (Oh, sweet black waves in the moonlight)
Then he tugged at his reins in the moonlight, and galloped away
      to the West.

Part Two

I

He did not come in the dawning; he did not come at noon;
And out of the tawny sunset, before the rise o' the moon,
When the road was a gypsy's ribbon, looping the purple moor,
A red-coat-troop came marching—
      Marching—marching—
King George's men came marching, up to the old inn-door.

II

They said no word to the landlord, they drank his ale instead;
But they gagged his daughter and bound her to the foot of her
     narrow bed.
Two of them knelt at her casement, with muskets at the side!
There was death at every window;
           And Hell at one dark window;
For Bess could see, through her casement, the road that *he* would
     ride.

III

They had tied her up to attention, with many a sniggering jest:
They had bound a musket beside her, with the barrel beneath her
     breast!
"Now keep good watch!" and they kissed her.
           She heard the dead man say—
Look for me by moonlight;
           Watch for me by moonlight;
I'll come to thee by moonlight, though Hell should bar the way!

IV

She twisted her hands behind her; but all the knots held good!
She writhed her hands till her fingers were wet with sweat and
     blood!
They stretched and strained in the darkness, and the hours crawled
     by like years;
Till, now, on the stroke of midnight,
     Cold, on the stroke of midnight,
The tip of one finger touched it! The trigger at least was hers!

V

The tip of one finger touched it; she strove no more for the rest!
Up, she stood to attention, with the barrel beneath her breast,
She would not risk their hearing: she would not strive again;
For the road lay bare in the moonlight,
           Blank and bare in the moonlight;
And the blood of her veins in the moonlight throbbed to her
     Love's refrain.

VI

Tlot-tlot; tlot-tlot! Had they heard it? The horse-hoofs ringing
    clear—
Tlot-tlot, tlot-tlot in the distance? Were they deaf that they did not
    hear?
Down the ribbon of moonlight, over the brow of the hill,
The highwayman came riding,
            Riding, riding!
The red-coats looked to their priming! She stood up straight and
    still!

VII

Tlot-tlot, in the frosty silence! *Tlot-tlot* in the echoing night!
Nearer he came and nearer! Her face was like a light!
Her eyes grew wide for a moment; she drew one last deep breath,
Then her finger moved in the moonlight,
            Her musket shattered the moonlight,
Shattered her breast in the moonlight and warned him—with her
    death.

VIII

He turned; he spurred him Westward; he did not know who stood
Bowed with her head o'er the musket, drenched with her own red
    blood!
Not till the dawn he heard it, and slowly blanched to hear
How Bess, the landlord's daughter,
            The landlord's black-eyed daughter,
Had watched for her Love in the moonlight, and died in the dark-
    ness there.

IX

Back, he spurred like a madman, shrieking a curse to the sky,
With the white road smoking behind him, and his rapier bran-
    dished high!
Blood-red were his spurs i' the golden noon; wine-red was his vel-
    vet coat;
When they shot him down on the highway,

Down like a dog on the highway,
And he lay in his blood on the highway, with the bunch of lace at
his throat.

*   *   *   *   *

And still of a winter's night, they say, when the wind is in the
trees,
When the moon is a ghostly galleon tossed upon cloudy seas,
When the road is a ribbon of moonlight over the purple moor,
A highwayman comes riding—
        Riding—riding—
A highwayman comes riding, up to the old inn-door.

x

Over the cobbles he clatters and clangs in the dark inn-yard;
And he taps with his whip on the shutters, but all is locked and
barred:
He whistles a tune to the window, and who should be waiting there
But the land-lord's black-eyed daughter,
        Bess, the landlord's daughter,
Plaiting a dark red love-knot into her long black hair.

The Seeing Eye

WILL JAMES

≈ ≈ ≈ *Will James, who was a cowboy himself before he became a writer, loved to tell stories about horses. This is one of his best, about one of the best horses Will ever knew. It is written the way cowboys used to talk.* —From Horses I Have Known

It's worse than tough for anybody to be blind but I don't think it's as tough for an indoor born and raised person as it is for one whose life is with the all out-of-doors the most of his life from childhood on. The outdoor man misses his freedom to roam over the hills and the sight of 'em ever changing. A canary would die outside his cage but a free-born eagle would dwindle away inside of one.

Dane Gruger was very much of an out-of-door man. He was born on a little ranch along a creek bottom, in the heart of the cow country, growed up with it to be a good cowboy, then, like his dad, went on in the cow business. A railroad went thru the lower part of the ranch but stations and little towns was over twenty miles away either way.

He had a nice little spread when I went to work for him, was married and had two boys who done some of the riding. I'd been riding for Dane for quite a few days before I knew he was blind, not totally blind, but, as his boys told me, he couldn't see any further than his outstretched hand, and that was blurred. He couldn't read, not even big print, with any kind of glasses so he never wore any.

That's what fooled me, and he could look you "right square in the eye" while talking to you. What was more he'd go straight down to the corral, catch his horse, saddle him and ride away like any man with full sight. The thing I first noticed and wondered at was that he never rode with us, and after the boys told me, I could understand. It was that he'd be of no use out on the range and away from the ranch.

Dane had been blind a few years when I come there and he'd of course got to know every foot of the ten miles which the ranch covered on the creek bottom before that happened. The ranch itself was one to two miles wide in some places and taking in some brakes. The whole of that was fenced and cross-fenced into pastures and hay lands, and Dane knew to within an inch when he came to every fence, gate or creek crossing. He knew how many head of cattle or horses might be in each pasture, how all was faring, when some broke out or some broke in, and where. He could find bogged cattle, cow with young calf needing help, and know everything that went well or wrong with what stock would be held on the ranch.

He of course seldom could do much towards helping whatever stock needed it or fix the holes he found in the fences, but when he'd get back to the ranch house he could easy tell the boys when there was anything wrong, and the exact spot where, in which field or pasture, how far from which side of the creek or what fence and what all the trouble might be. It would then be up to the boys to set things to rights, and after Dane's description of the spot it was easy found.

During the time I was with that little outfit I got to know Dane pretty well, well enough to see that I don't think he could of lived if he hadn't been able to do what he was doing. He was so full of life and gumption and so appreciating of all around him that he could feel, hear and breathe in. I'd sometimes see him hold his horse to a standstill while he only listened to birds or the faraway bellering of cattle, even to the yapping of prairie dogs which most cowboys would rather not hear the sound of.

To take him away from all of that, the open air, the feel of his saddle and horse under him and set him on a chair to do nothing but sit and babble and think, would of brought a quick end to him.

With the riding he done he felt satisfied he was doing something worth doing instead of just plain riding. He wouldn't of cared for that, and fact was he well took the place of an average rider.

But he had mighty good help in the work he was doing, and that was the two horses he used, for they was both as well trained to his wants and care as the dogs that's used nowadays to lead the blind and which are called "The Seeing Eye."

Dane had the advantage of the man with the dog, for he didn't have to walk and use a cane at every step. He rode, and he had more confidence in his horses' every step than he had in his own, even if he could of seen well. As horses do, they naturally sensed every foot of the earth under 'em without ever looking down at it, during sunlight, darkness or under drifted snow.

Riding into clumps of willows or thickets which the creek bottoms had much of, either of the two horses was careful to pick out a wide enough trail thru so their rider wouldn't get scratched or brushed off. If they come to a place where the brush was too thick and Dane was wanting to go thru that certain thicket, the ponies, regardless of his wants, would turn back for a ways and look for a better opening. Dane never argued with 'em at such times. He would just sort of head 'em where he wanted to go and they'd do the rest to pick out the best way there.

Them horses was still young when I got to that outfit, seven or eight years of age, and would be fit for at least twenty years more with the little riding and good care they was getting. Dane's boys had broke 'em especially for their dad's use that way and they'd done a fine job of it.

One of the horses, a gray of about a thousand pounds, was called Little Eagle. That little horse never missed a thing in sight, or sound. With his training the rustling of the brush close by would make him investigate and learn the cause before leaving that spot. Dane would know by his actions whether it was a new-born calf that had been hid or some cow in distress. It was the same at the boggy places along the creek or alkali swamps. If Little Eagle rode right on around and without stopping, Dane knew that all was well. If he stopped at any certain spot, bowed his neck and snorted low, then Dane knew that some horse or cow was in trouble. Keeping his hand on Little Eagle's neck he'd have him go on, and by the bend of that horse's neck as he went, like pointing, Dane could tell the exact location of where that animal was that was in trouble, or whatever it was that was wrong.

Sometimes, Little Eagle would line out on a trot, of his own accord and as tho there was something needed looking into right away. At times he'd even break into a lope, and then Dane wouldn't know what to expect, whether it was stock breaking thru a fence, milling around an animal that was down, or what. But most always it would be when a bunch of stock, horses or cattle, would be stringing out in single file, maybe going to water or some other part of the pasture.

At such times, Little Eagle would get just close enough to the stock so Dane could count 'em by the sound of the hoofs going by, a near impossible thing to do for a man that can see, but Dane got so he could do it and get a mighty close count on what stock was in each pasture that way. Close enough so he could tell if any had got out or others got in.

With the horses in the pastures, there was bells on the leaders of every bunch and some on one of every little bunch that sort of held together and separate from others. Dane knew by the sound of every bell which bunch it was and about how many there would be to each. The boys kept him posted on that every time they'd run a bunch in for some reason or other. Not many horses was ever kept under fence, but there was quite a few of the pure bred cattle for the upbreeding of the outside herds.

At this work of keeping tab on stock, Little Eagle was a cowboy by himself. With his natural intellect so developed as to what was wanted of him, he could near tell of what stock was wanted or not and where they belonged. The proof of that was when he turned a bunch of cattle out of a hayfield one time, and other times, and drove 'em to the gate of the field where they'd broke out of, circled around 'em when the gate was reached and went to it for Dane to open. He then drove the cattle thru, none got away, not from Little Eagle, and Dane would always prepare to ride at such times, for if any did try to break away Little Eagle would be right on their tail to bring 'em back, and for a blind man, not knowing when his horse is going to break into a sudden run, stop or turn, that's kind of hard riding, on a good cowhorse.

About all Dane would have to go by most of the time was the feel of the top muscles on Little Eagle's neck, and he got to know by them about the same as like language to him. With one hand most always on these muscles he felt what the horse seen. Tenseness, wonder, danger, fear, relaxation and about all that a human feels at the sight of different things. Places, dangerous or smooth, trouble or peace.

Them top muscles told him much more, and more plainly than if another rider had been riding constantly alongside of him and telling him right along of what he seen. That was another reason why Dane liked to ride alone. He felt more at ease, no confusion, and wasn't putting anybody out of their way by talking and describing when maybe they wouldn't feel like it.

And them two horses of Dane's, they not only took him wherever he wanted to go but never overlooked any work that needed to be done. They took it onto themselves to look for work which, being they always felt so good, was like play to them. Dane knew it when such times come and he then would let 'em go as they chose.

Neither of the horses would of course go out by themselves without a rider and do that work. They wouldn't of been interested doing that without Dane's company. What's more they couldn't have opened the gates that had to be gone thru, and besides they wasn't wanted to do that. They was to be the company of Dane and with him in whatever he wanted to do.

Dane's other horse was a trim bay about the same size as Little Eagle, and even tho just as good he had different ways about him. He was called Ferret, and a ferret he was for digging up and finding out things, like a cow with new-born calf or mare with colt, and he was even better than Little Eagle for finding holes in fences or where some was down.

All that came under the special training the boys had given him and Little Eagle, and if it wasn't for automobiles these days, such as them would be mighty valuable companions in the city, even more useful in the streets than the dog is, for the horse would soon know where his rider would want to go after being ridden such places a few times.

Unlike most horses it wasn't these two's nature to keep wanting to turn back to the ranch (home) when Dane would ride 'em away, and they wouldn't turn back until they knew the ride was over and it was time to. Sometimes Dane wouldn't show up for the noon meal, and that was all right with the ponies too, for he'd often get off 'em and let 'em graze with reins dragging. There was no danger of either of them ever leaving Dane, for they seemed as attached to him as any dog could be to his master.

It was the same with Dane for them, and he had more confidence in their trueness and senses than most humans have in one another.

A mighty good test and surprising outcome of that came one day as a powerful big cloudburst hit above the ranch a ways and left Dane acrost the creek from home. The creek had turned into churning wild waters the size of a big river in a few minutes, half a mile wide in some places and licking up close to the higher land where the ranch buildings and corrals was.

It kept on a-raining hard after the cloudburst had fell and it didn't act like it was going to let up for some time, and the wide river wouldn't be down to creek size or safe to cross, at least not for a day or so.

The noise of the rushing water was a-plenty to let Dane know of the cloudburst. It had come with a sudden roar and without a drop of warning, and Dane's horse, he was riding Little Eagle that day, plainly let him know the danger of the wide stretch of swirling fast waters. It wasn't the danger of the water only but uprooted trees and all kinds of heavy timber speeding along would make the crossing more than dangerous, not only dangerous but it would about mean certain death.

Little Eagle would of tackled the swollen waters or anything Dane would of wanted him to, but Dane knew a whole lot better than to make that wise horse go where he didn't want to, any time.

Dane could tell by the noise, and riding to the edge of the water and the location where he was, how wide the body of wild waters was. He knew that the stock could keep out of reach of it on either side without being jammed against the fences, but he got worried about the ranch, wondering if the waters had got up to the buildings. He worried too about his family worrying about him, and maybe try to find and get to him.

That worrying got him to figuring on ways of getting back. He sure couldn't stay where he was until the waters went down, not if he could help it. It wouldn't be comfortable being out so long in the heavy rain either, even if he did have his slicker on, and it wouldn't do to try to go to the neighbor's ranch which was fifteen miles away. He doubted if he could find it anyway, for it was acrost a bunch of rolling hills, nothing to go by, and Little Eagle wouldn't know that there would be where Dane would be wanting him to go. Besides there was the thought of his family worrying so about him and maybe risking their lives in trying to find him.

He'd just have to get home, somehow, and it was at the thought of his neighbor's ranch and picturing the distance and country to it in his mind, that he thought of the railroad, for he would of had to cross it to get there, and then, thinking of the railroad, the thought came of the trestle crossing along it and over the creek. Maybe he could make that. That would be sort of dangerous crossing, too, but the more he thought of it the more he figured it worth taking the chances of trying. That was the only way of his getting on the other side of the high waters and back to the ranch.

The railroad and trestle was only about half a mile from where he now was and that made it all the more tempting to try. So, after thinking it over in every way, including the fact that he'd be taking chances with losing his horse also, he finally decided to take the chance, at the risk of both himself and his horse, that is if his horse seen it might be safe enough. He felt it had to be done, and could be done, and there went to show his faith and confidence in that Little Eagle horse of his.

And that confidence sure wasn't misplaced, for, a cooler-headed, brainier horse never was.

There was two fences to cross to get to the railroad and trestle, and it wasn't at all necessary to go thru gates to get there, for the swollen waters with jamming timbers had laid the fence down for quite a ways on both sides of the wide river, some of the wire strands to break and snap and coil all directions.

A strand of barbed wire, even if flat to the ground, is a mighty dangerous thing to ride over, for a horse might pick it up with a hoof, and, as most horses will scare, draw their hind legs up under 'em and act up. The result might be a wicked sawing wire cut at the joint by the hock, cutting veins and tendons and often crippling a horse for life. In such cases the rider is also very apt to get tangled up in the wire, for that wicked stuff seems to have the ways of the tentacles of a devil-fish at such times.

Loose wire laying around on the ground is the cowboys' worst fear, especially so with Dane, for, as he couldn't see it was many times more threatening as he rode most every day from one fenced-in field to the other. But the confidence he had in his two cool-headed ponies relieved him of most all his fear of the dangerous barbed wire, and either one of 'em would stop and snort a little at the sight of a broken strand coiled to the ground. Dane knew what that meant and it always brought a chill to his spine. He'd get down off his saddle, feel around carefully in front of his horse, and usually the threatening coil would be found to within a foot or so of his horse's nose. The coil would then be pulled and fastened to the fence, to stay until a ranch hand who, with team and buckboard, would make the rounds of all fences every few months, done a general fixing of 'em.

It's too bad barbed wire *has* to be used for fences. It has butchered and killed many good horses, and some riders. But barbed wire is about the only kind of fence that will hold cattle, most of the time, and when there has to be many long miles of it, even with the smaller ranches, that's about the only kind of fence that can be afforded or used. Cattle (even the wildest) seldom get a scratch by it, even in breaking thru a four-strand fence of it, or going over it while it's loose and coiled on the ground, for they don't get rattled when in wire as a horse does, and they hold their hind legs straight back when going thru, while the horse he draws 'em under him instead and goes to tearing around.

Both Little Eagle and Ferret had been well trained against scaring and fighting wire if they ever got into it, and stop whenever coming to some that was loose on the ground. That training had been done with a rope and a piece of smooth wire at one end, and being they was naturally cool-headed they soon learned all the tricks of the wire and how to behave when they come near any of that coiled on the ground.

There was many such coils as the flood waters rampaged along the creek bottom, and as Dane headed Little Eagle towards the railroad and trestle he then let him pick his own way thru and around the two fence entanglements on the way there, along the edge of the rushing water.

Little Eagle done considerable winding around and careful stepping as he come to the fences that had been snapped and washed to scattering, dangerous strands over the field. Dane gave him his time, let him go as he choose, and finally the roar of the waters against the high banks by the trestle came to his ears. It sounded as tho it was near up to the trestle, which he knew was plenty high, and that gave him a good idea of what a cloudburst it had been.

He then got mighty dubious about trying to cross the trestle, for it was a long one, there was no railing of any kind on the sides, and part of it might be under water or even washed away. There was some of the flood water in the ditch alongside the railroad grade and it wasn't so many feet up it to the track level.

Riding between the rails a short ways he come to where the trestle begin and there he stopped Little Eagle. The swirling waters made a mighty roar right there, and how he wished he could of been able to see then, more than any time since his blindness had overtook him.

Getting off Little Eagle, there he felt his way along to the first ties to the trestle, of the space between each, which was about five inches, and just right for Little Eagle's small hoofs to slip in between, Dane thought. One such slip would mean a broken leg, and the horse would have to be shot right there, to lay between the rails. The rider would be mighty likely to go over the side of the trestle, too.

Dane hardly had any fear for himself, but he did have for Little Eagle. Not that he feared he would put a foot between the ties, for that little horse was too wise, cool-headed and careful to do anything like that, Dane knew. What worried him most was if the trestle was still up and above water all the way acrost. There would be no turning back, for in turning is when Little Eagle would be mighty liable to slip a hoof between the ties. The rain had let up but the wind was blowing hard and the tarred ties was slippery as soaped glass.

It all struck Dane as fool recklessness to try to cross on that long narrow trestle at such a time, but he felt he should try, and to settle his dubiousness he now left it to Little Eagle and his good sense as to whether to tackle it or not.

If he went he would *ride* him across, not try to crawl, feel his way and lead him, for in leading the horse he wouldn't be apt to pay as much attention to his footing and to nosing every dangerous step he made. Besides, Dane kind of felt that if Little Eagle should go over the side he'd go with him.

So, getting into the saddle again, he let Little Eagle stand for a spell, at the same time letting him know that he wanted to cross the trestle, for him to size it up and see if it could be done. It was up to him, and the little gray well understood.

It might sound unbelievable, but a good sensible horse and rider have a sort of feel-language which is mighty plain between 'em, and when comes a particular dangerous spot the two can discuss the possibilities of getting over or acrost it as well as two humans can, and even better, for the horse has the instinct which the human lacks. He can tell danger where the human can't, and the same with the safety.

It was that way with Little Eagle and Dane, only even more so, because as Little Eagle, like Ferret, had been trained to realize Dane's affliction, cater and sort of take care of him, they was always watchful. Then with Dane's affection and care for them, talking to 'em and treating 'em like the true pardners they was, there was an understanding and trust between man and horse that's seldom seen between man and man.

Sitting in his saddle with his hand on Little Eagle's neck the two "discussed" the dangerous situation ahead in such a way that the loud roar of the water foaming by and under the trestle didn't interfere any with the decision that was to come.

There was a tenseness in the top muscles of Little Eagle's neck as he looked over the scary, narrow, steel-ribboned trail ahead, nervous at the so careful investigation, that all sure didn't look well. But he'd now left

it all to Little Eagle's judgment, and Dane had about expected he'd
be against trying, Little Eagle, still all tense and quivering some,
planted one foot on the first tie, and crouching a bit, all nerves and
muscles steady, started on the way of the dangerous crossing.

Every step by step from the first seemed like a long minute to Dane.
The brave little horse, his nose close to the ties, at the same time
looking ahead, was mighty careful how he placed each foot, and sure
that the hind one would come up to the exact same place afterwards,
right where that front one had been. He didn't just plank his hoof and
go on, but felt for a sure footing on the wet and slippery tarred ties
before putting any weight on it and making another step. Something
like a mountain climber feeling and making sure of his every hold
while going on with his climbing.

The start wasn't the worst of the crossing. That begin to come as
they went further along and nearer to the center. There, with the
strong wind blowing broadside of 'em, the swift waters churning,
sounding like to the level of the slippery ties would seem about scary
enough to chill the marrow in any being. But there was more piled
onto that, for as they neared the center it began to tremble and sway as
if by earth tremors. This was by the high rushing waters swirling
around the tall and now submerged supporting timbers.

Little Eagle's step wasn't so sure then, and as careful as he was there
come a few times when he slipped, and a time or two when a hoof
went down between the ties, leaving him to stand on three shaking legs
until he got his hoof up and on footing again.

With most any other horse it would of been the end of him and his
rider then. As it was, Little Eagle went on, like a tightrope walker,
with every muscle at work. And Dane, riding mighty light on him, his
heart up his throat at every slip or loss of footing, done his best not to
get him off balance but help him that way when he thought he could.

If the shaking, trembling and swaying of the trestle had been steady
it would have been less scary and some easier, but along with the
strong vibrations of the trestle there'd sometimes come a big uprooted
tree to smash into it at a forty-mile speed. There'd be a quiver all along
the trestle at the impact. It would sway and bend dangerously, to ship
back again as the tree would be washed under and on.

Such goings on would jar Little Eagle's footing to where he'd again
slip a hoof between the ties, and Dane would pray, sometimes cuss a

little. But the way Little Eagle handled his feet and every part of himself, sometimes on the tip of his toes, the sides of his hoofs and even to his knees, he somehow managed to keep right side up.

Good thing, Dane thought, that the horse wasn't shod, for shoes without sharp calks would of been much worse on than none on the slippery ties. As it was, and being his shoes had been pulled off only a couple of days before to ease his feet some between shoeings, his hoofs was sharp at the edges and toe, and that gave him more chance.

The scary and most dangerous part of the trestle was reached, the center, and it was a good thing maybe that Dane couldn't see while Little Eagle sort of juggled himself over that part, for the trestle had been under repair and some of the old ties had been taken away in a few places, to later be replaced by new ones; but where each tie had been taken away that left an opening of near two feet wide. Mighty scary for Little Eagle too, but he eased over them gaps without Dane knowing.

Dane felt as tho it was long weary miles and took about that much time to finally get past the center and most dangerous part of the five-hundred-yard trestle, for them five hundred yards put more wear on him during that time than five hundred miles would of.

And he was far from near safe going as yet, for he'd just passed center, and the trestle was still doing some tall trembling and dangerous weaving, when, as bad and spooky as things already was, there come the sound of still worse fear and danger, and Dane's heart stood still. It was a train whistle he'd heard above the roar of the waters. It sounded like the train was coming his way, facing him, and there'd sure be no chance for him to turn and make it back, for he'd crossed over half of the trestle, the worst part, and going back would take a long time.

All the dangers and fears piling together now, instead of exciting Dane, seemed to cool and steady him, like having to face the worst and make the best of it. He rode right on towards the coming train.

He knew from memory that the railroad run a straight line to the trestle, that there was no railroad crossing nor other reason for the engineer to blow his whistle, unless it was for him, himself. Then it came to him that the engineer must of seen him on the trestle and would sure stop his train, if he could.

Standing up in his stirrups he raised his big black hat high as he could and waved it from side to side as a signal for the engineer to stop his train. Surely they could see that black hat of his and realize the predicament he was in. That getting off the trestle would mean almost certain death.

But the train sounded like it was coming right on, and at that Dane wondered if maybe it was coming too fast to be able to stop. He got a little panicky then, and for a second he was about to turn Little Eagle off the trestle and swim for it. It would of been a long and risky swim, maybe carried for miles down country before they could of reached either bank, and it would of taken more than luck to've succeeded. But if they'd got bowled over by some tree trunk and went down the churning waters that would be better, Dane thought, than to have Little Eagle smashed to smithereens by the locomotive. He had no thought for himself.

About the only thing that made him take a bigger chance and ride on some more was that he knew that the whole train and its crew would be doomed before it got halfways on the trestle, and what if it was a passenger train?

At that thought he had no more fear of Little Eagle keeping his footing on the trestle. His fear now went for the many lives there might be on the train, and he sort of went wild and to waving his big black hat all the more in trying to warn of the danger.

But he didn't put on no such action as to unbalance the little gray in any way. He still felt and helped with his every careful step, and then there got to be a prayer with each one, like the beads of the Rosary.

He rubbed his moist eyes and also prayed he could see, now of all times and if only just for this once, and then the train whistle blew again, so close this time that it sounded like it was on the trestle, like coming on, and being mighty near to him.—Dane had done his best, and now was his last and only chance to save Little Eagle and himself, by sliding off the trestle. He wiped his eyes like as tho to better see, and went to reining Little Eagle off the side of the trestle. But to his surprise, Little Eagle wouldn't respond to the rein. It was the first time excepting amongst the thick brush or bad creek crossings that horse had ever went against his wishes that way. But this was now very different, and puzzled, he tried him again and again, with no effect, and then, all at once, *he could see.*

Myself and one of Dane's boys had been riding, looking for Dane as soon as the cloudburst hit, and seeing the stopped passenger train with the many people gathered by the engine we high-loped towards it, there to get the surprise of seeing Dane and Little Eagle on the trestle and carefully making each and every dangerous step towards us and solid ground.

We seen we sure couldn't be of no use to the little gray nor Dane only maybe a hindrance, and being there was only a little ways more we held our horses and watched. Looking on the length of the trestle we noticed that only the rails and ties showed above the high water, there was quite a bend in it from the swift and powerful pressure and the rails and ties was leaning, like threatening to break loose at any time.

How the little horse and Dane ever made it, with the strong wind, slippery ties and all a-weaving, was beyond us. So was it with the passengers who stood with gaping mouths and tense watching. What if they'd known that the rider had been blind while he made the dangerous crossing?

And as the engineer went on to tell the spellbound passengers how that man and horse on the trestle had saved all their lives, they was more than thankful, for, as the heavy cloudburst had come so sudden and hit in one spot, there'd been no report of it, and, as the engineer said, he might of drove onto the trestle a ways before knowing. Then it would of been too late.

But Little Eagle was the one who played the biggest part in stopping what would have been a terrible happening. He was the one who decided to make the dangerous crossing, the one who had to use his head and hoofs with all his skill and power, also the one who at the last of the stretch would not heed Dane's pull of the reins to slide off the trestle. His first time not to do as he was wanted to. He'd disobeyed and had saved another life. He'd been "The Seeing Eye."

The fuss over with as Dane finally rode up on solid ground and near the engine, we then was the ones due for a big surprise. For Dane *spotted* us out from the crowd, and smiling, rode straight for us and looked us both "square in the eye."

The shock and years he lived crossing that trestle, then the puzzling over Little Eagle not wanting to turn at the touch of the rein had done the trick, had brought his sight back.

After that day, Little Eagle and Ferret was sort of neglected, neglected knee deep in clover, amongst good shade and where clear spring water run. The seeing eyes was partly closed in contentment.

And Shall Trelawny Die?

R. S. HAWKER

A good sword and a trusty hand!
    A merry heart and true!
King James's men shall understand
    What Cornish lads can do.

And have they fixed the where and when?
    And shall Trelawny die?
Here's twenty thousand Cornish men
    Will know the reason why!

Out spake their captain brave and bold,
    A merry wight was he:
'If London Tower were Michael's hold,
    We'll set Trelawny free!

'We'll cross the Tamar, land to land,
    The Severn is no stay,
With "one and all," and hand in hand,
    And who shall bid us nay?

'And when we come to London Wall,
    A pleasant sight to view,
Come forth! come forth, ye cowards all,
    Here's men as good as you.

'Trelawny he's in keep and hold,
    Trelawny he may die;
But here's twenty thousand Cornish bold
    Will know the reason why!'

The Way of a Lion

ALDEN STEVENS

≈ ≈ ≈ *Many charming and many silly stories have been written about lions by men who knew little about them. This one
was written by a man who knew lions well. It tells how lions
really live, particularly how they must kill in order to live.*

In the African dusk that fades swiftly into night, a dense cloud of tiny
birds wheeled with a fluttering roar of wings across the end of the
shallow valley and disappeared over the hill.

The tumult of their passing was startling, but it did not disturb the
great black-maned lion where he crouched tense in a clump of yellow
grass. The dark mass of hair that covered his neck and shoulders stirred
with the evening breeze. He lay there in the grass, massive head on
outstretched paws. The dark round pupils of his eyes were large now
as the darkness gathered. He stared intently up the little valley that lay
like a shallow trough between its rounded hills.

Except for the call of a night bird all was quiet. It was not the quiet
of peace, however. Perhaps the pose of the beast himself suggested a
calm that precedes some storm of action. He waited for something. A
ripple ran up the great tawny back, and the flat cords of muscle in his
tremendous forelegs quivered and writhed with a contained excitement
that pervaded the silent night.

This lion was larger than the average of his kind, weighing near to
five hundred pounds. Stretched flat as he now lay, he measured ten and
a half feet from the tip of his broad muzzle to the black, hairy tuft
at the end of his tail. Black hair grew low on his forehead, and over chest
and shoulders. The barrel of chest curved sharply up into a lean belly.
His color ranged from a deep brown along the spine, to a golden yellow. Six years old perhaps, no scar yet marred the smooth beauty of his
skin. Muscle overlaid his bones in rippling bands of power. Within
him was a swift intelligence and the capacity for lightning action. Here
was a creature of beauty and grace, of menace and strength.

The chill wind that blew into the lion's flaring nostrils brought the scent of a little herd of zebra that fed—wary but unalarmed—up there in the darkness. Another message came on the night wind. The lion scented his mate. The familiar odor of her distant body told him that she was playing her part and that her snarling voice would soon shatter the peace of the night.

Just over the crest of one of the hills that bounded the valley, the lioness moved swiftly through the darkness. Her belly swayed as she trotted. From time to time she stopped and listened. At last she reached a point just opposite to where the zebra were feeding. She could see the black mass of them below, less than two hundred yards from where she crouched. Her amber eyes stared intently into the dark and the temptation was strong to charge in and try for a kill. But she knew that the chances were against her. Before she had covered half the distance the zebra would be aware of her approach. There would be a snort of warning from the leader and then with a thunder of hoofs, the whole band would be gone over the opposite ridge. The plan of the hunt would be ruined. She thought of her mate, remembering where he waited in the grass at the narrow entrance to the valley. Her powerful body relaxed and she trotted on along the hillside.

Perhaps a quarter of a mile beyond where the zebra fed, the big lioness turned sharply to the left and went down the hill into the valley. Now the feeding animals were between her and her lord. Head thrust forward, she swept down toward her unsuspecting prey. She was less than three hundred yards from the zebra when they became aware of her. There was a loud snort of alarm and warning from the leader, shrill whinnies of fright from the mares as they gathered their colts. Before the oncoming lioness, straight down the valley, the herd of zebra fled in drumming thunder. The wind with its smell of death was at their heels. Death was before them too, waiting there in the grass at the mouth of the valley.

The great black-maned lion tensed himself for the kill. He heard the oncoming beat of hundreds of hoofs. Now he could see them, the mad dark mass of them, rushing directly at him out of the night. Now the sharp smell of sweat, the dust of flying forms about him. Here a fat mare, anxious for the little yellow colt that labored at her heels. There a fleeting stallion, the whistle of effort in his nostrils.

With a blaring snarl that shook the night with its depth and ferocity, a giant form shot from the grass and loomed an instant over the fat mare. Steel-like claws closed over her straining face. Others gripped her just below the ears. There was a dexterous twist of mighty muscles, and the sharp report of her breaking neck was followed by a scream of utter agony. The zebra was dead as she fell, and her colt stumbled over her, his long slender legs kicking in frantic fear. The little creature had just regained his feet when the lioness was upon him. Her fangs closed over the back of his neck and met in a crushing bite that severed spine and flesh.

The herd of zebra was gone. Somewhere on the open plain they would gather trembling, listening, their eyes straining into the night, their nostrils flaring wide to catch the scent of enemies. In the dark hour before dawn, they would feed again.

The big lion growled and the lioness answered him. Then he sniffed at her, their noses touching gently. She dropped on the grass as though tired, then rolled over lazily like a cat and lay extended. Her mate dropped his shaggy head, then raising it suddenly gave forth a tremendous blast of sound, a bellowing roar that filled all the world about. Then he dropped his head again, only to raise it once more as his roar shook the night. Jackals, yapping on the starlit plains, ceased their clamor and it seemed as though every creature within range of that mighty voice, cowered and listened. For a full minute after the last roar, the night hung empty and still as though suspended in the cold spaces among the stars.

There had been a growing radiance along the rim of low-lying mountains to the eastward, and now the edge of a lemon-yellow moon appeared, its rays lighting the scene where the lions surveyed their kill. Lazily, the female watched her mate as his mighty forearm swung the dead zebra into position for the work ahead of him. Holding the striped body in place, with one paw, the lion raked the tender belly in tearing sweeps, ripping through the skin and flesh until an opening appeared. Then growling fiercely, he scooped again and again, his big paw thrusting into the still warm body until it was completely emboweled. No human hunter, armed with knife and spear, could have done it more expertly.

While her mate was engaged in this savage operation, the lioness had watched him, growling deep encouragement. Now she rose slowly to her feet, padded to the edge of a patch of thorny bush and began to dig, her claws tearing through sod and brown earth. The steady sweep of leg and paw soon produced a considerable hole and into it the two beasts tumbled the intestines of the zebra, scraping earth, leaves and grass over the mass until the depression was filled. Thus buried, the swiftly decomposing insides would not taint the air, and alert noses of scavenging hyenas and jackals would be less likely to scent the kill. Here was food for at least two meals, and the killers had no desire to share their meat with lesser beasts who would be lured to the scene by the seductive odor of corruption.

Paws pushing against the strain of clamping fangs, the lions began to feast. They tore first at the meaty insides of the hind legs. Occasionally their bloody muzzles would touch and the lioness would growl fiercely, slapping her mate in a lightning swift jab. Hind quarters reared high, massive head and chest bent low, he ate in noisy satisfaction. She, stretched flat on spreading belly, gripped the prey between razor-keen claws, thrusting her tusks into the tender meat as she fed.

The two had eaten for a very short time when the lioness raised her head and looked about her. Then she rose heavily to her feet. A shiver rippled the skin along the length of her tawny body. There was something of physical weariness in her action as she turned and, with low-hanging head, disappeared into the black shadows of the thorn scrub. The big male stopped his feeding for an instant and stared after her.

Threading her way slowly through the tangled bush, the lioness soon came into an open plain and crossed a flat expanse of short grass to the foot of a low rocky hill that rose abruptly from the land. It was shaped somewhat like a loaf of bread, broad and rounded at the top, several hundred yards wide across its base—perhaps half a mile long. A dim trail zig-zagged upward along the face of the hill, winding amid low growing bush and rocks. Up this faint path the lioness made her slow way. At a point close by a great boulder she stopped and looked out and downward, resting as she gazed.

The flat stare of her yellow eyes encompassed the scene completely; the way she had come, the rolling vastness of the plains, the dark distant line that was forest, the starry bowl of the African sky arching mightily over the silent wilderness. These things she saw, and comprehended them for what they were. But more insistently her gaze focused on the dark patch of bush at the mouth of the little valley. Down there her black-maned mate was snarling over the body of the zebra. Hunger assailed her and a slow clear drool dripped from her black lips, but a need as old and even more urgent than hunger was now upon her. She turned away, following the path that led sharply up-ward.

Where a tumbled mass of boulders rose beyond a narrow ledge, a low opening showed black against the moonlit rocks. Without hesita-tion the lioness went into this cave, her belly swaying and almost dragging the ground as she crouched slightly at the dark entrance.

The cave was deep and dry. Lying in a rocky hollow at the far end, the big sinewy body stretched wearily and a sound very like a deep groan came from her. A glaze of pain filmed the clear eyes. Within her the life she had been carrying for nine months struggled urgently for exit into the world. Her cubs were about to be born and she awaited them.

The moon had set and only the stars looked in at the three squirming cubs and the lioness. The cubs—born with eyes wide open—looked out and saw the stars, then huddled close to the warmth of the great furry body that sheltered them, sucking vigorously at the generous breasts of their mother. They drank until filled, then slept to awake and drink again. The lioness, relaxed and content, cleansed the cubs with her rough tongue, stretched out and slept.

ALONE IN THE BUSH

At the age of five months the young male cub was a third again as large as his sisters. He was powerful and rangy, but with the clumsiness of cubhood showing in his shambling loose-gaited walk, and great paws so out of proportion to his yet slender legs and unformed mus-cles. That he was still a cub was also evident because each day brought him into some escapade or painful dilemma that age and experience would have avoided. The episode with the porcupine was typical. He still needed his parents and had much to learn from them, such as what beasts, snakes and insects to avoid, many ways and stratagems concern-ing the stalking and killing of game—all the essential things that only experience coupled with parental protection could give.

The rains moved westward across the land, turning the grass from yellow to green, bringing a million flowers, swelling the streams and water-holes. Behind the rains came the great herds of wildebeest—hundreds of thousands of them, blackish clumps that drifted slowly toward the distant Victoria Nyanza and the Congo border. They filled the eye, ever moving through the heat of day and the chill of the high equatorial night. Days passed and still they came. With the wildebeest moved others; kongoni, eland, gazelle, reedbuck and waterbuck, impala, zebra in countless thousands, elephant following the rains in their endless quest for water, giraffe, buffalo; a seemingly infinite host of four-footed ones cropping the grasses, drifting ever to the westward.

Killing was easy. The cubs and their parents feasted nightly. The night hours were filled with the drumming thunder of hoofs, with the deep roars of the killers. Lion, leopard, cheetah, hyena, jackal, and vulture had their fill of meat. And man, too, for the pulsing rhythm of drums sounded across the plains from little thorn-walled villages where savage herdsmen filled their bellies.

A night came when the big black-maned lion, his mate and the six-month-old cubs crouched in the shadow of an area of thorn thicket. They were motionless, waiting. On the plain that surrounded their place of concealment, creatures moved and fed on the grasses under the newly risen moon. The lions could smell them and hear the sounds they made—the stamp of a hoof, the steady crunching of grass as it was torn from its root, a snort, a whistle from a reedbuck near some pool of water, a low bellow.

Thorny branches crackled in brittle protest against some moving body that pushed its way through the bush. The lions crouched lower, tensed and waiting, so utterly motionless that they seemed part of the shadows. With a final snapping of branches a dark form thrust out from the cover and stood revealed in a moonlit space. It was a very young buffalo calf innocently unaware of his danger. He raised his wet muzzle and blew gently, then bawled softly. It was the last sound he ever made. Even before his mother's answering voice could reach him he was dead, the big lion's fangs at his throat. But as he went down under the crushing force of the lion's spring, the gentle *blatting* note in his throat turned to a bellow of terror.

In that instant when a calf's fear-stricken bawl ended in a choking cough, all the surrounding bush crashed with the movement of vast black bulks. The herd of buffalo were moving in on their enemies in a relentless narrowing circle. Hardly had the big lion brought his prey to earth when the calf's mother was upon him. Her swift charge caught him in the act of springing to safety, but he was too late. The cow's curving horn ripped through ribs, lungs and heart and her stamping hoofs crushed his writhing body to stillness. Snarling, the lioness fled, belly to earth, apparently uncaring for the fate of her cubs.

Frightened, ignorant of the nature of the danger about him, the male cub lay flat and motionless. The bush was full of bellowings and great forms that moved in crashing thunder. Dust and flying twigs filled the air. No past experience told the trembling cub that the beasts closing in on him possessed the keenest sense of smell and hearing in all the animal world. He did not know the keen vindictive intelligence of the great beasts now looking for him in that tangle of bush. His escape was a miracle.

Only the lightning-swift message of brain to muscles saved the cub from the menace that closed upon him. A great sword-like horn swept the earth where he had crouched but an instant before. His desperate leap for safety carried him well into the bush. And then he ran—ran belly to ground, ran alone and full of fear until, exhausted, he dropped in the grass by a little flat-topped thorn tree, wild-eyed and panting. Night though it was, he slept at last, and did not wake until dawn colored the east.

It was a frightened and bewildered awakening. If he had been a human animal he would have known keen sorrow as well as fright and loneliness. He could not mourn his father's death because he knew nothing of the meaning of death. He had not the sort of brain and mentality that could raise the desperate question as to whether his mother had escaped or whether his sisters lay by their father, smashed to death in the thorny bushland. All he knew was that he was alone and missed the companionship of his family. And fear was still with him in the form of memory of last night's experience. The world seemed strange and filled with the menace of the unknown.

As the dawn grew brighter the young lion surveyed the country about him. He lay on the rounded top of a grassy hill. On all sides the land fell away to rolling plains that swept off to distant horizons. Far to the northeast a mountain thrust its stupendous blue-white summit against a pale sky. Northward the plains lost themselves in blue un-guessed distance. To the south piled mountain masses were dark against white clouds. A golden haze shimmered to the eastward where dust rose from moving herds of zebra.

It was all strange to the lonely cub. He stared at his surroundings, seeking some landmark that was familiar. Never in his life had he been more than half a mile distant from the shelter of the home cave on the

Hill of the Buffalo. A kind of terror that comes to the young of any species when it finds itself alone and unprotected, must have gripped the cub in those hours he spent under the little thorn tree. Finally he rose from the clump of grass where he lay and began casting about in ever-widening circles.

His progress was slow. At the rustle of some unknown creature—perhaps a bird or some small animal fleeing before him through the grass—he would stop, crouch, remain tense and motionless for minutes at a time, waiting until his nose, ears or eyes assured him that no enemy was close. The hour of sunset found him at the foot of the hill, less than half a mile westward from its crest where he had lain the night before. A rabbit hopped from the shelter of thick-growing thorn, realizing his mistake too late. The cub's darting paw was swifter than the rabbit's leap for flight and the bunny rolled across the grass with a broken neck. Even in the instant of this little kill, the cub made no sound, no growl or snarl of triumph. Caution made him silent, for he feared that unfriendly ears might hear him. With the body of the rabbit in his mouth, he went back to the top of the hill. It was the only place he knew now that was not utterly strange. In the clump of grass under the little thorn tree he ate the rabbit, then lay quiet—still hungry—while day faded and the stars came out. The moon rose early and the lanky cub watched its slow ascent above the dark eastern hills. A far drumbeat stirred the air.

The howls of the hyenas sounded at intervals and jackals barked. Far below, on the silvery plains, herds of animals fled from some terror of the night. Once, toward dawn, the night trembled to the roars of distant lions and the sound brought the cub's head erect as he stared into the darkness, listening to the savage voices of his kind. Twice during the night, he made timid sorties a little way down the hill, driven by hunger and the instinct to roam in the dark.

The following day he went directly to the spot where he had killed the rabbit. It was very early in the morning, and the bush was astir with small animals. Half an hour of careful stalking resulted in the death of another rabbit which was eaten on the spot. Eyes and ears alert, and senses keenly tuned for the approach of enemies, the young lion started back for the hilltop. A swift leap and high-stretched paws snatched a spur-fowl from the air in the instant it rose from the grass before him. With the bird in his jaws he went on up the hill. He never reached its top.

The big hyena slouched from behind a bush directly in the path of the cub. Both animals were startled. Of the two, it is probable that the hyena was the more frightened. Where there was a young lion, there was usually a mother and father lion close by. The great hairless scar that ran its livid course down the hyena's rear flank bore testimony to a narrow escape from death not many months past, when a lion's slashing claws had raked him. The hyena's roving eye scanned the hillside and saw nothing to alarm him. This lion before him was apparently alone. Also he was young and defenseless, and the spur-fowl between his jaws was tempting.

The cub was frightened, and well might he be frightened, for the powerful beast confronting him was more than his equal—a scarred veteran three times his size. The stench of rotten meat on which the hyena had been feeding filled the cub's nostrils, quenching the fresh warm odor of the bird in his mouth. It was only for the space of an instant that the scene held motionless on the sunny hillside.

The hyena snarled and lunged forward. The cub whirled and fled, a yellow flash of speed. It is probable that if he had dropped the spur-fowl, the chase would have ended, but instinctively and stubbornly his jaws clamped tighter on the yielding feathers. Down the hill over short grass, in and out through a wide belt of flat-topped thorn trees and thick bush, down into the bed of a long-dried-up river where the burning sand and jagged stones brought blood from the tender pads of his young feet, up the opposite bank and through a fringe of tearing thorns on to an open plain; thus the chase went.

The cub's first burst of speed had given him a good lead over the great mustard-colored beast behind, but now both strength and speed were ebbing and the hyena was closing the gap in a clumsy tireless lope that seemed never to slacken. But for the squat gnarled tree that stood alone in the grassy plain, it is likely there would have been a swift end to the young lion. The most powerful jaws in the whole animal kingdom were less than ten feet behind when the cub's desperate leap carried him into the lower crotch of the lone tree. The way above was easy, and he scrambled upward as far as he could go. His young claws were not yet dulled by time and, although he was not naturally a tree-climbing animal, he climbed. Perched some fifteen feet above the ground in a sort of nest where three branches came together, he looked down at his enemy. The hyena was at the base of the tree, baffled, hot and angry. He panted, while sweat ran from his tongue. Then he would close his mouth to growl fearsomely.

It was not until sunset that the chill evening breeze brought some attractive odor to the hyena compelling enough in its promise of food to lure him away from his all-day siege. As he trotted off across the plain he looked back over his shoulder once or twice as though reluctant to leave, but he was gone at last, a black, menacing silhouette against the sky as he stood for a moment on a distant ridge.

It was nearly an hour later, and quite dark when the weary cub relaxed his clutching perch. Climbing down was not as easy as climbing up and he fell, but landed on his feet, like any other member of the cat family.

The spur-fowl was still in his mouth. He slunk away from the tree and, at a safe distance, ate silently in the shadow of a bush. He lay there all night, afraid to move. Life stirred all about him. Once a great black bulk passed his hiding-place, passed, snuffed loudly, then came back to stand a few paces distant, listening, sniffing. Finally it moved off in the darkness snorting suspiciously. It was the closest view of a rhinoceros the young lion had ever had. Three hyenas loped by, fortunately up-wind from the sheltering thornbush. A little herd of wildebeest cropped the grass nearby, only to whistle with alarm and thunder off into the night when their keen noses scented the poor cowering cub. They smelled a lion and that was reason enough for flight. Had they known it was only a young and frightened one that had alarmed them, they need not have gone at all.

The dawn was chill and a cold rain fell from heavy clouds. The shivering orphan drank from a pool of rain water, stood uncertainly a moment in the driving storm and then trotted slowly off to the westward, a small forlorn figure soon lost to view in the mist of rain.

NEW HUNTING-GROUND

Now the young male lion entered that period of his life which was free from danger. He knew no hardships. The activity of hunting kept him in good condition. He grew amazingly with the passing months, grew in strength and size and beauty. Memory of the past still lingered. The big scarred hyena that had come near to killing him still haunted his dreams. He yet trembled when he recalled the image of those three tall Masai warriors who had passed so close to his hiding place. The nights of his long journey to the westward, when unknown creatures sniffed and snorted close to him in the dark, remained vivid in his mind. Especially did he remember the terror of that night of death when the warm scent of buffaloes filled his nostrils and their great black forms crashed about him and his family.

He explored every square foot of the high table-land where he lived. Each grassy little plain, each rocky gorge where the baboons brought up their families along stony slopes, silent forests and quiet pools, blind pockets in the tiny hills—all these he came to know. From the grassy edge of this vast land, he looked out over the world below, a world whose green or yellow plains washed up like waves of the sea against the deeply eroded sides of the plateau.

The timeless days of Africa merged into months. The color of the landscape changed with the changing season. The awkward Cub had become a Lion—a creature of size, a beast of prey. Here on this lofty kingdom the seasons brought physical changes to him. At two years the dark stripe that once ran along his spine was no longer a stripe, but just a gradually deepening area of coloring along the line of his back, brown in the center and merging from there into the lighter tawny-buff of sides and flanks. At three years of age, the spots of his cubhood could hardly be seen. At this age his mane began to show, a darker growth on head, chest and shoulders, extending in a line along his belly. Even at this age he was as large as his father had been in full maturity. His full growth would not be attained until he was six years old, but even now he was a creature of immense power, unscarred by battle, truly a king of the world he inhabited.

An experience which occurred during the fourth year of his life might well have meant an abrupt end to that life had it not been for the lithe strength within him. As it was, the happening merely added to his store of knowledge.

On a night when the moon shone white and clear, he hunted along the forest edge with a light chill wind in his face. In an open glade where the grasses grew high and lush, a small herd of eland grazed. The beautiful large animals were well in the open, removed from the sharp black shadows of bush and forest. A bit apart from the others a cow eland cropped the grass and by her side was her half-grown calf. They fed into the wind. From time to time they raised their heads, in common with the rest of the herd, and gazed about them, munching contentedly. The young lion moved in toward these two with extreme caution. The long grass parted slowly before his stealthy approach. For long minutes he lay belly to grass, waiting for the right moment to resume his stalk. At about twenty feet from the unsuspicious animals, he gathered for the spring. Then he launched himself, a terrifying spectacle as his great claws unsheathed to strike the young calf and fangs flashed long and white for the killing bite.

The reactions of animals are faster than those of humans. The quick message of eye or nose gives rise to instant action. In that space, probably no more than a second, that elapsed between the Lion's spring and the impact of his flying body against the young eland, the mother had seen and acted. As she saw the flying death that menaced her offspring, she charged. In mid-air our lion saw her coming. He could not halt his spring. He struck the calf, and the blow rolled the bawling youngster over and over. Even as he struck the earth, the Lion turned sideways and his claws dug the earth as he whirled, lightning-swift, to escape. An instant later and he would have been disemboweled, but his speed and quick mind saved him. Snarling with rage and pain he crossed the open glade in long bounds. Blood streamed from his left rear flank. The long black dagger that was the mother eland's horn had ripped through flesh and hide, a foot-long gash that gaped redly for many a day before it healed. Fortunately the wound involved no tendons or major nerve centers, so no lameness resulted. In time, a long hairless scar marked the wound, and this he carried through all the years of his life.

From about that time the Lion felt a growing restlessness. Sourceless angers stirred in him. Irritability marked his days. A feeling for the need to expend his tremendous strength moved him to a fury of excess action in the ordinary affairs of life. He no longer walked, a slow, graceful figure across familiar landscapes, but, instead, trotted or loped as though by moving more rapidly, time itself would the more quickly pass. The nightly kill and feeding were done in an abandon of fury. Whatever need it was that stirred within him was obscure, and no natural instinct could function in behalf of this beast, living his hermit life on the high plateau, because he was cut off by the barriers of habit and the fears and suspicions of his youth from the companionship of his own kind.

Now, well along in the fifth year of life, the Lion became a creature of menace, a truly dangerous creature, full of truculent moods and fierce repressions. But again, as in the days when he wandered, a lonely cub, to safety across a lonely land, fate and circumstance were to play their dual part in bringing needed change.

The long rains had passed their season and now was the month of May. The days were filled with flooding sunlight, the skies were a deeper blue. Now the plains and bush-encircled prairies were no longer a dull and tired yellow, but a bright, fresh green. The thorn thickets were in flower and the once gray and dusty leaves were shining. The blue haze of distance that is Africa's was lifted, and far mountains stood stark and clear.

One afternoon the Lion lay in the shade of a bush close to the edge of the table-land. Eyes blinking sleepily, he seemed to drowse unwitting of the world about him. Yet he was not unwitting, for the light breeze that rippled his mane brought him many familiar scents that were all part of his life. Suddenly his massive head rose alertly. An intent look of concentration came into his yellow eyes. A new smell was in his wide nostrils, exciting, compelling. Nose and vision swung into the wind and at the sight that greeted him. The Lion flattened himself into the grass. His long quivering body was hidden, but he could see clearly through the waving grass tips.

Some hundred yards away, a lioness, young, lithe, golden-yellow, drew herself over the edge of the abrupt slope that led to the plains below. She stood looking about her for a moment, then walked slowly into the cover of some high bush that grew nearby, and disappeared. She was in country that was strange to her, but not to the Lion. Every stick, bush, tree and stone was familiar to him. He had roamed every narrow game trail that threaded the forests, knew each little valley, whether it was a blind one or led into a maze of similar valleys and ravines. Crouching low, and ever with the wind in his nose, he slipped silently into the thickets.

When he sighted her again, the lioness stood at the edge of open country looking interestedly at little herds of game that fed there. Finally she walked across the plain and went on over a hill. The Lion followed her. From the crest of the hill he saw her in the shallow depression below him. She was standing by the remains of his last night's kill. He could hear her low growl as she sniffed the sward where he had lain but a few hours before. The odor of his big body where it had pressed the earth must have been very plain, for the lioness quickly raised her head and looked intently about her. Then, without warning, she dropped low and ran swiftly into the thicket of wild olive. The Lion did not follow her at once. In fact he did not follow her at all, but after a short wait, made a detour that would intercept her. He trotted swiftly, a short cut by way of a dim game trail, and crouched there waiting to glimpse her again. But she had eluded him, using a craftiness of her own as though she suspected she was being followed.

During the rest of the daylight hours the Lion hunted her, but caught never a glimpse of the beautiful creature. Seeing her, the first sight of his kind since the separation from his parents four years before, excited him, and with the excitement was mingled, strangely enough, a soothing sense of contentment. As night fell, he sat on a hilltop searching the surrounding land for some movement that would betray her whereabouts. In him was a feeling of loss and loneliness that he had not known since his cubhood. From another hilltop a hundred yards distant, the lioness lay flat in the grass and watched him.

That night he sought his kill early. With the light breeze blowing in his face he worked cautiously up a shallow valley where a little herd of zebra grazed in the darkness. At the rate of his progress it would be half an hour or more before he would be within charging distance of his prey. Suddenly, out of the night ahead, there came a loud snort of alarm, followed by the wild drumming sound of flying hoofs. The zebra were in flight—but not away from him. They were surging toward the Lion, the black mass of them coming at him in noise and straining terror, flying from some menace behind them.

Selecting a fat mare, he leaped with a blaring snarl, towering over her for an instant. As his weight hit the running animal she stumbled and fell, her scream of agony choked to silence by dust and death. One of the Lion's paws enveloped her face, another clutched her neck. Great forelegs wrenched and the zebra's neck snapped. Thus she fell, and hitting the earth, fangs met behind her ears and severed her spinal cord.

The herd of zebra thundered off into the darkness and the Lion listened to the sound of their flight. He lay with his front paws on the head of his victim, growling deeply, an endless rumble that followed his breathing. A sharp fluttering snarl from the near thornbush brought him to his feet with bared fangs. The lioness walked slowly toward him and they faced each other across the dead zebra. Then she dropped to her belly, watching him, growling gently. Warily, with rasping menace in his throat, he disemboweled the zebra. The lioness crept closer. And as he sunk his fangs into the tender inside of one of the hind legs, she seized the other with claws and teeth. His eyes blazed and one great paw lifted as though to strike. But the lioness tore at the meat, apparently unconcerned with the antics of this noisy, threatening male. He dropped his head and fed. Once their bloody muzzles touched and they ceased eating abruptly to stare at each other. Together they devoured the meatiest parts of their prey. At dawn they buried the zebra's entrails and as the sun rose, walked off side by side into the bushy thicket.

Jerusalem

WILLIAM BLAKE

≈ ≈ ≈ *From* Milton

And did those feet in ancient time
Walk upon England's mountains green?
And was the holy Lamb of God
On England's pleasant pastures seen?

And did the Countenance Divine
Shine forth upon our clouded hills?
And was Jerusalem builded here
Among these dark Satanic hills?

Bring me my bow of burning gold!
Bring me my arrows of desire!
Bring me my spear! O clouds, unfold!
Bring me my chariot of fire!

I will not cease from mental fight,
Nor shall my sword sleep in my hand,
Till we have built Jerusalem
In England's green and pleasant land.

In Panoply of Spears

CHARLES G. D. ROBERTS

≈ ≈ ≈ *This is the only story I know about that curious creature the porcupine. It tells how porcupines live and how they fight when they meet their animal enemies in the North woods.* —*From* The Kindred of the Wild

There was a pleasant humming all about the bee-tree, where it stood solitary on the little knoll upon the sunward slope of the forest. It was an ancient maple, one side long since blasted by lightning, and now decayed to the heart; while the other side yet put forth a green bravery of branch and leaf. High up under a dead limb was a hole, thronged about with diligent bees who came and went in long diverging streams against the sunsteeped blue. A mile below, around the little, straggling backwoods settlement, the buckwheat was in bloom; and the bees counted the longest day too short for the gathering of its brown and fragrant sweets.

In fine contrast to their bustle and their haste was a moveless dark brown figure clinging to a leafy branch on the other and living side of the tree. From a distance it might easily have been taken for a big bird's-nest. Far out on the limb it sat, huddled into a bristling ball. Its nose, its whole head indeed, were hidden between its fore paws, which childlishly but tenaciously clutched at a little upright branch. In this position, seemingly so precarious, but really, for the porcupine, the safest and most comfortable that could be imagined, it dozed away the idle summer hours.

From the thick woods at the foot of the knoll emerged a large black bear, who lifted his nose and eyed shrewdly the humming streams of workers converging at the hole in the bee-tree. For some time the bear stood contemplative, till an eager light grew in his small, cunning, half-humourous eyes. His long red tongue came out and licked his lips, as he thought of the summer's sweetness now stored in the hollow tree. He knew all about that prosperous bee colony. He remembered when, two years before, the runaway swarm from the settlement had taken possession of the hole in the old maple. That same autumn he had tried to rifle the treasure-house, but had found the wood about the entrance still too sound and strong for even such powerfully rending claws as his. He had gone away surly with disappointment, to scratch a few angry bees out of his fur, and wait for the natural processes of decay to weaken the walls of the citadel.

On this particular day he decided to try again. He had no expectation that he would succeed; but the thought of the honey grew irresistible to him as he dwelt upon it. He lumbered lazily up the knoll, reared his dark bulk against the trunk, and started to climb to the attack.

But the little workers in the high-set hive found an unexpected protector in this hour of their need. The dozing porcupine woke up, and took it into his head that he wanted to go somewhere else. Perhaps in his dreams a vision had come to him of the lonely little oat-field in the clearing, where the young grain was plumping out and already full of milky sweetness. As a rule he preferred to travel and feed by night. But the porcupine is the last amid the wild kindreds to let convention interfere with impulse, and he does what seems good to the whim of the moment. His present whim was to descend the bee-tree and journey over to the clearing.

The bear had climbed but seven or eight feet, when he heard the scraping of claws on the bark above. He heard also the light clattering noise, unlike any other sound in the wilderness. He knew it at once as the sound of the loose-hung, hollow quills in a porcupine's active tail; and looking up angrily, he saw the porcupine curl himself downward from a crotch and begin descending the trunk to meet him.

The bear weighed perhaps four hundred or five hundred pounds. The porcupine weighed perhaps twenty-five pounds. Nevertheless, the bear stopped; and the porcupine came on. When he saw the bear, he gnashed his teeth irritably, and his quills, his wonderful panoply of finely barbed spears, erected themselves all over his body till his usual bulk seemed doubled. At the same time his colour changed. It was almost as if he had grown suddenly pale with indignation; for when the long quills stood up from among his blackish-brown fur they showed themselves all white save for their dark keen points. Small as he was in comparison with his gigantic opponent, he looked, nevertheless, curiously formidable. He grunted and grumbled querulously, and came on with confidence, obstinately proclaiming that no mere bear should for a moment divert him from his purpose.

Whether by instinct, experience, or observation, the bear knew something about porcupines. What would honey be to him, with two or three of those slender and biting spear-points embedded in his nose? As he thought of it, he backed away with increasing alacrity. He checked a rash impulse to dash the arrogant little hinderer from the tree and annihilate him with one stroke of his mighty paw,—but the mighty paw cringed, winced, and drew back impotent, as its sensitive nerves considered how it would feel to be stuck full, like a pin-cushion, with inexorably penetrating points. At last, thoroughly outfaced, the bear descended to the ground, and stood aside respectfully for the porcupine to pass.

The porcupine, however, on reaching the foot of the trunk, dis-covered an uncertainty in his mind. His whim wavered. He stopped, scratched his ears thoughtfully first with one fore paw and then with the other, and tried his long, chisel-like front teeth, those matchless gnawing machines, on a projecting edge of bark. The bear eyed him for some moments, then lumbered off into the woods indifferently, convinced that the bee-tree would be just as interesting on some other day. But before that other day came around, the bear encountered Fate, lying in wait for him, grim and implacable, beneath a trapper's deadfall in the heart of the tamarack swamp. And the humming tribes in the bee-tree were left to possess their honeyed commonwealth in peace.

Soon after the bear had left the knoll, the porcupine appeared to make up his mind as to what he wanted to do. With an air of fixed purpose he started down the knoll, heading for the oat-field and the clearing which lay some half-mile distant through the woods. As he moved on the ground, he was a somewhat clumsy and wholly gro-tesque figure. He walked with a deliberate and precise air, very slowly, and his legs worked as if the earth were to them an unfamiliar element. He was about two and a half feet long, short-legged, solid and sturdy looking, with a nose squared off so that it should not get in the way of his gnawing. As he confronted you, his great chisel teeth, bared and conspicuous, appeared a most formidable weapon. Effec-tive as they were, however, they were not a weapon which he was apt to call into use, save against inanimate and edible opponents; because he could not do so without exposing his weak points to attack,—his nose, his head, his soft, unprotected throat. His real weapon of offence was his short, thick tail, which was heavily armed with very powerful quills. With this he could strike slashing blows, such as would fill an enemy's face or paws with spines, and send him howling from the encounter. Clumsy and inert it looked, on ordinary occasions; but when need arose, its muscles had the lightning action of a strong steel spring.

As the porcupine made his resolute way through the woods, the manner of his going differed from that of all the other kindreds of the wild. He went not furtively. He had no particular objection to making a noise. He did not consider it necessary to stop every little while, stiffen himself to a monument of immobility, cast wary glances about the gloom, and sniff the air for the taint of enemies. He did not care who knew of his coming; and he did not greatly care who came. Behind his panoply of biting spears he felt himself secure, and in that security he moved as if he held in fee the whole green, shadowy, perilous woodland world.

A wood-mouse, sitting in the door of his burrow between the roots of an ancient fir-tree, went on washing his face with his dainty paws as the porcupine passed within three feet of him. Almost any other forest traveller would have sent the timid mouse darting to the depths of his retreat; but he knew that the slow-moving figure, however terrible to look at, had no concern for wood-mice. The porcupine had barely passed, however, when a weasel came in view. In a flash the mouse was gone, to lie hidden for an hour, with trembling heart, in the furthest darkness of his burrow.

Continuing his journey, the porcupine passed under a fallen tree. Along the horizontal trunk lay a huge lynx, crouched flat, movelessly watching for rabbit, chipmunk, mink, or whatever quarry might come within his reach. He was hungry, as a lynx is apt to be. He licked his chaps, and his wide eyes paled with savage fire, as the porcupine dawdled by beneath the tree, within easy clutch of his claws. But his claws made no least motion of attack. He, too, like the bear, knew something about porcupines. In a few moments, however, when the porcupine had gone on some ten or twelve feet beyond his reach, his feelings overcame him so completely that he stood up and gave vent to an appalling scream of rage. All the other wild things within hearing trembled at the sound, and were still; and the porcupine, startled out of his equipoise, tucked his nose between his legs, and bristled into a ball of sharp defiance. The lynx eyed him venomously for some seconds, then dropped lightly from the perch, and stole off to hunt in other neighbourhoods, realising that his reckless outburst of bad temper had warned all the coverts for a quarter of a mile around. The porcupine, uncurling, grunted scornfully and resumed his journey.

Very still, and lonely and bright the clearing lay in the flooding afternoon sunshine. It lay along beside a deeply rutted, grass-grown backwoods road which had been long forgotten by the attentions of the road-master. It was enclosed from the forest in part by a dilapi-dated wall of loose stones, in part by an old snake fence, much patched with brush. The cabin which had once presided over its solitude had long fallen to ruin; but its fertile soil had saved it from being forgotten. A young farmer-lumber-man from the settlement a couple of miles away held possession of it, and kept its boundaries more or less intact, and made it yield him each year a crop of oats, barley, or buckwheat.

Emerging from the woods, the porcupine crawled to the top of the stone wall and glanced about him casually. Then he descended into the cool, light-green depths of the growing oats. Here he was completely hidden, though his passage was indicated as he went by the swaying and commotion among the oat-tops.

The high plumes of the grain, of course, were far above the porcu-pine's reach; and for a healthy appetite like his it would have been tedious work indeed to pull down the stalks one by one. At this point, he displayed an ingenious resourcefulness with which he is seldom credited by observers of his kind. Because he is slow in movement, folk are apt to conclude that he is slow in wit; whereas the truth is that he has fine reserves of shrewdness to fall back on in emergency. Instead of pulling and treading down the oats at haphazard, he moved through the grain in a small circle, leaning heavily inward. When he had thus gone around the circle several times, the tops of the grain lay together in a convenient bunch. This succulent sheaf he dragged down, and devoured with relish.

When he had abundantly satisfied his craving for young oats, he crawled out upon the open sward by the fence, and carelessly sampled the bark of a seedling apple-tree. While he was thus engaged a big, yellow dog came trotting up the wood-road, poking his nose inquisi-tively into every bush and stump in the hope of finding a rabbit or chipmunk to chase. He belonged to the young farmer who owned the oat-field; and when, through the rails of the snake fence, he caught sight of the porcupine, he was filled with noisy wrath. Barking and yelping,—partly with excitement, and partly as a signal to his master, who was trudging along the road far behind him,—he clambered over the fence, and bore down upon the trespasser.

The porcupine was not greatly disturbed by this loud onslaught, but he did not let confidence make him careless. He calmly tucked his head under his breast, set his quills in battle array, and awaited the event with composure.

Had he discovered the porcupine in the free woods, the yellow dog would have let him severely alone. But in his master's oat-field, that was a different matter. Moreover, the knowledge that his master was coming added to his zeal and rashness; and he had long cherished the ambition to kill a porcupine. He sprang forward, open-jawed,—and stopped short when his fangs were just within an inch or two of those bristling and defiant points. Caution had come to his rescue just in time.

For perhaps half a minute he ran, whining and baffled, around the not-to-be daunted ball of spines. Then he sat down upon his haunches, lifted up his muzzle, and howled for his master to come and help him.

As his master failed to appear within three seconds, his impatience got the better of him, and he again began running around the porcupine, snapping fiercely, but never coming within two or three inches of the militant points. For a few moments these two or three inches proved to be a safe distance. Such a distance from the shoulders, back, and sides was all well enough. But suddenly, he was so misguided as to bring his teeth together within a couple of inches of the armed but quiescent tail. This was the instant for which the porcupine had been waiting. The tail flicked smartly. The big dog jumped, gave a succession of yelping cries, pawed wildly at his nose, then tucked his tail between his legs, scrambled over the fence, and fled away to his master. The porcupine unrolled himself, and crawled into an inviting hole in the old stone wall.

About ten minutes later a very angry man, armed with a fence-stake, appeared at the edge of the clearing with a cowed dog at his heels. He wanted to find the porcupine which had stuck those quills into his dog's nose. Mercifully merciless, he had held the howling dog in a grip of iron while he pulled out the quills with his teeth; and now he was after vengeance. Knowing a little, but not everything, about porcupines, he searched every tree in the immediate neighbourhood, judging that the porcupine, after such an encounter, would make all haste to his natural retreat. But he never looked in the hole in the wall; and the yellow dog, who had come to doubt the advisability of finding porcupines, refused firmly to assist in the search. In a little while, when his anger began to cool, he gave over the hunt in disgust, threw away the fence-stake, bit off a goodly chew from the fig of black tobacco which he produced from his hip-pocket, and strode away up the grassy wood-road.

For perhaps half an hour the porcupine dozed in the hole among the stones. Then he woke up, crawled out, and moved slowly along the top of the wall.

There was a sound of children's voices coming up the road; but the porcupine, save for a grumble of impatience, paid no attention. Presently the children came in sight,—a stocky little boy of nine or ten, and a lank girl of perhaps thirteen, making their way homeward from school by the short cut over the mountain. Both were barefooted and barelegged, deeply freckled, and with long, tow-coloured locks. The boy wore a shirt and short breeches of blue-gray homespun, the breeches held up precariously by one suspender. On his head was a tattered and battered straw; and in one hand he swung a little dinner-pail. The girl wore the like blue-gray homespun for a petticoat, with a waist of bright red calico, and carried a limp pink sunbonnet on her arm.

"Oh, see the porkypine!" cried the girl, as they came abreast of the stone wall.

"By gosh! Let's kill it!" exclaimed the stocky little boy, starting forward eagerly, with a prompt efflorescence of primitive instincts. But his sister clutched him by the arm and anxiously restrained him.

"My lands, Jimmy, you mustn't go near a porkypine like that!" she protested, more learned than her brother in the hoary myths of the settlements. "Don't you know he can fling them quills of his'n at you, an' they'll go right through an' come out the other side?"

"By gosh!" gasped the boy, eyeing the unconcerned animal with apprehension, and edging off to the furthermost ditch. Hand in hand, their eyes wide with excitement, the two children passed beyond the stone wall. Then, as he perceived that the porcupine had not seemed to notice them, the boy's hunting instinct revived. He stopped, set down the tin dinner-pail, and picked up a stone.

"No, you don't, Jimmy!" intervened the girl, with mixed emotions of kindliness and caution, as she grabbed his wrist and dragged him along.

"Why, Sis?" protested the boy, hanging back, and looking over his shoulder longingly. "Jest let me fling a stone at him!"

"No!" said his sister, with decision. "He ain't a-hurtin' us, and he's mindin' his own business. An' I reckon maybe he can fling quills as fur as you can fling stones!"

Convinced by this latter argument, the boy gave up his design, and suffered his wise sister to lead him away from so perilous a neighbour-hood. The two little figures vanished amid the green glooms beyond the clearing, and the porcupine was left untroubled in his sovereignty.

II

That autumn, late one moonlight night, the porcupine was down by a little forest lake feasting on lily pads. He occupied a post of great advantage, a long, narrow ledge of rock jutting out into the midst of the lilies, and rising but an inch or two above the water. Presently, to his great indignation, he heard a dry rustling of quills behind him, and saw another porcupine crawl out upon his rock. He faced about, bristling angrily and gnashing his teeth, and advanced to repel the intruder.

The intruder hesitated, then came on again with confidence, but making no hostile demonstrations what ever. When the two met, the expected conflict was by some sudden agreement omitted. They touched blunt noses, squeaked and grunted together for awhile till a perfect understanding was established; then crawled ashore and left the lily pads to rest, broad, shiny, and unruffled in the moonlight, little platters of silver on the dark glass of the lake.

The newcomer was a female; and with such brief wooing the big porcupine had taken her for his mate. Now he led her off to show her the unequalled den which he had lately discovered. The den was high in the side of a heap of rocks, dry in all weathers, and so overhung by a half-uprooted tree as to be very well concealed from passers and prowlers. Its entrance was long and narrow, deterrent to rash investi-gators. In fact, just after the porcupine had moved in, a red fox had discovered the doorway and judged it exactly to his liking; but on finding that the occupant was a porcupine, he had hastily decided to seek accommodation elsewhere. In this snug house the two porcupines settled contentedly for the winter.

The winter passed somewhat uneventfully for them, though for the rest of the wood-folk it was a season of unwonted hardship. The cold was more intense and more implacable than had been known about the settlements for years. Most of the wild creatures, save those who could sleep the bitter months away and abide the coming of spring, found themselves face to face with famine. But the porcupines feared neither famine nor cold. The brown fur beneath their quills was thick and warm, and hunger was impossible to them with all the trees of the forest for their pasturage. Sometimes, when the cold made them sluggish, they would stay all day and all night in a single balsam-fir or hemlock, stripping one branch after another of leaf and twig, indifferent to the monotony of their diet. At other times, however, they were as active and enterprising as if all the heats of summer were loosing their sinews. On account of the starvation-madness that was everywhere ranging the coverts, they were more than once attacked as they crawled lazily over the snow; but on each occasion the enemy, whether lynx or fox, fisher or mink, withdrew discomfited, with something besides hunger in his hide to think about.

Once, in midwinter, they found a prize which added exquisite variety to their bill of fare. Having wandered down to the outskirts of the settlements, they discovered, cast aside among the bushes, an empty firkin which had lately contained salt pork. The wood, saturated with brine, was delicious to the porcupines. Greedily they gnawed at it, returning night after night to the novel banquet, till the last sliver of the flavoured wood was gone. Then, after lingering a day or two longer in the neighbourhood, expecting another miracle, they returned to their solitudes and their hemlock.

When the winter was drawing near its close, but spring had not yet sent the wilderness word of her coming, the porcupines got her message in their blood. They proclaimed it abroad in the early twilight from the tops of the high hemlocks, in queer, half-rhythmical choruses of happy grunts and squeaks. The sound was far from melodious, but it pleased every one of the wild kindred to whose ears it came; for they knew that when the porcupines got trying to sing, then the spring thaws were hurrying up from the south.

At last the long desired one came; and every little rill ran a brawling brook in the fulness of its joy. And the ash-buds swelled rich purple;

and the maples crimsoned with their misty blooms; and the skunk cabbage began to thrust up bold knobs of emerald, startling in their brightness, through the black and naked leaf-mould of the swamp. And just at this time, when all the wild kindred, from the wood-mouse to the moose, felt sure that life was good, a porcupine baby was born in the snug den among the rocks.

It was an astonishingly big baby,—the biggest, in proportion to the size of its parents, of all the babies of the wild. In fact it was almost as big as an average bear cub. It was covered with long, dark brown, silky fur, under which the future panoply of spear-points was already beginning to make way through the tender skin. Its mother was very properly proud, and assiduous in her devotion. And the big father, though seemingly quite indifferent, kept his place contentedly in the den instead of going off sourly by himself to another lair as the porcupine male is apt to do on the arrival of the young.

One evening about dusk, when the young porcupine was but three days old, a weasel glided noiselessly up to the door of the den, and sniffed. His eyes, set close together and far down toward his malignant, pointed nose, were glowing red with the lust of the kill. Fierce and fearless as he was, he knew well enough that a porcupine was something for him to let alone. But this, surely, was his chance to feed fat an ancient grudge; for he hated everything that he could not hope to kill. He had seen the mother porcupine feeding comfortably in the top of a near-by poplar. And now he made assurance doubly sure by sniffing at her trail, which came out from the den and did not return. As for the big male porcupine, the prowler took it for granted that he had followed the usage of his kind, and gone off about other business. Like a snake, he slipped in, and found the furry baby all alone. There was a strong, squeaking cry, a moment's struggle; and then the weasel drank eagerly at the blood of his easy prey. The blood, and the fierce joy of the kill, were all he wanted, for his hunting was only just begun.

The assassin stayed but a minute with his victim, then turned swiftly to the door of the den. But the door was blocked. It was filled by an ominous, bristling bulk, which advanced upon him slowly, inexorably, making a sharp, clashing sound with its long teeth. The big porcupine had come home. And his eyes blazed more fiercely red than those of the weasel.

The weasel, fairly caught, felt that doom was upon him. He backed away, over the body of his victim, to the furthest depth of the den. But, though a ruthless murderer, the most cruel of all the wild kindred, he was no coward. He would evade the slow avenger if he could; but if not, he would fight to the last gasp.

Against this foe the porcupine scorned his customary tactics, and depended upon his terrible, cutting teeth. At the same time he knew that the weasel was desperate and deadly. Therefore he held his head low, shielding his tender throat. When he reached the wider part of the den, he suddenly swung sidewise, thus keeping the exit still blocked.

Seeing now that there was no escape, the weasel gathered his forces for one last fight. Like lightning he sprang, and struck; and being, for speed, quite matchless among the wild folk, he secured a deadly hold on the porcupine's jaw. The porcupine squeaked furiously and tried to shake his adversary off. With a sweep of his powerful neck, he threw the weasel to one side, and then into the air over his head.

The next instant the weasel came down, sprawling widely, full upon the stiffly erected spears of the porcupine's back. They pierced deep into his tender belly. With a shrill cry he relaxed his hold on the avenger's jaw, shrank together in anguish, fell to the ground, and darted to the exit. As he passed he got a heavy slap from the porcupine's tail, which filled his face and neck with piercing barbs. Then he escaped from the den and fled away toward his own lair, carrying his death with him. Before he had gone a hundred yards one of the quills in his belly reached a vital part. He faltered, fell, stretched his legs out weakly, and died. Then a red squirrel, who had been watching him in a quiver of fear and hate, shot from his hiding-place, ran wildly up and down his tree, and made the woods ring with his sharp, barking chatter of triumph over the death of the universal enemy.

In the midst of the squirrel's shrill rejoicings the porcupine emerged from his den. He seemed to hesitate, which is not the way of a porcupine. He looked at his mate, still foraging in the top of her poplar, happily unaware for the present of how her little world had changed. He seemed to realise that the time of partings had come, the time when he must resume his solitude. He turned and looked at his den,— he would never find another like it! Then he crawled off through the cool, wet woods, where the silence seemed to throb sweetly with the stir and fulness of the sap. And in a hollow log, not far from the bee-tree on the knoll, he found himself a new home, small and solitary.

Ulysses

ALFRED, LORD TENNYSON

It little profits that an idle king,
By this still hearth, among these barren crags,
Match'd with an aged wife, I mete and dole
Unequal laws unto a savage race,
That hoard, and sleep, and feed, and know not me.
I cannot rest from travel; I will drink
Life to the lees. All times I have enjoy'd
Greatly, have suffer'd greatly, both with those
That loved me, and alone; on shore, and when
Thro' scudding drifts the rainy Hyades
Vext the dim sea. I am become a name;
For always roaming with a hungry heart
Much have I seen and known,—cities of men
And manners, climates, councils, governments,
Myself not least, but honor'd of them all.—
And drunk delight of battle with my peers,
Far on the ringing plains of windy Troy.
I am a part of all that I have met;
Yet all experience is an arch wherethro'
Gleams that untravell'd world whose margin fades
For ever and for ever when I move.
How dull it is to pause, to make an end,
To rust unburnish'd, not to shine in use!
As tho' to breathe were life! Life piled on life
Were all too little, and of one to me
Little remains; but every hour is saved
From that eternal silence, something more,
A bringer of new things; and vile it were
For some three suns to store and hoard myself,
And this gray spirit yearning in desire
To follow knowledge like a sinking star,

Beyond the utmost bound of human thought.
  This is my son, mine own Telemachus,
To whom I leave the sceptre and the isle,—
Well-loved of me, discerning to fulfill
This labor, by slow prudence to make mild
A rugged people, and thro' soft degrees
Subdue them to the useful and the good.
Most blameless is he, centred in the sphere
Of common duties, decent not to fail
In offices of tenderness, and pay
Meet adoration to my household gods,
When I am gone. He works his work, I mine.
  There lies the port, the vessel puffs her sail;
There gloom the dark broad seas. My mariners,
Souls that have toil'd, and wrought, and thought with me,—
That ever with a frolic welcome took
The thunder and the sunshine, and opposed
Free hearts, free foreheads,—you and I are old;
Old age hath yet his honor and his toil.
Death closes all; but something ere the end,
Some work of noble note, may yet be done,
Not unbecoming men that strove with Gods.
The lights begin to twinkle from the rocks;
The long day wanes; the slow moon climbs; the deep
Moans round with many voices. Come, my friends.
'T is not too late to seek a newer world.
Push off, and sitting well in order smite
The sounding furrows; for my purpose holds
To sail beyond the sunset, and the baths
Of all the western stars, until I die.
It may be that the gulfs will wash us down;
It may be we shall touch the Happy Isles,
And see the great Achilles, whom we knew.
Tho' much is taken, much abides; and tho'
We are not now that strength which in old days
Moved earth and heaven, that which we are, we are,—
One equal temper of heroic hearts,
Made weak by time and fate, but strong in will
To strive, to seek, to find, and not to yield.

After Twenty Years

O. HENRY

≈ ≈ ≈ *The short story with a surprise ending was O. Henry's specialty. In this clever anecdote he tricks his readers with artful ease.*

The policeman on the beat moved up the avenue impressively. The impressiveness was habitual and not for show, for spectators were few. The time was barely 10 o'clock at night, but chilly gusts of wind with a taste of rain in them had well nigh depeopled the streets.

Trying doors as he went, twirling his club with many intricate and artful movements, turning now and then to cast his watchful eye adown the pacific thoroughfare, the officer, with his stalwart form and slight swagger, made a fine picture of a guardian of the peace. The vicinity was one that kept early hours. Now and then you might see the lights of a cigar store or of an all-night lunch counter; but the majority of the doors belonged to business places that had long since been closed.

When about midway of a certain block the policeman suddenly slowed his walk. In the doorway of a darkened hardware store a man leaned, with an unlighted cigar in his mouth. As the policeman walked up to him the man spoke up quickly. "It's all right, officer," he said, reassuringly. "I'm just waiting for a friend. It's an appointment made twenty years ago. Sounds a little funny to you, doesn't it? Well, I'll explain if you'd like to make certain it's all straight. About that long ago there used to be a restaurant where this store stands—'Big Joe' Brady's restaurant."

"Until five years ago," said the policeman. "It was torn down then."

The man in the doorway struck a match and lit his cigar. The light showed a pale, square-jawed face with keen eyes, and a little white scar near his right eyebrow. His scarfpin was a large diamond, oddly set.

"Twenty years ago to-night," said the man, "I dined here at 'Big Joe'

Brady's with Jimmy Wells, my best chum, and the finest chap in the world. He and I were raised here in New York, just like two brothers, together, I was eighteen and Jimmy was twenty. The next morning I was to start for the West to make my fortune. You couldn't have dragged Jimmy out of New York; he thought it was the only place on earth. Well, we agreed that night that we would meet here again exactly twenty years from that date and time, no matter what our conditions might be or from what distance we might have to come. We figured that in twenty years each of us ought to have our destiny worked out and our fortunes made, whatever they were going to be."

"It sounds pretty interesting," said the policeman. "Rather a long time between meets, though, it seems to me. Haven't you heard from your friend since you left?"

"Well, yes, for a time we corresponded," said the other. "But after a year or two we lost track of each other. You see, the West is a pretty big proposition, and I kept hustling around it pretty lively. But I know Jimmy will meet me here if he's alive, for he always was the truest, stanchest old chap in the world. He'll never forget. I came a thousand miles to stand in this door to-night, and it's worth it if my old partner turns up."

The waiting man pulled out a handsome watch, the lids of it set with small diamonds.

"Three minutes to ten," he announced. "It was exactly ten o'clock when we parted here at the restaurant door."

"Did pretty well out West, didn't you?" asked the policeman.

"You bet! I hope Jimmy has done half as well. He was a kind of plodder, though, good fellow as he was. I've had to compete with some of the sharpest wits going to get my pile. A man gets in a groove in New York. It takes the West to put a razor-edge on him."

The policeman twirled his club and took a step or two.

"I'll be on my way. Hope your friend comes around all right. Going to call time on him sharp?"

"I should say not!" said the other. "I'll give him half an hour at least. If Jimmy is alive on earth he'll be here by that time. So long, officer."

"Good-night, sir," said the policeman, passing on along his beat, trying doors as he went.

There was now a fine, cold drizzle falling, and the wind had risen from its uncertain puffs into a steady blow. The few foot passengers astir in that quarter hurried dismally and silently along with coat collars turned high and pocketed hands. And in the door of the hardware store the man who had come a thousand miles to fill an appointment, uncertain almost to absurdity, with the friend of his youth, smoked his cigar and waited.

About twenty minutes he waited, and then a tall man in a long overcoat, with collar turned up to his ears, hurried across from the opposite side of the street. He went directly to the waiting man.

"Is that you, Bob?" he asked, doubtfully.

"Is that you, Jimmy Wells?" cried the man in the door.

"Bless my heart!" exclaimed the new arrival, grasping both the other's hands with his own. "It's Bob, sure as fate. I was certain I'd find you here if you were still in existence. Well, well, well!—twenty years is a long time. The old restaurant's gone, Bob; I wish it had lasted, so we could have had another dinner there. How has the West treated you, old man?"

"Bully; it has given me everything I asked it for. You've changed lots, Jimmy. I never thought you were so tall by two or three inches."

"Oh, I grew a bit after I was twenty."

"Doing well in New York, Jimmy?"

"Moderately. I have a position in one of the city departments. Come on, Bob; we'll go around to a place I know of, and have a good long talk about old times."

The two men started up the street, arm in arm. The man from the West, his egotism enlarged by success, was beginning to outline the history of his career. The other, submerged in his overcoat, listened with interest.

At the corner stood a drug store, brilliant with electric lights. When they came into this glare each of them turned simultaneously to gaze upon the other's face.

The man from the West stopped suddenly and released his arm.

"You're not Jimmy Wells," he snapped. "Twenty years is a long time, but not long enough to change a man's nose from a Roman to a pug."

"It sometimes changes a good man into a bad one," said the tall man. "You've been under arrest for ten minutes, 'Silky' Bob. Chicago thinks you may have dropped over our way and wires us she wants to have a chat with you. Going quietly, are you? That's sensible. Now, before we go to the station here's a note I was asked to hand to you. You may read it here at the window. It's from Patrolman Wells."

The man from the West unfolded the little piece of paper handed him. His hand was steady when he began to read, but it trembled a little by the time he had finished. The note was rather short.

Bob: I was at the appointed place on time. When you struck the match to light your cigar I saw it was the face of the man wanted in Chicago. Somehow I couldn't do it myself, so I went around and got a plain clothes man to do the job.

Jimmy.

A Reproof of Gluttony

HILAIRE BELLOC

The Elephant will eat of hay
Some four and twenty tons a day,
    And in his little eyes express
    His unaffected thankfulness
That Providence should deign to find
Him food of this delicious kind.
While they that pay for all the hay
Will frequently be heard to say
How highly privileged they feel
To help him make so large a meal.

The Boa Constrictor
    dotes on goats;
The Horse is quite content with oats,
Or will alternatively pass
A happy morning munching grass.
The great Ant Eater of Taluz
Consumes—or people say he does—
Not only what his name implies
But even ordinary flies:
And Marmosets and Chimpanzees
Are happy on the nuts of trees.

    The Lion from the burning slopes
    Of Atlas lives on Antelopes,
And only adds the flesh of men
    By way of relish now and then;
    As Cheetahs—yes, and Tigers, too,
    And Jaguars of the Andes—do.

The Lobster, I have heard it said,
Eats nobody till he is dead;
And Cobras, though they have the sense
            To poison you in self-defence,
Restrict their food to birds and hares:
Which also may be true of Bears.

Indeed wherever we survey
Our Humble Friends we find that they
Confine their appetites to what
May happen to be on the spot.
Simplicity and moderation
Distinguish all the Brute Creation
But Man—proud man! (as Dryden sings)
Though wolfing quantities of things—
Smoked Salmon in transparent slices,
And Turbot à la Reine,
                    and Ices,
      And Truffled Pies
         and Caviare,
      And Chinese Ginger
                    from the Jar;
And Oysters; and a kind of stuff
Called Cassouletto (good enough!)
And Mutton duly steeped in claret
(Or jumped with young shallot and carrot),
And Chicken Livers done with rice,
And Quails (which, I am told, are Mice),
And Peaches from a sunny wall,
And—Lord! I don't know what and all!—

            Oh! Yes! And Sausages
                    —is not
      Contented with his Prandial lot.

MORAL

The Moral is (I think, at least)
That Man is an UNGRATEFUL BEAST.

The Monkey's Paw

W. W. JACOBS

⇋ ⇋ ⇋ *This is a story of supernatural horror, one of the finest ever written. Notice the skill with which the author refuses to describe frightful things, but leaves you to imagine them for yourself.*

Without, the night was cold and wet, but in the small parlor of Lakesnam Villa the blinds were drawn and the fire burned brightly. Father and son were at chess, the former, who possessed ideas about the game involving radical changes, putting his king into such sharp and unnecessary perils that it even provoked comment from the white-haired old lady knitting placidly by the fire.

"Hark at the wind," said Mr. White, who, having seen a fatal mistake after it was too late, was amiably desirous of preventing his son from seeing it.

"I'm listening," said the latter, grimly surveying the board as he stretched out his hand. "Check."

"I should hardly think that he'd come tonight," said his father, with his hand poised over the board.

"Mate," replied the son.

"That's the worst of living so far out," bawled Mr. White, with sudden and unlooked-for violence; "of all the beastly, slushy, out-of-the-way places to live in, this is the worst. Pathway's a bog, and the road's a torrent. I don't know what people are thinking about. I suppose because only two houses on the road are let, they think it doesn't matter."

"Never mind, dear," said his wife soothingly; "perhaps you'll win the next one."

Mr. White looked up sharply, just in time to intercept a knowing glance between mother and son. The words died away on his lips, and he hid a guilty grin in his thin gray beard.

"There he is," said Herbert White, as the gate banged to loudly and heavy footsteps came toward the door.

The old man rose with hospitable haste, and opening the door, was heard condoling with the new arrival. The new arrival also condoled with himself, so that Mrs. White said, "Tut, tut!" and coughed gently as her husband entered the room, followed by a tall burly man, beady of eye and rubicund of visage.

"Sergeant-Major Morris," he said, introducing him.

The sergeant-major shook hands, and taking the proffered seat by the fire, watched contentedly while his host got out whisky and tumblers and stood a small copper kettle on the fire.

At the third glass his eyes got brighter, and he began to talk, the little family circle regarding with eager interest this visitor from distant parts, as he squared his broad shoulders in the chair and spoke of strange scenes and doughty deeds, of wars and plagues and strange peoples.

"Twenty-one years of it," said Mr. White, nodding at his wife and son. "When he went away he was a slip of a youth in the warehouse. Now look at him."

"He don't look to have taken much harm," said Mrs. White politely.

"I'd like to go to India myself," said the old man, "just to look around a bit, you know."

"Better where you are," said the sergeant-major, shaking his head. He put down the empty glass, and sighing softly, shook it again.

"I should like to see those old temples and fakirs and jugglers," said the old man. "What was that you started telling me the other day about a monkey's paw or something, Morris?"

"Nothing," said the soldier hastily. "Leastways, nothing worth hearing."

"Monkey's paw?" said Mrs. White curiously.

"Well, it's just a bit of what you might call magic, perhaps," said the sergeant-major off-handedly.

His three listeners leaned forward eagerly. The visitor absent-mindedly put his empty glass to his lips and then set it down again. His host filled it for him.

"To look at," said the sergeant-major, fumbling in his pocket, "it's just an ordinary little paw, dried to a mummy."

He took something out of his pocket and proffered it. Mrs. White drew back with a grimace, but her son, taking it, examined it curiously.

"And what is there special about it?" inquired Mr. White, as he took it from his son and, having examined it, placed it upon the table.

"It had a spell put on it by an old fakir," said the sergeant-major, "a very holy man. He wanted to show that fate ruled people's lives, and that those who interfered with it did so to their sorrow. He put a spell on it so that three separate men could each have three wishes from it."

His manner was so impressive that his hearers were conscious that their light laughter jarred somewhat.

"Well, why don't you have three, sir?" said Herbert White cleverly.

The soldier regarded him in the way that middle age is wont to regard presumptuous youth. "I have," he said quietly, and his blotchy face whitened.

"And did you really have the three wishes granted?" asked Mrs. White.

"I did," said the sergeant-major, and his glass tapped against his strong teeth.

"And has anybody else wished?" inquired the old lady.

"The first man had his three wishes, yes," was the reply. "I don't know what the first two were, but the third was for death. That's how I got the paw."

His tones were so grave that a hush fell upon the group.

"If you've had your three wishes, it's no good to you now, then, Morris," said the old man at last. "What do you keep it for?"

The soldier shook his head. "Fancy, I suppose," he said slowly. "I did have some idea of selling it, but I don't think I will. It has caused enough mischief already. Besides, people won't buy. They think it's a fairy tale, some of them, and those who do think anything of it want to try it first and pay me afterward."

"If you could have another three wishes," said the old man, eyeing him keenly, "would you have them?"

"I don't know," said the other. "I don't know."

He took the paw, and dangling it between his front finger and thumb, suddenly threw it upon the fire. White, with a slight cry, stooped down and snatched it off.

"Better let it burn," sad the soldier solemnly.

"If you don't want it, Morris," said the old man, "give it to me."

"I won't," said his friend doggedly. "I threw it on the fire. If you keep it, don't blame me for what happens. Pitch it on the fire again, like a sensible man."

The other shook his head and examined his new possession closely.

"How do you do it?" he inquired.

"Hold it up in your right hand and wish aloud," said the sergeant-major, "but I warn you of the consequences."

"Sounds like the *Arabian Nights*," said Mrs. White, as she rose and began to set the supper. "Don't you think you might wish for four pairs of hands for me?"

Her husband drew the talisman from his pocket and then all three burst into laughter as the sergeant-major, with a look of alarm on his face, caught him by the arm.

"If you must wish," he said gruffly, "wish for something sensible."

Mr. White dropped it back into his pocket, and placing chairs, motioned his friend to the table. In the business of supper the talisman was partly forgotten, and afterward the three sat listening in an enthralled fashion to a second installment of the soldier's adventures in India.

"If the tale about the monkey paw is not more truthful than those he has been telling us," said Herbert, as the door closed behind their guest, just in time for him to catch the last train, "we shan't make much out of it."

"Did you give him anything for it, father?" inquired Mrs. White, regarding her husband closely.

"A trifle," said he coloring slightly. "He didn't want it, but I made him take it. And he pressed me again to throw it away."

"Likely," said Herbert, with pretended horror. "Why, we're going to be rich, and famous, and happy. Wish to be an emperor, father, to begin with; then you can't be henpecked."

He darted round the table, pursued by the maligned Mrs. White armed with an antimacassar.

Mr. White took the paw from his pocket and eyed it dubiously. "I don't know what to wish for, and that's a fact," he said slowly. "It seems to me I've got all I want."

"If you only cleared the house, you'd be quite happy, wouldn't you?" said Herbert, with his hand on his shoulder. "Well, wish for two hundred pounds, then; that'll just do it."

His father, smiling shamefacedly at his own credulity, held up the talisman, as his son, with a solemn face somewhat marred by a wink at his mother, sat down at the piano and struck a few impressive chords.

"I wish for two hundred pounds," said the old man distinctly.

A fine crash from the piano greeted the words, interrupted by a shuddering cry from the old man. His wife and son ran toward him.

"It moved," he cried, with a glance of disgust at the object as it lay on the floor. "As I wished it twisted in my hands like a snake."

"Well, I don't see the money," said his son, as he picked it up and placed it on the table, "and I bet I never shall."

"It must have been your fancy, father," said his wife, regarding him anxiously.

He shook his head. "Never mind, though; there's no harm done, but it gave me a shock all the same."

They sat down by the fire again while the two men finished their pipes. Outside, the wind was higher than ever, and the old man started nervously at the sound of a door banging upstairs. A silence unusual and depressing settled upon all three, which lasted until the old couple rose to retire for the night.

"I expect you'll find the cash tied up in a big bag in the middle of your bed,' said Herbert, as he bade them good night, "and something horrible squatting up on top of the wardrobe watching you as you pocket your ill-gotten gains."

II

In the brightness of the wintry sun next morning as it streamed over the breakfast table Herbert laughed at his fears. There was an air of prosaic wholesomeness about the room which it had lacked on the previous night, and the dirty, shriveled little paw was pitched on the sideboard with a carelessness which betokened no great belief in its virtues.

"I suppose all old soldiers are the same," said Mrs. White. "The idea of our listening to such nonsense! How could wishes be granted in these days? And if they could, how could two hundred pounds hurt you, father?"

"Might drop on his head from the sky," said the frivolous Herbert.

"Morris said the things happened so naturally," said the father, "that you might if you so wished attribute it to coincidence."

"Well, don't break into the money before I come back," said Herbert, as he rose from the table. "I'm afraid it'll turn you into a mean, avaricious man, and we shall have to disown you."

His mother laughed, and following him to the door, watched him down the road, and returning to the breakfast table, was very happy at the expense of her husband's credulity. All of which did not prevent her from scurrying to the door at the postman's knock, nor prevent her from referring somewhat shortly to retired sergeant-majors of bibulous habits when she found that the post brought a tailor's bill.

"Herbert will have some more of his funny remarks, I expect, when he comes home," she said, as they sat at dinner.

"I dare say," said Mr. White, pouring himself out some beer; "but for all that, the thing moved in my hand; that I'll swear to."

"You thought it did," said the old lady soothingly.

"I say it did," replied the other. "There was no thought about it; I had just—What's the matter?"

His wife made no reply. She was watching the mysterious movements of a man outside, who, peering in an undecided fashion at the house, appeared to be trying to make up his mind to enter. In mental connection with the two hundred pounds, she noticed that the stranger was well dressed and wore a silk hat of glossy newness. Three times he paused at the gate, and then walked on again. The fourth time he stood with his hand upon it, and then with sudden resolution flung it open and walked up the path. Mrs. White at the same moment placed her hands behind her, and hurriedly unfastening the strings of her apron, put that useful article of apparel beneath the cushion of her chair.

She brought the stranger, who seemed ill at ease, into the room. He gazed furtively at Mrs. White, and listened in a preoccupied fashion as the old lady apologized for the appearance of the room, and her husband's coat, a garment which he usually reserved for the garden. She then waited as patiently as her sex would permit for him to broach his business, but he was at first strangely silent.

"I—was asked to call," he said at last, and stooped and picked a piece of cotton from his trousers. "I come from Maw and Meggins."

The old lady started. "Is anything the matter?" she asked breathlessly. "Has anything happened to Herbert? What is it? What is it?"

Her husband interposed. "There, there, mother," he said hastily. "Sit down, and don't jump to conclusions. You've not brought bad news, I'm sure," and he eyed the other wistfully.

"I'm sorry—" began the visitor.

"Is he hurt?" demanded the mother.

The visitor bowed in assent. "Badly hurt," he said quietly, "but he is not in any pain."

"Oh, thank God!" said the old woman, clasping her hands. "Thank God for that! Thank—"

She broke off suddenly as the sinister meaning of the assurance dawned upon her and she saw the awful confirmation of her fears in the other's averted face. She caught her breath, and turning to her slower-witted husband, laid her trembling old hand upon his. There was a long silence.

"He was caught in the machinery," said the visitor at length, in a low voice.

"Caught in the machinery," repeated Mr. White, in a dazed fashion, "yes."

He sat staring blankly out at the window, and taking his wife's hand between his own, pressed it as he had been wont to do in their old courting days nearly forty years before.

"He was the only one left to us," he said, turning gently to the visitor. "It is hard."

The other coughed, and rising, walked slowly to the windows. "The firm wished me to convey their sincere sympathy with you in your great loss," he said, without looking around. "I beg that you will understand I am only their servant and merely obeying orders."

There was no reply; the old woman's face was white, her eyes staring, and her breath inaudible; on the husband's face was a look such as his friend the sergeant might have carried into his first action.

"I was to say that Maw and Meggins disclaim all responsibility," continued the other. "They admit no liability at all, but in consideration of your son's services they wish to present you with a certain sum as compensation."

Mr. White dropped his wife's hand, and rising to his feet, gazed with a look of horror at his visitor. His dry lips shaped the words, "How much?"

"Two hundred pounds," was the answer.

Unconscious of his wife's shrieks, the old man smiled faintly, put out his hands like a sightless man, and dropped, a senseless heap, to the floor.

III

In the huge new cemetery, some two miles distant, the old people buried their dead, and came back to a house steeped in shadow and silence. It was all over so quickly that at first they could hardly realize it, and remained in a state of expectation as though of something else to happen—something else which was to lighten this load, too heavy for old hearts to bear. But the days passed, and expectation gave place to resignation—the hopeless resignation of the old, sometimes mis-called apathy. Sometimes they hardly exchanged a word, for now they had nothing to talk about, and their days were long to weariness.

It was about a week after that that the old man, waking suddenly in the night, stretched out his hand and found himself alone. The room was in darkness, and the sound of subdued weeping came from the window. He raised himself in bed and listened.

"Come back," he said tenderly. "You will be cold."

"It is colder for my son," said the old woman, and wept afresh.

The sound of her sobs died away on his ears. The bed was warm, and his eyes heavy with sleep. He dozed fitfully, and then slept until a sudden wild cry from his wife awoke him with a start.

"The monkey's paw!" she cried wildly. "The monkey's paw!"

He started up in alarm. "Where? Where is it? What's the matter?"

She came stumbling across the room toward him. "I want it," she said quietly. "You've not destroyed it?"

"It's in the parlor, on the bracket," he replied, marveling, "Why?"

She cried and laughed together, and bending over, kissed his cheek.

"I only just thought of it," she said hysterically. "Why didn't I think of it before? Why didn't you think of it?"

"Think of what?" he questioned.

"The other two wishes," she replied rapidly. "We've only had one."

"Was not that enough?" he demanded fiercely.

"No," she cried triumphantly; "we'll have one more. Go down and get it quickly, and wish our boy alive again."

The man sat up in bed and flung the bedclothes from his quaking limbs. "Good God, you are mad!" he cried, aghast.

"Get it," she panted; "get it quickly, and wish—Oh, my boy, my boy!"

Her husband struck a match and lit the candle. "Get back to bed," he said unsteadily. "You don't know what you are saying."

"We had the first wish granted," said the old woman feverishly; "why not the second?"

"A coincidence," stammered the old man.

"Go and get it and wish," cried the old woman, and dragged him toward the door.

He went down in the darkness, and felt his way to the parlor, and then to the mantelpiece. The talisman was in its place, and a horrible fear that the unspoken wish might bring his mutilated son before him ere he could escape from the room seized upon him, and he caught his breath as he found that he lost the direction of the door. His brow cold with sweat, he felt his way round the table, and groped along the wall until he found himself in the small passage with the unwholesome thing in his hand.

Even his wife's face seemed changed as he entered the room. It was white and expectant, and to his fears seemed to have an unnatural look upon it. He was afraid of her.

"Wish!" she cried, in a strong voice.

"It is foolish and wicked," he faltered.

"Wish!" repeated his wife.

He raised his hand. "I wish my son alive again."

The talisman fell to the floor, and he regarded it shudderingly. Then he sank trembling into a chair as the old woman, with burning eyes, walked to the window and raised the blind.

He sat until he was chilled with the cold, glancing occasionally at the figure of the old woman peering through the window. The candle end, which had burnt below the rim of the china candlestick, was throwing pulsating shadows on the ceiling and walls, until, with a flicker larger than the rest, it expired. The old man, with an unspeakable sense of relief at the failure of the talisman, crept back to his bed, and a minute or two afterward the old woman came silently and apathetically beside him.

Neither spoke, but both lay silently listening to the ticking of the clock. A stair creaked, and a squeaky mouse scurried noisily through the wall. The darkness was oppressive, and after lying for some time screwing up his courage, the husband took the box of matches, and striking one, went downstairs for a candle.

At the foot of the stairs the match went out, and he paused to strike another, and at the same moment a knock, so quiet and stealthy as to be scarcely audible, sounded on the front door.

The matches fell from his hand. He stood motionless, his breath suspended until the knock was repeated. Then he turned and fled swiftly back to his room, and closed the door behind him. A third knock sounded through the house.

"*What's that?*" cried the old woman, starting up.

"A rat," said the old man, in shaking tones—"a rat. It passed me on the stairs."

His wife sat up in bed listening. A loud knock resounded through the house.

"It's Herbert!" she screamed. "It's Herbert!"

She ran to the door, but her husband was before her, and catching her by the arm, held her tightly.

"What are you going to do?" he whispered hoarsely.

"It's my boy; it's Herbert!" she cried, struggling mechanically. "I forgot it was two miles away. What are you holding me for? Let go. I must open the door."

"For God's sake don't let it in," cried the old man, trembling.

"You're afraid of your own son," she cried, struggling. "Let me go. I'm coming, Herbert; I'm coming."

There was another knock, and another. The old woman with a sudden wrench broke free and ran from the room. Her husband followed to the landing, and called after her appealingly as she hurried downstairs. He heard the chain rattle back and the bottom bolt drawn slowly and stiffly from the socket. Then the old woman's voice, strained and panting.

"The bolt," she cried loudly. "Come down. I can't reach it."

But her husband was on his hands and knees groping wildly on the floor in search of the paw. If he could only find it before the thing outside got in. A perfect fusillade of knocks reverberated through the house, and he heard the scraping of a chair as his wife put it down in the passage against the door. He heard the creaking of the bolt as it came slowly back, and at the same moment, he found the monkey's paw, and frantically breathed his third and last wish.

The knocking ceased suddenly, although the echoes of it were still in the house. He heard the chair drawn back and the door opened. A cold wind rushed up the staircase, and a long loud wail of disappointment and misery from his wife gave him courage to run down to her side, and then to the gate beyond. The street lamp flickering opposite shone on a quiet and deserted road.

Lepanto

G. K. CHESTERTON

≋ ≋ ≋ The battle of Lepanto was fought in 1571 between Spanish, Venetian, and papal galleys and a Turkish fleet. Don John of Austria, the Christian commander, won a great victory. The Sultan of the Turks was called the Soldan by the Christians, and Mohammed, founder of the religion of Islam, was called Mahound. The Christians of that time thought of him as a demon. This wonderful poem is a song of triumph.

And the Soldan of Byzantium is smiling as they run;
There is laughter like the fountains in that face of all men feared,
It stirs the forest darkness, the darkness of his beard;
It curls the blood-red crescent, the crescent of his lips;
For the inmost sea of all the earth is shaken with his ships.
They have dared the white republics up the capes of Italy,
They have dashed the Adriatic round the Lion of the Sea,
And the Pope has cast his arms abroad for agony and loss,
And called the kings of Christendom for swords about the Cross.
The cold Queen of England is looking in the glass;
The shadow of the Valois is yawning at the Mass;
From evening isles fantastical rings faint the Spanish gun,
And the Lord upon the Golden Horn is laughing in the sun,

Dim drums throbbing, in the hills half heard,
Where only on a nameless throne a crownless prince has stirred,
Where, risen from a doubtful seat and half-attainted stall,
The last knight of Europe takes weapons from the wall,
The last and lingering troubadour to whom the bird has sung,
That once went singing southward when all the world was young.
In that enormous silence, tiny and unafraid,
Comes up along a winding road the noise of the Crusade.
Strong gongs groaning as the guns boom far,

Don John of Austria is going to the war;
Stiff flags straining in the night-blasts cold
In the gloom black-purple, in the glint old-gold,
Torchlight crimson on the copper kettle-drums,
Then the tuckets, then the trumpets, then the cannon, and he
    comes.
Don John laughing in the brave beard curled,
Spurning of his stirrups like the thrones of all the world,
Holding his head up for a flag of all the free.
Love-light of Spain—hurrah!
Death-light of Africa!
Don John of Austria
Is riding to the sea.

Mahound is in his paradise above the evening star,
(*Don John of Austria is going to the war.*)
He moves a mighty turban on the timeless houri's knees,
His turban that is woven of the sunset and the seas.
He shakes the peacock gardens as he rises from his ease,
And he strides among the tree-tops and is taller than the trees;
And his voice through all the garden is a thunder sent to bring
Black Azrael and Ariel and Ammon on the wing.
Giants and the Genii,
Multiplex of wing and eye,
Whose strong obedience broke the sky
When Solomon was king.

They rush in red and purple from the red clouds of the morn,
From temples where the yellow gods shut up their eyes in scorn;
They rise in green robes roaring from the green hells of the sea
Where fallen skies and evil hues and eyeless creatures be,
On them the sea-valves cluster and the grey sea-forests curl,
Splashed with a splendid sickness, the sickness of the pearl;
They swell in sapphire smoke out of the blue cracks of the ground,—
They gather and they wonder and give worship to Mahound.
And he saith, "Break up the mountains where the hermit-folk may
    hide,
And sift the red and silver sands lest bone of saint abide,
And chase the Giaours flying night and day, not giving rest,

For that which was our trouble comes again out of the west.
We have set the seal of Solomon on all things under sun,
Of knowledge and of sorrow, and endurance of things done.
But a noise is in the mountains, in the mountains, and I know
The voice that shook our palaces—four hundred years ago:
It is he that saith not 'Kismet': it is he that knows not Fate;
It is Richard, it is Raymond, it is Godfrey in the gate!
It is he whose loss is laughter when he counts the wager worth,
Put down your feet upon him, that our peace be on the earth."
For he heard drums groaning and he heard drums jar,
(*Don John of Austria is going to the war.*)
Sudden and still—hurrah!
Bolt from Iberia!
Don John of Austria
Is gone by Alcalar.

St. Michael's on his Mountain in the sea-roads of the north
(*Don John of Austria is girt and going forth.*)
Where the grey seas glitter and the sharp tides shift
And the sea folk labour and the red sails lift.
He shakes his lance of iron and he claps his wings of stone;
The noise is gone through Normandy; the noise is gone alone;
The North is full of tangled things and texts and aching eyes,
And dead is all the innocence of anger and surprise,
And Christian killeth Christian in a narrow dusty room,
And Christian dreadeth Christ that hath a newer face of doom,
And Christian hateth Mary that God kissed in Galilee,—
But Don John of Austria is riding to the sea.
Don John calling through the blast and the eclipse,
Crying with the trumpet, with the trumpet of his lips,
Trumpet that sayeth *ha!*
    Domino gloria!
Don John of Austria
Is shouting to the ships.

King Philip's in his closet with the Fleece about his neck
(*Don John of Austria is armed upon the deck.*)
The walls are hung with velvet that is black and soft as sin,
And little dwarfs creep out of it and little dwarfs creep in.

He holds a crystal phial that has colours like the moon,
He touches, and it tingles, and he trembles very soon,
And his face is like a fungus of a leprous white and grey
Like plants in the high houses that are shuttered from the day,
And death is in the phial, and the end of noble work,
But Don John of Austria has fired upon the Turk.
Don John's hunting, and his hounds have bayed—
Booms away past Italy the rumour of his raid.
Gun upon gun, ha! ha!
Gun upon gun, hurrah!
Don John of Austria
Has loosed the cannonade.

The Pope was in his chapel before day or battle broke,
(*Don John of Austria is hidden in the smoke.*)
The hidden room in a man's house where God sits all the year,
The secret window whence the world looks very small and very
    dear.
He sees as in a mirror on the monstrous twilight sea
The crescent of his cruel ships whose name is mystery;
They fling great shadows foe-wards, making Cross and Castle dark,
They veil the plumèd lions on the galleys of St. Mark;
And above the ships are palaces of brown, black-bearded chiefs,
And below the ships are prisons, where with multitudinous griefs,
Christian captives sick and sunless, all a labouring race repines
Like a race in sunken cities, like a nation in the mines.
They are lost like slaves that swat, and in the skies of morning
    hung
The stairways of the tallest gods when tyranny was young.
They are countless, voiceless, hopeless as those fallen or fleeing on
Before the high King's horses in the granite of Babylon.
And many a one grows witless in his quiet room in hell
Where a yellow face looks inward through the lattice of his cell,
And he finds his God forgotten, and he seeks no more a sign—
(*But Don John of Austria has burst the battle-line!*)
Don John pounding from the slaughter-painted poop,
Purpling all the ocean like a bloody pirate's sloop,
Scarlet running over on the silvers and the golds,
Breaking of the hatches up and bursting of the holds,

Thronging of the thousands up that labour under sea
White for bliss and blind for sun and stunned for liberty.
Vivat Hispania!
Domino Gloria!
Don John of Austria
Has set his people free!

Cervantes on his galley sets the sword back in the sheath
(*Don John of Austria rides homeward with a wreath.*)
And he sees across a weary land a straggling road in Spain,
Up which a lean and foolish knight forever rides in vain,
And he smiles, but not as Sultans smile, and settles back the
    blade. . . .
(*But Don John of Austria rides home from the Crusade.*)

The Leader of the People

JOHN STEINBECK

≈ ≈ ≈ *Forty years ago in the West there were still old men alive who could remember their adventures crossing the great plains and mountains in covered wagons. The ranch where Jody lived with his parents was in California. Jody's grandfather had been one of the pioneers.* —From The Red Pony

On Saturday afternoon, Billy Buck, the ranch-hand, raked together the last of the old year's haystack and pitched small forkfuls over the wire fence to a few mildly interested cattle. High in the air small clouds like puffs of cannon smoke were driven eastward by the March wind. The wind could be heard whishing in the brush on the ridge crests, but no breath of it penetrated down into the ranch-cup.

The little boy, Jody, emerged from the house eating a thick piece of buttered bread. He saw Billy working on the last of the haystack. Jody tramped down scuffing his shoes in a way he had been told was destructive to good shoe-leather. A flock of white pigeons flew out of the black cypress tree as Jody passed, and circled the tree and landed again. A half-grown tortoise-shell cat leaped from the bunkhouse porch, galloped on stiff legs across the road, whirled and galloped back again. Jody picked up a stone to help the game along, but he was too late, for the cat was under the porch before the stone could be discharged. He threw the stone into the cypress tree and started the white pigeons on another whirling flight.

Arriving at the used-up haystack, the boy leaned against the barbed wire fence. "Will that be all of it, do you think?" he asked.

The middle-aged ranch-hand stopped his careful raking and stuck his fork into the ground. He took off his black hat and smoothed down his hair. "Nothing left of it that isn't soggy from ground moisture," he said. He replaced his hat and rubbed his dry leathery hands together.

"Ought to be plenty mice," Jody suggested.

"Lousy with them," said Billy. "Just crawling with mice."

"Well, maybe, when you get all through, I could call the dogs and hunt the mice."

"Sure, I guess you could," said Billy Buck. He lifted a forkful of the damp ground-hay and threw it into the air. Instantly three mice leaped out and burrowed frantically under the hay again.

Jody sighed with satisfaction. Those plump, sleek, arrogant mice were doomed. For eight months they had lived and multiplied in the haystack. They had been immune from cats, from traps, from poison and from Jody. They had grown smug in their security, overbearing and fat. Now the time of disaster had come; they would not survive another day.

Billy looked up at the top of the hills that surrounded the ranch. "Maybe you'd better ask your father before you do it," he suggested.

"Well, where is he? I'll ask him right now."

"He rode up to the ridge ranch after dinner. He'll be back pretty soon."

Jody slumped against the fence post. "I don't think he'd care."

As Billy went back to his work he said ominously, "You'd better ask him anyway. You know how he is."

Jody did know. His father, Carl Tiflin, insisted upon giving permission for anything that was done on the ranch, whether it was important or not. Jody sagged farther against the post until he was sitting on the ground. He looked up at the little puffs of wind-driven cloud. "Is it like to rain, Billy?"

"It might. The wind's good for it, but not strong enough."

"Well, I hope it don't rain until after I kill those damn mice." He looked over his shoulder to see whether Billy had noticed the mature profanity. Billy worked on without comment.

Jody turned back and looked at the side-hill where the road from the outside world came down. The hill was washed with lean March sunshine. Silver thistles, blue lupins and a few poppies bloomed among the sage bushes. Halfway up the hill Jody could see Doubletree Mutt, the black dog, digging in a squirrel hole. He paddled for a while and then paused to kick bursts of dirt out between his hind legs, and he dug with an earnestness which belied the knowledge he must have had that no dog had ever caught a squirrel by digging a hole.

Suddenly, while Jody watched, the black dog stiffened, and backed out of the hole and looked up the hill toward the cleft in the ridge where the road came through. Jody looked up too. For a moment Carl Tiflin on horseback stood out against the pale sky and then he moved down the road toward the house. He carried something white in his hand.

The boy started to his feet. "He's got a letter," Jody cried. He trotted away toward the ranch house, for the letter would probably be read aloud and he wanted to be there. He reached the house before his father did, and ran in. He heard Carl dismount from his creaking saddle and slap the horse on the side to send it to the barn where Billy would unsaddle it and turn it out.

Jody ran into the kitchen. "We got a letter!" he cried.

His mother looked up from the pan of beans. "Who has?"

"Father has. I saw it in his hand."

Carl strode into the kitchen then, and Jody's mother asked, "Who's the letter from, Carl?"

He frowned quickly. "How did you know there was a letter?"

She nodded her head in the boy's direction. "Big-Britches Jody told me."

Jody was embarrassed.

His father looked down at him contemptuously. "He is getting to be a Big-Britches," Carl said. "He's minding everybody's business but his own. Got his big nose into everything."

Mrs. Tiflin relented a little. "Well, he hasn't enough to keep him busy. Who's the letter from?"

Carl still frowned on Jody. "I'll keep him busy if he isn't careful." He held out a sealed letter. "I guess it's from your father."

Mrs. Tiflin took a hairpin from her head and slit open the flap. Her lips pursed judiciously. Jody saw her eyes snap back and forth over the lines. "He says," she translated, "he says he's going to drive out Saturday to stay for a little while. Why, this is Saturday. The letter must have been delayed." She looked at the postmark. "This was mailed day before yesterday. It should have been here yesterday." She looked up questioningly at her husband, and then her face darkened angrily. "Now what have you got that look on you for? He doesn't come often."

Carl turned his eyes away from her anger. He could be stern with her most of the time, but when occasionally her temper arose, he could not combat it.

"What's the matter with you?" she demanded again.

In his explanation there was a tone of apology Jody himself might have used. "It's just that he talks," Carl said lamely. "Just talks."

"Well, what of it? You talk yourself."

"Sure I do. But your father only talks about one thing."

"Indians!" Jody broke in excitedly. "Indians and crossing the plains!"

Carl turned fiercely on him. "You get out, Mr. Big-Britches! Go on, now! Get out!"

Jody went miserably out the back door and closed the screen with elaborate quietness. Under the kitchen window his shamed, downcast eyes fell upon a curiously shaped stone, a stone of such fascination that he squatted down and picked it up and turned it over in his hands.

The voices came clearly to him through the open kitchen window. "Jody's damn well right," he heard his father say. "Just Indians and crossing the plains. I've heard that story about how the horses got driven off about a thousand times. He just goes on and on, and he never changes a word in the things he tells."

When Mrs. Tiflin answered her tone was so changed that Jody, outside the window, looked up from his study of the stone. Her voice had become soft and explanatory. Jody knew how her face would have changed to match the tone. She said quietly, "Look at it this way, Carl. That was the big thing in my father's life. He led a wagon train clear across the plains to the coast, and when it was finished, his life was done. It was a big thing to do, but it didn't last long enough. Look!" she continued, "it's as though he was born to do that, and after he finished it, there wasn't anything more for him to do but think about it, and talk about it. If there'd been any farther west to go, he'd have gone. He's told me so himself. But at last there was the ocean. He lives right by the ocean where he had to stop."

She had caught Carl, and entangled him in her soft tone.

"I've seen him," he agreed quietly. "He goes down and stares off west over the ocean." His voice sharpened a little. "And then he goes up to the Horseshoe Club in Pacific Grove, and he tells people how the Indians drove off the horses."

She tried to catch him again. "Well, it's everything to him. You might be patient with him and pretend to listen."

Carl turned impatiently away. "Well, if it gets too bad, I can always go down to the bunkhouse and sit with Billy," he said irritably. He walked through the house and slammed the front door after him.

Jody ran to his chores. He dumped the grain to the chickens without chasing any of them. He gathered the eggs from the nests. He trotted into the house with the wood and interlaced it so carefully in the wood-box that two armloads seemed to fill it to overflowing.

His mother had finished the beans by now. She stirred up the fire and brushed off the stove-top with a turkey wing. Jody peered cautiously at her to see whether any rancor toward him remained. "Is he coming today?" Jody asked.

"That's what his letter said."

"Maybe I'd better walk up the road to meet him."

Mrs. Tiflin clanged the stove-lid shut. "That would be nice," she said. "He'd probably like to be met."

"I guess I'll just do it then."

Outside, Jody whistled shrilly to the dogs. "Come on up the hill," he commanded. The two dogs waved their tails and ran ahead. Along the roadside the sage had tender new tips. Jody tore off some pieces and rubbed them on his hands until the air was filled with the sharp wild smell. With a rush the dogs leaped from the road and yapped into the brush after a rabbit. That was the last Jody saw of them, for when they failed to catch the rabbit, they went back home.

Jody plodded on up the hill toward the ridge top. When he reached the little cleft where the road came through, the afternoon wind struck him and blew up his hair and ruffled his shirt. He looked down on the little hills and ridges below and then out at the huge green Salinas Valley. He could see the white town of Salinas far out in the flat and the flash of its windows under the waning sun. Directly below him, in an oak tree, a crow congress had convened. The tree was black with crows all cawing at once.

Then Jody's eyes followed the wagon road down from the ridge where he stood, and lost it behind a hill, and picked it up again on the other side. On that distant stretch he saw a cart slowly pulled by a bay horse. It disappeared behind the hill. Jody sat down on the ground and watched the place where the cart would reappear again. The wind sang on the hilltops and the puff-ball clouds hurried eastward.

Then the cart came into sight and stopped. A man dressed in black dismounted from the seat and walked to the horse's head. Although it was so far away, Jody knew he had unhooked the check-rein, for the horse's head dropped forward. The horse moved on, and the man walked slowly up the hill beside it. Jody gave a glad cry and ran down the road toward them. The squirrels bumped along off the road, and a road-runner flirted its tail and raced over the edge of the hill and sailed out like a glider.

Jody tried to leap into the middle of his shadow at every step. A stone rolled under his foot and he went down. Around a little bend he raced, and there, a short distance ahead, were his grandfather and the cart. The boy dropped from his unseemly running and approached at a dignified walk.

The horse plodded stumble-footedly up the hill and the old man walked beside it. In the lowering sun their giant shadows flickered darkly behind them. The grandfather was dressed in a black broad-cloth suit and he wore kid congress gaiters and a black tie on a short, hard collar. He carried his black slouch hat in his hand. His white beard was cropped close and his white eyebrows overhung his eyes like moustaches. The blue eyes were sternly merry. About the whole face and figure there was a granite dignity, so that every motion seemed an impossible thing. Once at rest, it seemed the old man would be stone, would never move again. His steps were slow and certain. Once made, no step could ever be retraced; once headed in a direction, the path would never bend nor the pace increase or slow.

When Jody appeared around the bend, Grandfather waved his hat slowly in welcome, and he called, "Why, Jody! Come down to meet me, have you?"

Jody sidled near and turned and matched his step to the old man's step and stiffened his body and dragged his heels a little. "Yes, sir," he said. "We got your letter only today."

"Should have been here yesterday," said Grandfather. "It certainly should. How are all the folks?"

"They're fine, sir." He hesitated and then suggested shyly, "Would you like to come on a mouse hunt tomorrow?"

"Mouse hunt, Jody?" Grandfather chuckled. "Have the people of this generation come down to hunting mice? They aren't very strong, the new people, but I hardly thought mice would be game for them."

"No, sir. It's just play. The haystack's gone. I'm going to drive out the mice to the dogs. And you can watch, or even beat the hay a little."

The stern, merry eyes turned down on him. "I see. You don't eat them, then. You haven't come to that yet."

Jody explained, "The dogs eat them, sir. It wouldn't be much like hunting Indians, I guess."

"No, not much—but then later, when the troops were hunting Indians and shooting children and burning teepees, it wasn't much different from your mouse hunt."

They topped the rise and started down into the ranch-cup, and they lost the sun from their shoulders. "You've grown," Grandfather said. "Nearly an inch, I should say."

"More," Jody boasted. "Where they mark me on the door I'm up more than an inch since Thanksgiving even."

Grandfather's rich throaty voice said, "Maybe you're getting too much water and turning to pith and stalk. Wait until you head out, and then we'll see."

Jody looked quickly into the old man's face to see whether his feelings should be hurt, but there was no will to injure, no punishing nor putting-in-your-place light in the keen blue eyes. "We might kill a pig," Jody suggested.

"Oh, no! I couldn't let you do that. You're just humoring me. It isn't the time and you know it."

"You know Riley, the big boar, sir?"

"Yes. I remember Riley well."

"Well, Riley ate a hole into that same haystack, and it fell down on him and smothered him."

"Pigs do that when they can," said Grandfather.

"Riley was a nice pig, for a boar, sir. I rode him sometimes, and he didn't mind."

A door slammed at the house below them, and they saw Jody's mother standing on the porch waving her apron in welcome. And they saw Carl Tiflin walking up from the barn to be at the house for their arrival.

The sun had disappeared from the hills by now. The blue smoke from the house chimney hung in flat layers in the purpling ranch-cup The puff-ball clouds, dropped by the falling wind, hung listlessly in the sky.

Billy Buck came out of the bunkhouse and flung a wash basin of soapy water on the ground. He had been shaving in mid-week, for Billy held Grandfather in reverence, and Grandfather said that Billy was one of the few men of the new generation who had not gone soft. Although Billy was in middle age, Grandfather considered him a boy. Now Billy was hurrying toward the house too.

When Jody and grandfather arrived, the three were waiting for them in front of the yard gate.

Carl said, "Hello, sir. We've been looking for you."

Mrs. Tiflin kissed Grandfather on the side of his beard, and stood still while his big hand patted her shoulder. Billy shook hands solemnly, grinning under his straw moustache. "I'll put up your horse," said Billy, and he led the rig away.

Grandfather watched him go, and then, turning back to the group, he said as he had said a hundred times before, "There's a good boy. I knew his father, old Mule-tail Buck. I never knew why they called him Mule-tail except he packed mules."

Mrs. Tiflin turned and led the way into the house. "How long are you going to stay, Father? Your letter didn't say."

"Well, I don't know. I thought I'd stay about two weeks. But I never stay as long as I think I'm going to."

In a short while they were sitting at the white oilcloth table eating their supper. The lamp with the tin reflector hung over the table. Outside the dining-room windows the big moths battered softly against the glass.

Grandfather cut his steak into tiny pieces and chewed slowly. "I'm hungry," he said. "Driving out here got my appetite up. It's like when we were crossing. We all got so hungry every night we could hardly wait to let the meat get done. I could eat about five pounds of buffalo meat every night."

"It's moving around does it," said Billy. "My father was a government packer. I helped him when I was a kid. Just the two of us could about clean up a deer's ham."

"I knew your father, Billy," said Grandfather. "A fine man he was. They called him Mule-tail. I don't know why except he packed mules."

"That was it," Billy agreed. "He packed mules."

Grandfather put down his knife and fork and looked around the table. "I remember one time we ran out of meat—" His voice dropped to a curious low sing-song, dropped into a tonal groove the story had worn for itself. "There were no buffalo, no antelope, not even rabbits. The hunters couldn't even shoot a coyote. That was the time for the leader to be on the watch. I was the leader, and I kept my eyes open. Know why? Well, just the minute the people begin to get hungry they'd start slaughtering the team oxen. Do you believe that? I've heard of parties that just ate up their draft cattle. Started from the middle and worked toward the ends. Finally they'd eat the lead pair, and then the wheelers. The leader of a party had to keep them from doing that."

In some manner a big moth got into the room and circled the hanging kerosene lamp. Billy got up and tried to clap it between his hands. Carl struck with a cupped palm and caught the moth and broke it. He walked to the window and dropped it out.

"As I was saying," Grandfather began again, but Carl interrupted him. "You'd better eat some more meat. All the rest of us are ready for our pudding."

Jody saw a flash of anger in his mother's eyes. Grandfather picked up his knife and fork. "I'm pretty hungry, all right," he said. "I'll tell you about that later."

When supper was over, when the family and Billy Buck sat in front of the fireplace in the other room, Jody anxiously watched Grandfather. He saw the signs he knew. The bearded head leaned forward; the eyes lost their sternness and looked wonderingly into the fire; the big lean fingers laced themselves on the black knees. "I wonder," he began, "I just wonder whether I ever told you how those thieving Piutes drove off thirty-five of our horses."

"I think you did," Carl interrupted. "Wasn't it just before you went up into the Tahoe country?"

Grandfather turned quickly toward his son-in-law, "That's right. I guess I must have told you that story."

"Lots of times," Carl said cruelly, and he avoided his wife's eyes. But he felt the angry eyes on him, and he said, " 'Course I'd like to hear it again."

Grandfather looked back at the fire. His fingers unlaced and laced again. Jody knew how he felt, how his insides were collapsed and empty. Hadn't Jody been called a Big-Britches that very afternoon? He arose to heroism and opened himself to the term Big-Britches again. "Tell about Indians," he said softly.

Grandfather's eyes grew stern again. "Boys always want to hear about Indians. It was a job for men, but boys want to hear about it. Well, let's see. Did I ever tell you how I wanted each wagon to carry a long iron plate?"

Everyone but Jody remained silent. Jody said, "No. You didn't."

"Well, when the Indians attacked, we always put the wagons in a circle and fought from between the wheels. I thought that if every wagon carried a long plate with rifle holes, the men could stand the plates on the outside of the wheels when the wagons were in a circle and they would be protected. It would save lives and that would make up for the extra weight of the iron. But of course the party wouldn't do it. No party had done it before and they couldn't see why they should go to the expense. They lived to regret it, too."

Jody looked at his mother, and knew from her expression that she was not listening at all. Carl picked at a callus on his thumb and Billy Buck watched a spider crawling up the wall.

Grandfather's tone dropped into its narrative groove again. Jody knew in advance exactly what words would fall. The story droned on, speeded up for the attack, grew sad over the wounds, struck a dirge at the burials on the great plains. Jody sat quietly watching Grandfather. The stern blue eyes were detached. He looked as though he were not very interested in the story himself.

When it was finished, when the pause had been politely respected as the frontier of the story, Billy Buck stood up and stretched and hitched his trousers. "I guess I'll turn in," he said. Then he faced Grandfather. "I've got an old powder horn and a cap and ball pistol down to the bunkhouse. Did I ever show them to you?"

Grandfather nodded slowly. "Yes, I think you did, Billy. Reminds me of a pistol I had when I was leading the people across." Billy stood politely until the little story was done, and then he said, "Good night," and went out of the house.

Carl Tiflin tried to turn the conversation then. "How's the country between here and Monterey? I've heard it's pretty dry."

"It is dry," said Grandfather. "There's not a drop of water in the Laguna Seca. But it's a long pull from '87. The whole country was powder then, and in '61 I believe all the coyotes starved to death. We had fifteen inches of rain this year."

"Yes, but it all came too early. We could do with some now." Carl's eye fell on Jody. "Hadn't you better be getting to bed?"

Jody stood up obediently. "Can I kill the mice in the old haystack, sir?"

"Mice? Oh! Sure, kill them all off. Billy said there isn't any good hay left."

Jody exchanged a secret and satisfying look with Grandfather. "I'll kill every one tomorrow," he promised.

Jody lay in his bed and thought of the impossible world of Indians and buffaloes, a world that had ceased to be forever. He wished he could have been living in the heroic time, but he knew he was not of heroic timber. No one living now, save possibly Billy Buck, was worthy to do the things that had been done. A race of giants had lived then, fearless men, men of a staunchness unknown in this day. Jody thought of the wide plains and of the wagons moving across like centipedes. He thought of Grandfather on a huge white horse, marshaling the people. Across his mind marched the great phantoms, and they marched off the earth and they were gone.

He came back to the ranch for a moment, then. He heard the dull rushing sound that space and silence make. He heard one of the dogs, out in the doghouse, scratching a flea and bumping his elbow against the floor with every stroke. Then the wind arose again and the black cypress groaned and Jody went to sleep.

He was up half an hour before the triangle sounded for breakfast. His mother was rattling the stove to make the flames roar when Jody went through the kitchen. "You're up early," she said. "Where are you going?"

"Out to get a good stick. We're going to kill the mice today."

"Who is 'we'?"

"Why, Grandfather and I."

"So you've got him in it. You always like to have someone in with you in case there's blame to share."

"I'll be right back," said Jody. "I just want to have a good stick ready for after breakfast."

He closed the screen door after him and went out into the cool blue morning. The birds were noisy in the dawn and the ranch cats came down from the hill like blunt snakes. They had been hunting gophers in the dark, and although the four cats were full of gopher meat, they sat in a semi-circle at the back door and mewed piteously for milk. Doubletree, Mutt and Smasher moved sniffing along the edge of the brush, performing the duty with rigid ceremony, but when Jody whistled, their heads jerked up and their tails waved. They plunged down to him, wriggling their skins and yawning. Jody patted their heads seriously, and moved on to the weathered scrap pile. He selected an old broom handle and a short piece of inch-square scrap wood. From his pocket he took a shoelace and tied the ends of the stick loosely together to make a flail. He whistled his new weapon through the air and struck the ground experimentally, while the dogs leaped aside and whined with apprehension.

Jody turned and started down past the house toward the old haystack ground to look over the field of slaughter, but Billy Buck, sitting patiently on the back steps, called to him, "You better come back. It's only a couple of minutes till breakfast."

Jody changed his course and moved toward the house. He leaned his flail against the steps. "That's to drive the mice out," he said. "I'll bet they're fat. I'll bet they don't know what's going to happen to them today."

"No, nor you either," Billy remarked philosophically, "nor me, nor anyone."

Jody was staggered by this thought. He knew it was true. His imagination twitched away from the mouse hunt. Then his mother came out on the back porch and struck the triangle, and all thoughts fell in a heap.

Grandfather hadn't appeared at the table when they sat down. Billy nodded at his empty chair. "He's all right? He isn't sick?"

"He takes a long time to dress," said Mrs. Tiflin. "He combs his whiskers and rubs up his shoes and brushes his clothes."

Carl scattered sugar on his mush. "A man that's led a wagon train across the plains has got to be pretty careful how he dresses."

Mrs. Tiflin turned on him. "Don't do that, Carl! Please don't!" There was more threat than of request in her tone. And the threat irritated Carl.

"Well, how many times do I have to listen to the story of the iron plates, and the thirty-five horses? That time's done. Why can't he forget it, now it's done?" He grew angrier while he talked, and his voice rose. "Why does he have to tell them over and over? He came across the plains. All right! Now it's finished. Nobody wants to hear about it over and over."

The door into the kitchen closed softly. The four at the table sat frozen. Carl laid his mush spoon on the table and touched his chin with his fingers.

Then the kitchen door opened and Grandfather walked in. His mouth smiled tightly, and his eyes were squinted. "Good morning," he said, and he sat down and looked at his mush dish.

Carl could not leave it there. "Did—did you hear what I said?"

Grandfather jerked a little nod.

"I don't know what got into me, sir. I didn't mean it. I was just being funny."

Jody glanced in shame at his mother, and he saw that she was looking at Carl, and that she wasn't breathing. It was an awful thing that he was doing. He was tearing himself to pieces to talk like that. It was a terrible thing to him to retract a word, but to retract it in shame was infinitely worse.

Grandfather looked sidewise. "I'm trying to get right side up," he said gently. "I'm not being mad. I don't mind what you said, but it might be true, and I would mind that."

"It isn't true," said Carl. "I'm not feeling well this morning. I'm sorry I said it."

"Don't be sorry, Carl. An old man doesn't see things sometimes.

Maybe you're right. The crossing is finished. Maybe it should be forgotten, now it's done."

Carl got up from the table. "I've had enough to eat. I'm going to work. Take your time, Billy!" He walked quickly out of the dining-room. Billy gulped the rest of his food and followed soon after. But Jody could not leave his chair.

"Won't you tell any more stories?" Jody asked.

"Why, sure I'll tell them, but only when—I'm sure people want to hear them."

"I like to hear them, sir."

"Oh! Of course you do, but you're a little boy. It was a job for men, but only little boys like to hear about it."

Jody got up from his place. "I'll wait outside for you, sir. I've got a good stick for those mice."

He waited by the gate until the old man came out on the porch. "Let's go down and kill the mice now," Jody called.

"I think I'll just sit in the sun, Jody. You go kill the mice."

"You can use my stick if you like."

"No, I'll just sit here a while."

Jody turned disconsolately away, and walked down toward the old haystack. He tried to whip up his enthusiasm with thoughts of the fat juicy mice. He beat the ground with his flail. The dogs coaxed and whined about him, but he could not go. Back at the house he could see Grandfather sitting on the porch, looking small and thin and black.

Jody gave up and went to sit on the steps at the old man's feet.

"Back already? Did you kill the mice?"

"No, sir. I'll kill them some other day."

The morning flies buzzed close to the ground and the ants dashed about in front of the steps. The heavy smell of sage slipped down the hill. The porch boards grew warm in the sunshine.

Jody hardly knew when Grandfather started to talk. "I shouldn't stay here, feeling the way I do." He examined his strong old hands. "I feel as though the crossing wasn't worth doing." His eyes moved up the side-hill and stopped on a motionless hawk perched on a dead limb. "I tell those old stories, but they're not what I want to tell. I only know how I want people to feel when I tell them.

"It wasn't Indians that were important, nor adventures, nor even getting out here. It was a whole bunch of people made into one big crawling beast. And I was the head. It was westering and westering.

Every man wanted something for himself, but the big beast that was all of them wanted only westering. I was the leader, but if I hadn't been there, someone else would have been the lead. The thing had to have a head.

"Under the little bushes the shadows were black at white noonday. When we saw the mountains at last, we cried—all of us. But it wasn't getting here that mattered, it was movement and westering.

"We carried life out here and set it down the way those ants carry eggs. And I was the leader. The westering was as big as God, and the slow steps that made the movement piled up and piled up until the continent was crossed.

"Then we came down to the sea, and it was done." He stopped and wiped his eyes until the rims were red. "That's what I should be telling instead of stories."

When Jody spoke, Grandfather started and looked down at him. "Maybe I could lead the people some day," Jody said.

The old man smiled. "There's no place to go. There's the ocean to stop you. There's a line of old men along the shore hating the ocean because it stopped them."

"In boats I might, sir."

"No place to go, Jody. Every place is taken. But that's not the worst —no, not the worst. Westering has died out of the people. Westering isn't a hunger any more. It's all done. Your father is right. It is finished." He laced his fingers on his knee and looked at them.

Jody felt very sad. "If you'd like a glass of lemonade I could make it for you."

Grandfather was about to refuse, and then he saw Jody's face. "That would be nice," he said. "Yes, it would be nice to drink a lemonade."

Jody ran into the kitchen where his mother was wiping the last of the breakfast dishes. "Can I have a lemon to make a lemonade for Grandfather?"

His mother mimicked—"And another lemon to make a lemonade for you."

"No, ma'am. I don't want one."

"Jody! You're sick!" Then she stopped suddenly. "Take a lemon out of the cooler," she said softly. "Here, I'll reach the squeezer down to you."

Ivry:
A Song of the Huguenots

LORD MACAULAY

≋ ≋ ≋ *Henry IV, Henry of Navarre, was the French king who led the Protestant forces against the Catholic League at the Battle of Ivry. Mayenne was a duke in treasonous alliance with Spain. It doesn't matter who the others were. What matters is the hero worship, courage, and exultation expressed in this grand poem.*

Now glory to the Lord of Hosts, from whom all glories are!
And glory to our Sovereign Liege, King Henry of Navarre!
Now let there be the merry sound of music and of dance,
Through thy corn-fields green, and sunny vines, oh pleasant land
    of France!
And thou, Rochelle, our own Rochelle, proud city of the waters,
Again let rapture light the eyes of all thy mourning daughters.
As thou wert constant in our ills, be joyous in our joy,
For cold, and stiff, and still are they who wrought thy walls annoy.
Hurrah! hurrah! a single field hath turned the chance of war,
Hurrah! Hurrah! for Ivry, and Henry of Navarre.

Oh! how our hearts were beating, when, at the dawn of day.
We saw the army of the League drawn out in long array;
With all its priest-led citizens, and all its rebel peers,
And Appenzel's stout infantry, and Egmont's Flemish spears.
There rode the brood of false Lorraine, the curses of our land;
And dark Mayenne was in the midst, a truncheon in his hand;
And, as we looked on them, we thought of Seine's empurpled
    flood,
And good Coligni's hoary hair all dabbled with his blood;
And we cried unto the living God, who rules the fate of war,
To fight for his own holy name, and Henry of Navarre.

The King is come to marshal us, in all his armour drest,
And he has bound a snow-white plume upon his gallant crest.
He looked upon his people, and a tear was in his eye;
He looked upon the traitors, and his glance was stern and high.
Right graciously he smiled on us, as rolled from wing to wing,
Down all our line, a deafening shout, "God save our Lord the
    King."
"An if my standard-bearer fall, as fall full well he may,
For never saw I promise yet of such a bloody fray,
Press where ye see my white plume shine, amidst the ranks of war,
And be your oriflamme to-day the helmet of Navarre."

Hurrah! the foes are moving. Hark to the mingled din,
Of fife, and steed, and trump, and drum, and roaring culverin.
The fiery Duke is pricking fast across Saint André's plain,
With all the hireling chivalry of Guelders and Almayne.
Now by the lips of those ye love, fair gentlemen of France,
Charge for the golden lilies,—upon them with the lance.
A thousand spurs are striking deep, a thousand spears in rest,
A thousand knights are pressing close behind the snow-white
    crest;
And in they burst, and on they rushed, while, like a guiding star,
Amidst the thickest carnage blazed the helmet of Navarre.

Now, God be praised, the day is ours. Mayenne hath turned his
    rein.
D'Aumale hath cried for quarter. The Flemish count is slain.
Their ranks are breaking like thin clouds before a Biscay gale;
The field is heaped with bleeding steeds, and flags, and cloven
    mail.
And then we thought on vengeance, and, all along our van,
"Remember Saint Bartholomew, was passed from man to man.
But out spake gentle Henry, "No Frenchman is my foe:
Down, down, with every foreigner, but let your brethren go."
Oh! was there ever such a knight, in friendship or in war,
As our Sovereign Lord, King Henry, the soldier of Navarre?"

Right well fought all the Frenchmen who fought for France today;
And many a lordly banner God gave them for a prey.

But we of the religion have borne us best in fight;
And the good Lord of Rosny hath ta'en the cornet white.
Our own true Maximilian the cornet white hath ta'en,
The cornet white with crosses black, the flag of false Lorraine.
Up with it high; unfurl it wide; that all the host may know
How God hath humbled the proud house which wrought his
    church such woe.
Then on the ground, while trumpets sound their loudest point of
    war,
Fling the red shreds, a footcloth meet for Henry of Navarre.

Ho! maidens of Vienna; Ho! matrons of Lucerne;
Weep, weep, and rend your hair for those who never shall return.
Ho! Philip, send, for charity, thy Mexican pistoles,
That Antwerp monks may sing a mass for thy poor spearmen's
    souls.
Ho! gallant nobles of the League, look that your arms be bright;
Ho! burghers of Saint Genevieve, keep watch and ward to-night.
For our God hath crushed the tyrant, our God hath raised the
    slave,
And mocked the counsel of the wise, and the valour of the brave.
Then glory to his holy name, from whom all glories are;
And glory to our Sovereign Lord, King Henry of Navarre.

A Raid by the Crows

J. W. SCHULTZ

≈ ≈ ≈ *When J. W. Schultz was a young man nearly one hundred years ago, he lived with the Blackfoot Indians of Mon-
tana. He married an Indian girl called Nät-ah'-ki, fought enemy tribes, and learned to know the Indians as few men have
known them. These stories are taken from his book* My Life as
an Indian.

A big chinook wind in the latter part of February cleared the river of
ice, and the little snow in the coulées soon melted away. Grass showed
green in the bottom lands in March.

One evening a vast herd of buffalo had been discovered two or three
miles back from the river—a herd so large that it was said the valley of
Cow Creek and the hills on each side of it were black with them as far
as one could see. Soon after sunrise many hunters, with their women
following on travois horses, had gone out to run this herd and get
meat. An hour or so later they charged in among them on their trained
runners, splitting the herd in such a way that about a thousand or more
broke straight down the valley toward the camp, for the nearer to
camp the killing was done the easier it was to pack in the meat. Down
the valley the frightened animals fled, followed by their pursuers. We
in camp heard the thunder of hoofs and saw the cloud of dust before
the animals came in sight. Our lodges were pitched on the lower side
of the bottom, between the creek and a steep, bare, rocky ridge. Every
man, woman, and child of us had hurried outside to witness the chase.

It was really far more exciting to see such a run near at hand than to
take part in it. First of all, the huge, shaggy, oddly shaped beasts
charged madly by with a thunderous pounding of hoof and rattle of
horns, causing the ground to tremble as if from an earthquake; and
then the hunters, their long hair streaming in the wind, guiding their
trained mounts here and there in the thick of it all, singling out this fat
cow or that choice young bull, firing their guns, or leaning over and
driving an arrow deep into the vital part of the great beast. The plain

over which they passed became dotted with the dead, with great animals standing head down, swaying, staggering, as the life blood flowed from mouth and nostrils, finally crashing over on the ground, limp and lifeless heaps.

That is what we, standing by our lodges, saw that morning. No one cheered the hunters, nor spoke, nor laughed. It was too solemn a moment. We saw death abroad; huge, powerful beasts, full of tireless energy, suddenly stricken into so many heaps of meat and hide. Paradoxical as it may seem, the Blackfeet reverenced, regarded as "medicine," or sacred, these animals which they killed for food, whose hides furnished them with shelter and clothing.

A band of horses drinking at the river became frightened at the noise of the approaching herd. They bounded up the bank and raced out over the bottom, heads and tails up, running directly toward the herd, which swerved to the eastward, crossed the creek, and came tearing down our side of it. The rocky ridge hemming in the bottom was too steep for them to climb, so they kept on in the flat directly toward the lodges. Some in their terror ran wildly around, stopping behind one lodge a moment, then running to the shelter of another. Women screamed, children bawled, men shouted words of advice and command.

I seized hold of Nät-ah'-ki, ran with her over to one of Berry's wagons, and got her up in it. In a moment both his and Sorrel Horse's wagons were filled with people, others crouching under and standing in lines behind them. Persons in the vicinity of the ridge clambered up among the rocks. Those near the creek jumped into it, but many stood helplessly behind their lodges in the center of the camp.

Now, the leaders of the herd reached the outer edge of the village. They could not draw back, for those behind forced them forward, and they loped on, threading their way between the lodges, nimbly jumping from side to side to avoid them, kicking out wickedly at them as they passed. For all his great size and uncouth shape, the buffalo was quick and active on his feet.

I had taken shelter behind one of the wagons with many others and watched the brown, living stream surge by, winding in and out between the lodges as a river winds past the island and bars in its channel. We held our breath anxiously, for we well knew that almost anything—the firing of a gun or sight of some suspicious object ahead —might throw the herd into confusion. If it turned or bunched up in a compact mass, people would surely be trampled to death, lodges overturned, the greater part of camp reduced to ruin. Finally the last of the herd passed beyond the outer lodges into the river and across it to the opposite side.

No one had been hurt, not a lodge had been overturned. But long scaffolds of drying meat, many hides and pelts of various animals pegged out on the ground to dry, had either disappeared or been cut into small fragments. That, indeed, was an experience to be remembered; we were thankful to have escaped with our lives. When we thought what would have happened had we got in the way of the rushing herd, we shuddered.

The next day the trees and high bushes bordering the river were bright with the people's offerings to their Sun god. They gave always their best, their choicest and most prized ornaments and finery.

One warm, sunny day in the end of March, camp was broken, and crossing the wide, shallow ford of the river at Cow Island, we climbed the south slope of the valley and strung out over the plain. At such times Nät-ah′-ki and I frequently dropped behind and rode along a mile or more to the right or left of the trail on little side hunts. We were free to do this, for mother and her uncle's family took charge of our pack and travois horses, and herded them along with their own. And when we came back to camp in the evening we would find our lodge put up, the couches made, wood and water at hand, the tireless mother sitting by the fire awaiting our arrival. Sometimes Nät-ah′-ki would remonstrate with her for doing all this, but she would always say, "Young people should be happy. This my mother did for me when I was newly married. Some day you will likely be doing it for your daughter." Which remark would cause my woman to turn away in confusion, and she would pretend to be very busy about something. Alas! they thought that this carefree life was going to last forever. Even we white men little dreamed how soon the buffalo were to disappear.

On this lovely morning we rode gradually, slowly and obliquely away to the west until we were a couple of miles from the trail. Still farther out we could see several hunters now and then, as they passed over a rise of ground, and occasionally the long column of the moving camp was in sight. Sometimes we loitered, letting our horses feed as they walked, and again we would start them into a lope and keep it up until we were well abreast of the others. Nät-ah′-ki kept up a ceaseless chatter of gossip and story and questions about the country from which I had come.

Along toward noon we came to the head of a pine-clad coulée running into the far-away Judith, and in a little grove there was a small spring of clear, cold water. We drank, and then leading our animals up to the top of the slope where we could obtain a good view of the surrounding country we ate our lunch of bread, *depuyer*, and dried meat. A fox cub came trotting over the bench opposite us, ran down the slope into the grove and to the spring, and presently came out on our side, sniffing the air, undoubtedly having scented our food. It walked up to within thirty feet of us, stopped and stared at us and the grazing horses, then circled around and finally stretched out on its belly, head up watching us intently, and frequently sniffing the air, curiously working its slender, delicately contoured nose.

"Did I ever tell you," Nät-ah'-ki asked, "about my grandfather and his pet fox? No? Well then, listen.

"One night my grandfather's dream commanded him to catch a cub fox, tame it, and be kind to it. He thought long over this, and counseled with others as to its meaning, but none could understand it any more than he. The next night his dream told him the same things, and again on the third night, and lastly on the fourth night. Four times his dreams commanded him. Four is the sacred number. When he arose the fourth morning, he knew that he must obey his dream. He no longer asked why, or what was meant, but after eating he went out to catch a fox. There were many foxes. Every little way as he walked he saw them running or sitting by their dens into which they disappeared as he drew near. He had a long lariat, to an end of which he had tied a length of fine buckskin string. Making a running noose of the string, he would lay it in a circle around the entrance to the den, then go back as far as the lariat extended and lie down to watch for the animals. If one poked its head out, he would jerk the lariat, and the noose would tighten around its neck or body. Children catch ground squirrels in this way—he had done it himself in youthful days—and he believed that in like manner he could capture a fox.

"These animals have more than one entrance to their den, often as many as five or six. If my grandfather set the noose around a hole into which he saw a fox go, the animal was certain to look out from another opening, and seeing him lying nearby, would dodge back and appear no more, even though he waited a long time.

"Thus passed the first day, and the second. On the evening of the third he noosed one, but with a snap of its sharp teeth the fox cut the string and escaped. Tired and thirsty, and hungry, he was returning

home that evening, when on the side of a coulée he saw five young
foxes playing near the entrance to their den, the mother and father
sitting watching them. They were very small, so young that they tumbled over each other slowly and awkwardly. He sat down on the
opposite side of the coulée and watched them until the sun set and
night came on. Over and over he asked himself how he could catch one
of the young. He prayed, too, calling upon the gods, upon his dream,
to show him the way.

"Returning to his lodge, he ate and drank and filled and lighted his
pipe, again praying for help. And suddenly, as he sat there silently
smoking, the way was shown him. The gods had taken pity on him. He
went to bed and slept well. 'Go out and find a large buffalo shoulder
blade,' he said to my grandmother, after the morning meal, 'then take a
cowskin and accompany me.'

"They went to the den of young foxes. Very close to the place where
the little ones played was a large bunch of rye grass, and in the center
of it my grandfather began to cut away the sod, to loosen the earth
with his knife. My grandmother helped him, using the shoulder blade
as a white man does his shovel, removing the earth and piling it on the
cowskin, then carrying the load away and scattering it in the bottom of
the coulée. They worked and worked, cutting and digging, and scraping, until the hole was deep enough for my grandfather to stand in. His
eyes were even with the top of the ground, the fringe of the rye grass
still standing made a good screen. The foxes might scent him, but they
could not see him. 'Go home,' he said to my grandmother when they
had finished their work. 'Go home and make a sacrifice to the Sun and
pray that I may succeed in that which I have to do.'

"Then he got into the hole and stood very still, waiting, watching for
the little ones to come out. Long he waited. The sun seemed to travel
very slowly down toward the mountains. It was very hot. He became
thirsty. His legs ached, but he stood motionless as the ground itself,
always watching. A little while before sunset an old fox came out, and
walked halfway around the rye grass bunch. Then, suddenly, it scented
him, and ran swiftly away up the coulée. Soon afterward the little ones
came forth, one by one, slowly and lazily, yawning and stretching
themselves, blinking their eyes in the strong light. They began to play,
as they had done on the previous evening, and before long they
gathered in a scuffle at the edge of the rye grass. Then my grandfather
quickly reached out, and seized one by the back of the neck. 'Hai-yá,
little brother,' he cried, 'I have caught you.' Climbing out of the hole he

wrapped the cub in a fold of his robe and hurried to his lodge. He was happy. Four times his dream had spoken to him. On the fourth day he had fulfilled its command. He felt sure that in some way the taking of the fox was to be for his good.

"Puh'-po-kan—dream—my grandfather named the little animal. From the very beginning it had no fear of him, and soon made friends with the dogs of the lodge. The fox ate readily the bits of meat my grandfather gave it, and learned to drink water and soup. Grandfather forbade anyone to pet it, or feed it, or call it by name, so it was friendly only with him. It wanted to follow him wherever he went, and at night would crawl under the robes and sleep beside him. It was such a funny little one, always wanting to play with my grandfather or with the lodge dogs. When it was frightened by anything it would run to him, making short, gasping, hoarse little barks, just as we hear them at night out beyond the lodges. I did so want to play with it, take it up in my arms, and pet it, but always my mother would say, 'Don't you dare do it; it's a sacred one, and if you touch it something dreadful will happen to you. Perhaps you would go blind.'

"Not a mouse wandered in under the lodge-skin but Puh'-po-kan had found and killed it, and often he would bring home a bird or ground squirrel. When Puh'-po-kan had seen two winters, we were camping on the Little River, just north of the Bear's Paw Mountains. One night, after the lodge fires had all died out and everyone was asleep, Puh'-po-kan awoke my grandfather by backing up against his head and barking in a way it had when frightened. 'Stop that,' said my grandfather, reaching up and giving the little one a light slap. 'Stop barking and go to sleep.'

"But Puh'-po-kan would not stop. Instead he barked harder than ever, trembling because he was so excited. My grandfather raised up on his elbow and looked about. The moon was shining down through the smoke hole, so that he could make out the different objects in the lodge. Over by the doorway there was something that looked like a person crouching. 'Who are you?' he asked. 'What do you want here?'

"No answer.

"Then my grandfather spoke again: 'Tell me quickly who you are Get up and talk, or I will shoot you.'

"Still there was no answer. Puh'-po-kan kept on barking. My grandfather quietly reached out for his gun, which lay at the head of his bed, cocked it without noise, aimed and fired it. With a fearful scream a man sprang up and fell dead right in the hot ashes and coals of the fireplace, from which my grandfather quickly dragged him.

"A fire was quickly built and the light showed that the dead man was an enemy, a Sioux. He had no weapon except a long knife, still firmly gripped in his right hand. When the fox gave warning of his presence, he most likely thought that by remaining crouched on the ground he would not be discovered, and that those aroused would soon again fall asleep. He seemed to have come to the camp alone, for no trace of others could be found, no horses were stolen.

"All the talk in camp was about the fox, and my grandfather's dream. It was all great medicine. And my grandfather—how pleased he was! He made many sacrifices, prayed much, and loved Puh'-po-kan more than ever. Two more winters the little one lived, and then one summer night it was bitten by a rattlesnake and soon died. The women wrapped the swollen little body in robes and buried it on a scaffold they made in a cottonwood tree, just as if it had been a person."

I recinched our saddles. Nät-ah'-ki spread the remains of our lunch on a smooth flat stone. "Eat heartily, little brother," she said. We mounted and rode away, and looking back we saw the fox busily chewing a piece of meat.

Late in the afternoon we arrived in camp, which had been pitched near a small lake on the high plateau. The water was bad, but drinkable when made into tea. In the evening I was invited to a feast given by Big Lake. Rising Wolf was also a guest, along with a number of other staid and sober men. Young men seldom feasted and smoked with their elders, and in the camp were many coteries, or social sets, just as we find them in any civilized community, with the exception that there was no jealousy nor rivalry between them; no one of them felt that its members were in any way better than the members of another set.

We had smoked but one pipe, when a young man hurried in through the doorway, and said: "A war party of many men is near us."

"Ah!" all exclaimed, and then Big Lake: "Quick! tell us."

"I was hunting," said the young man, "and tied my horse to a bunch of sage while I crept up to a band of antelope. He got loose and ran away on his back trail and I started back afoot. At sundown I came to the top of a ridge and could see our camp, and over on another ridge near the Judith I saw at least fifty men. Saw them climb up and stand on its summit. They must have discovered our camp by the smoke from the lodge fires. I waited until it was dark, and hurried on. They will raid our horses tonight."

"Scatter out through camp, all of you," said Big Lake, quickly. "Tell the men to come here at once, warn the women not to scream or cry or run. Hurry!"

I went home and told Nät-ah'-ki the news, removed the cover of my rifle, and filled my coat pockets with cartridges. "Wait!" she said, grasping the barrel. "What are you going to do?"

"Why, Big Lake told us to meet at his lodge," I explained. "He has some good plan, I suppose."

"Yes, he is wise," she agreed, "but you are not going out there to be killed by a war party. Stay here with me."

"But our horses! I cannot remain here in the lodge and let the enemy run them off."

"They do not matter. Let them go."

"But," I said, "if I remained here people would call me a coward, they would say to you: 'Your white man has a woman's heart; why don't you make some dresses for him?'"

That ended the argument. She just sat down on the couch, covered her head with a shawl, and thus I left her.

Big Lake was a born tactician. In the few moments required to assemble the men he had thought out his plan of defense, and issued his orders in a few words. The various bands of the All Friends Society were told off into four groups, out to the north, south, east, and west of camp, and there they would await the arrival of the enemy. All others not of the society were to go with any one of the bands they chose. It was not feared that a war party would make an attack on the camp. They came, of course, to steal horses, and the plan was to go out where the herds were grazing and lie in wait. The really valuable animals were all tethered, as usual, near the lodges of their owners, and passing by the herds of common horses, the enemy would try to get in to them, cut their ropes and lead them away.

With the Crazy Dogs and Raven Carriers I moved out with thirty or forty others who, like myself, belonged to no organization. We spread out in a wide line, and after walking slowly and silently for about half a mile, word was passed to stop, whereupon we sat down in the cover of the sage and grease-wood brush. The moon was low in the western sky and due to set about midnight, so it was not very dark; we could see quite plainly the brush forty or fifty yards distant. The man nearest me on the right slowly crawled over and sat beside me.

"The night light is about to go out of sight," he whispered. "The war party will appear soon, if they come at all."

He spoke truly, for a little later we heard away out beyond a murmur of voices. Then there was silence, and then with soft tread and harsh swish of brush against their leggings, the raiders came into view, unsuspectingly advancing. Someone on my left fired first, and then the whole line shot an irregular volley. Sparks of the cheap black powder glowed and sparkled as they spouted from fuke and rifle into the darkness. The flashes blinded us for a moment, and when we could see again the enemy were running away. They had fired a number of shots in answer to ours, but as we afterward found, not one of their bullets had hit any of us.

Almost as one man our line sprang forward. Here were bodies, five of them, and one with life still in it. Thud went a war club and the recumbent figure sprawled out, face up, in the waning moonlight. In a trice the dead were scalped, their arms taken by those who came first to them. On sped our party, an occasional shot was fired at a dimly seen retreating figure. Behind us now came the three other divisions of the camp, shouting words of encouragement. But no enemy could be seen or heard, and our party stopped; it was useless to look further in the darkness.

Big Lake came up. "Spread out," he said, "spread out again and encircle the camp. Perhaps some of them are concealed in the brush closer in, and with daylight we will find them."

I shouldered my rifle and went home. Nät-ah'-ki was sitting up with her mother for company and I related all that had occurred.

"Why did you come back?" she asked, after I had finished. "Why didn't you stay out there with the rest as Big Lake ordered?"

"Hai-ya'!" I exclaimed. "How peculiar are women; one may not understand them. You begged me this evening to remain here with you. I came back because I am tired and hungry and sleepy, and now you are displeased because I returned. Well, to please you I'll go back and sit with the others until morning."

"Sit down, crazy man," she said, pushing me back on the couch from which I had started to rise. "You will stay right there. Here is your pipe; fill it and smoke while I broil some meat and make tea."

"You are the chief," I said to her, contentedly leaning back against a willow mat. "It shall be as you say."

Ode to a Nightingale

JOHN KEATS

≈ ≈ ≈

My heart aches, and a drowsy numbness pains
 My sense, as though of hemlock I had drunk,
Or emptied some dull opiate to the drains
 One minute past, and Lethe-wards had sunk:
'Tis not through envy of thy happy lot,
 But being too happy in thine happiness,—
  That thou, light-wingèd Dryad of the trees,
   In some melodious plot
 Of beechen green, and shadows numberless,
  Singest of summer in full-throated ease.

O for a draught of vintage! that hath been
 Cool'd a long age in the deep-delvèd earth,
Tasting of Flora and the country-green,
 Dance, and Provençal song, and sunburnt mirth!
O for a beaker full of the warm South,
 Full of the true, the blushful Hippocrene,
  With beaded bubbles winking at the brim,
   And purple-stained mouth;
 That I might drink, and leave the world unseen,
  And with thee fade away into the forest dim:

Fade far away, dissolve, and quite forget
 What thou among the leaves hast never known,
The weariness, the fever, and the fret
 Here, where men sit and hear each other groan;
Where palsy shakes a few, sad, last gray hairs,
 Where youth grows pale, and spectre-thin, and dies;
  Where but to think is to be full of sorrow
   And leaden-eyed despairs;

Where Beauty cannot keep her lustrous eyes,
    Or new Love pine at them beyond to-morrow.

Away! away! for I will fly to thee,
    Not charioted by Bacchus and his pards,
But on the viewless wings of Poesy,
    Though the dull brain perplexes and retards:
Already with thee! tender is the night,
    And haply the Queen-Moon is on her throne,
        Cluster'd around by all her starry Fays;
            But here there is no light,
    Save what from heaven is with the breezes blown
        Through verdurous glooms and winding mossy ways.

I cannot see what flowers are at my feet,
    Nor what soft incense hangs upon the boughs,
But, in embalmèd darkness, guess each sweet
    Wherewith the seasonable month endows
The grass, the thicket, and the fruit-tree wild;
    White hawthorn, and the pastoral eglantine;
        Fast fading violets cover'd up in leaves;
            And mid-May's eldest child,
    The coming musk-rose, full of dewy wine,
        The murmurous haunt of flies on summer eves.

Darkling I listen; and for many a time
    I have been half in love with easeful Death,
Call'd him soft names in many a mused rhyme,
    To take into the air my quiet breath;
Now more than ever seems it rich to die,
    To cease upon the midnight with no pain,
        While thou art pouring forth thy soul abroad
            In such an ecstasy!
    Still wouldst thou sing, and I have ears in vain—
        To thy high requiem become a sod.

Thou wast not born for death, immortal Bird!
    No hungry generations tread thee down;

The voice I hear this passing night was heard
  In ancient days by emperor and clown:
Perhaps the self-same song that found a path
    Through the sad heart of Ruth, when sick for home,
      She stood in tears amid the alien corn;
        The same that oft-times hath
    Charm'd magic casements, opening on the foam
      Of perilous seas, in faery lands forlorn.

Forlorn! the very word is like a bell
  To toll me back from thee to my sole self!
Adieu! the fancy cannot cheat so well
    As she is fam'd to do, deceiving elf.
Adieu! adieu! thy plaintive anthem fades
    Past the near meadows, over the still stream
      Up the hill-side; and now 'tis buried deep
        In the next valley-glades:
    Was it a vision, or a waking dream?
      Fled is that music:—do I wake or sleep?

Masai Spearmen:
The Bravest of the Brave

JOHN HUNTER

≈ ≈ ≈ *Lions are royal animals, but they are the enemies of the Masai tribesmen of East Africa, who hunt them to prove their courage and to protect their cattle. "Moran" means a Masai warrior, or a group of warriors. "Spoor" means animal tracks.* —*From* Hunter

I saw my first spear hunt when I was staying in a small Masai community not far from Lake Magadi. The night before, a lion had jumped the twelve-foot boma that surrounded the village, seized a cow, and leaped back over the barrier with the cow in his mouth. I know this feat sounds incredible, as the lion weighed no more than four hundred pounds and the cow probably weighed nearly twice that. Yet a male lion can perform this exploit with no more trouble than a fox has in carrying off a chicken.

A lion shows a special knack in getting partly under the carcass and shifting the weight onto his back while still holding the cow's throat in his mouth. When jumping the barricade, the lion's tail becomes absolutely rigid and seems to act as a balance. The Masai have assured me that a lion without a tail could not possible perform this feat.

I was prepared to start out on the lion's trail the next morning, but the moran in this community told me somewhat contemptuously that my help was not needed. They would handle the situation themselves. At that time, I found it hard to believe that a group of men could kill an adult lion with spears. I asked if I could go along and bring my gun. Permission was politely granted me. That night I loaded my .416 Rigby magazine rifle, never doubting that it would fall to my lot to kill any lions that we might find.

We started off at daybreak. I followed the spearmen. There were ten of them. Magnificent-looking men, slender but finely muscled, not one under six feet. To give their limbs free play, each man removed his one garment, the long piece of cloth they wear draped over their shoulders, and wrapped it around his left arm. They carried their brightly-painted shields balanced on their shoulders. Their spears were in their right hands. The warriors wore their ostrich-plume headdresses as though going into battle and bracelets of fur around their ankles. Otherwise, they were completely naked.

We picked up the spoor of the lion and the moran began to track. The lion had gorged on the cow during the night and was lying up in some dense cover. They threw stones into the bushes at random until the savage growls of the lion showed he had been hit: When the moran had spotted the cat by his angry grunts and snarls, they began to throw stones in good earnest; then the bushes began to shake. Suddenly the lion burst out a hundred yards from us and went bounding away across the plains, his gorged belly swinging from side to side as he ran.

Instantly the Masai were after him, giving their wild cries as they sped through the tall, yellow grass. The lion, still heavy with his great meal, did not run far. He stopped and turned at bay. The spearmen spread out to encircle him. The lion stood in the middle of the ring, looking this way and that, snarling in a way to make one's blood run cold as the spearmen slowly closed in.

The lion allowed the men to come within forty yards. Then I could tell that he was preparing to charge. His head was held low, just above his outstretched forepaws. His hindquarters were slightly arched so he could bring his rear legs well forward and get the maximum spring behind his rush. He began to dig his claws into the ground, much as a sprinter digs in with his spiked shoes to make sure he does not slip when he makes his first jump.

I concentrated on the sinister inverted curve of the lion's tail. Just before he charges, a lion always twitches the tasseled tip of his tail three times in rapid succession. On the third twitch he comes for you at amazing speed, going so fast he seems only a small part of his real size.

The spearmen knew as well as I did that the lion was preparing to attack. By what seemed to be a single impulse, all their spear arms moved back together for the cast. The men were so tense with excitement that their taut shoulder muscles twitched slightly, making ripples of sunlight play along the spear blades. You could have driven a nail into any one of them without his feeling it.

Suddenly the tip of the lion's tail began to twitch. One! Two! Three! Then he charged for the ring of spearmen. At once half a dozen spears leaped through the air toward him. I saw one plunge into his shoulder and the next instant the spear head broke through the hide on his other side. The lion never paused in his stride. In his path stood one of the moran, a youngster on his first hunt. The boy never flinched. He braced himself to meet the charge, holding his shield in front of him and swaying back slightly so as to put the whole weight of his body into his spear thrust. The lion sprang for the boy. With one blow he knocked the young moran's shield out of his hand as though it were cardboard. Then he reared up, trying to sweep the boy toward him with his outstretched paws.

The boy drove his spear a good two feet into the lion's chest. The mortally wounded beast sprang on him, fixing his hind claws in the boy's belly to insure his grip while at the same time he seized the boy's shoulders in his jaws.

The young warrior went down under the weight of the great cat. Instantly all the other moran were around the dying lion. It was too close quarters for spears. The men used their double-edged simis, heavy knives about two feet long. Shouldering each other out of the way, they hacked like madmen at the lion's head. In a matter of seconds, they had sliced the head to pieces, starting with the muzzle and shearing off an inch or so at a time. I saw one man deliver a terrible blow that split the lion's skull open, but whether the animal was still alive at the moment I can hardly say.

I had been quite unable to use my gun during this battle. A man with a gun is a positive menace at such times. Once the frenzied warriors began to circle the lion, a rifleman cannot fire without running a grave chance of hitting them.

I examined the wounded boy. His wounds were truly frightful yet he seemed completely indifferent to them. I sewed him up with a needle and thread. He paid no more attention to the process than if I were patting him on the back.

The hide of the lion was so perforated with spear thrusts and simi-slashes that it was worthless as a trophy. It was simply a cut and bloody mass of dirty yellow hair. The dignity and majesty of the noble beast had completely departed, leaving only a sorry remnant.

When we returned to the Masai manyatta or village, the wounded boy was urged to eat great quantities of raw beef and then given cattle blood as a purgative so he could gorge himself again. Some of the other moran had been clawed by the lion but they made no attempt to guard against infection, except to wash their wounds with water. Later I saw some Masai communities soak the root of a bush called the "olilorite" in water, which gives it a permanganate of potash color. It seems to act as an antiseptic and promotes healing.

I hope the lad recovered. He certainly held top honors for the day, and the young girls were looking at him with such admiration that, if he lived, he would have no trouble picking out a suitable sweetheart.

The Masai believe that the bravest act a man can perform is to grab a lion by the tail and hold the animal so the other warriors can close in with their spears and simis. Any man who performs this feat four times is given the title of "melombuki" and ranks as a captain. It is also an unwritten law among them that any man who gains this title must be willing to fight anything living. I doubt if more than two out of a thousand Masai ever become melombuki, although the competition among the moran to gain this honor is very keen.

I have seen several of these "tail pullings" during Masai lion hunts and it is a wonder to me that the men attempting the feat ever come out alive. I remember one hunt in which fifty or more spearmen were involved. They had put up two lions and a lioness. The animals tried to reach some heavy scrub but the warriors cut them off. The lions retreated into a small clump of bush near a dry, sandy watercourse. When possible, a pursued lion nearly always makes for one of these dry stream beds with its canopies of overhanging bush. In a matter of minutes, the moran had the thicket surrounded and began to move forward for the kill.

As the circle of yelling warriors closed in, the concealed lions began to growl. Then without any warning, the largest of the lions broke from the cover and made a rush for freedom. He was a fine sight as he dashed along the stream bottom, tail down and going all out at a gallop. He was headed straight for two moran, who raised their spears and prepared to meet his charge. But the big male had no desire to fight; he wished only to escape. He gave a mighty bound straight over the heads of the two spearmen, spinning one of them around sideways with a blow from his flank.

The other moran made tongue-clicking sounds of disapproval, partly because the two young men had allowed the lion to escape and partly because the lion had refused to fight. I have often noticed that the old lions with the finest manes are more reluctant to give battle than young males or females. The same is true of elephants. An old bull with fine ivory is shyer than a young bull or cow. I suppose they learn discretion with the years. It has also seemed to me that lions are able to tell young, inexperienced moran and will deliberately direct their attack at these youngsters. This may be nothing but my imagination yet the younger men are apt to be hesitant and uncertain in their actions and I believe the lions can detect it.

As the spearmen closed in around the thicket, they bunched together, jostling each other in their desire to be first to spill blood. The remaining two lions were clearly visible in the bush, standing shoulder to shoulder and both giving grating roars. When the moran were within ten yards of the lions, spears began to fly. One of the spears struck the lioness in the loin and she came out with a scream of rage and pain. For an instant she stood up on her hind legs, pawing the air like the crest on a coat of arms. Then she dropped to bite at the spear in her flank. At that moment, one of the moran threw down his spear and, rushing forward, grabbed her by the root of her tail. A moran never grabs a lion by the tasseled end of the tail. A lion can make his tail as stiff as a gun barrel, and a man would be swept aside by a single jerk.

At once the moran's comrades dashed in, slashing with their simis. At moments like this, the spearmen work themselves up to a pitch of blind frenzy. They seem to be mere automatic stabbers. Their faces are expressionless. There is no teamwork; each man is out to do the killing by himself. The lioness was digging her hind feet into the ground to get purchase forward and the tail puller was dragging her back. Suddenly the lioness went up on her hind legs, striking left and right with her paws at the men around her. Although I saw her blows go home, the men never flinched. They told me afterward that they never feel any pain at the time of a mauling—they are at too high a pitch of excitement. Apparently neither does the lion. Both sides continue to fight until one drops from loss of blood.

Slowly the lioness fell to the ground. Then all I could see were the flashing blades of the simis as the men hacked away in their blind fury. When it was over, the animal's head was cut into shreds. There must have been a dozen spears in the body. It looked like a bloody pincushion.

From the noise on the other side of the clump of bush, I knew another group of spearmen were busy with the second lion. I saw a warrior kneel and hold out his shield in a taunting fashion. The next instant the lion had leaped on it, knocking the man flat. The prone warrior tried vainly to get in a spear thrust while the lion mauled his exposed shoulder. I shouted to the other men to keep back and let me get in a shot, but nothing could be heard above the wild, falsetto yells of the warriors and the deep grunts of the lion as he lacerated the prostrate man. I saw two spears plunge into the lion's body and then the moran fell on the raging beast with their simis.

Before the lion was dead, he had seriously wounded one of the attacking moran besides ripping open the shoulder of the warrior lying under the shield. I did what I could for the injured men. They both had deep claw and fang incisions and were losing considerable blood. As I sewed up one man's injuries, he glanced down casually at the terrible cuts and made the same contemptuous clicking sound with his tongue that the moran had made when they saw the first lion escape. The warrior's attitude seemed to be "What a nuisance!" yet a white man in a similar situation would have been wild with pain.

Strangely enough, I have never heard of any bones being broken by the lion's teeth. The wounds are all flesh wounds. Apparently the lion's fang teeth are wide enough apart to close around the bones. Yet when a lion grabs a man by the shoulder, his fangs often meet in his victim's body. If you pour disinfectant into the one wound it will run out the other.

The spearmen have assured me that a lion's most dangerous weapon is neither his teeth nor his claws proper but what might be called his dewclaws. On the inside of each lion's forelegs is an extra claw about two inches long. These claws roughly correspond to a man's thumbs. They are curved and very sharp. The dewclaws are usually kept folded against the lion's legs and are difficult to see, but the lion can extend them at will so they stand out almost at right angles. These two claws are keen as brush hooks, and very strong. A lion slashes with them and can disembowel a man with one blow of these terrible hooks.

The Masai spears are made by native smiths from bits of iron ore picked up in the streams. The smiths do not understand the art of tempering the metal so the spears are soft. A man can easily bend the blade over his knee. But the moran are able to throw their weapons with such skill that the spear will sometimes pass completely through an animal. If the spear strikes a bone, it will bend almost at right angles. The owner never straightens the blade until he returns to the village. The bent spear is proof positive that he was in at the kill, and so is highly prized.

While I was in the reserve, I also saw the Masai spear leopards. I consider this an even greater feat than killing lions. Although a leopard does not weigh more than two hundred pounds, he is far quicker and more aggressive than a lion. Leopards are cunning beasts and will lie quietly until you are almost on top of them. Then they will suddenly charge with the deadliest speed and determination. Also, leopards lie up in caves and other dark recesses, while lions prefer the open bush. A man crawling among boulders after a leopard is in an unenviable position.

I accompanied three spearmen who were after a leopard that had been killing their goats. Unlike the noble lions, a leopard will kill for the sheer lust of killing. This cat had left several dead goats behind him, never even bothering to eat their flesh. After considerable track-ing, the moran finally marked the animal down in a narrow belt of high grass. If the cat had been a lion, a few stones would have brought him charging or at least forced him to growl and show his hiding place. But a leopard is a wily brute and, although we threw a bushel of stones into the grass, he gave no sign. Unfortunately, I did not have my dogs with me so there was nothing for it but to drive the animal out.

With only three spearmen, I was able to use my gun without fear of hitting one of the men. I told the moran to spread out on either side of me and keep well back. I knew when the leopard came, he would come fast. I was sure that the men would not have time to use their spears, and I would have scarcely time for a quick snap shot at the cat as he sprang. I was underrating the moran, but I still did not realize their marvelous skill with their long, delicate blades.

We moved slowly through the waist-high grass, much as though beating for pheasants. The moran kept a few paces behind me, their shields held before them and their spears raised for the cast. We moved forward a foot at a time, stopping constantly to look around for the big cat. The strip of grass was not long, but this slow progress was nerve-racking, especially as we were all at a high point of tension.

Suddenly the leopard exploded out of the grass a yard or so in front of me and to my right. He made a great bound for me. Before I could get my rifle up, the moran on my right had transfixed the beast with his spear. The leopard had scarcely left the ground before the thin blade was through him. The spear hit the leopard between the neck and shoulders, pinning him to the ground. He lay there squirming and snarling, unable to free himself. Immediately the moran drew his simi and leaped forward to finish him off. I had great difficulty restraining him until I had time to put a bullet into the skewered animal and save a good skin from being slashed to ribbons.

When a moran is about to throw his spear, he takes up a position just like a shooting stance with his left foot slightly advanced for balance. When he throws, the whole weight of his body goes into the cast. The spear seems to shiver as it flies through the air. Most of the spears have a narrow ridge on either side of the blade and I believe this may cause the spear to rotate slightly in flight, somewhat like a rifle bullet. A moran is absolutely accurate with his spear up to twenty yards, even when throwing at a moving target.

At the end of three months, I started back to Nairobi with two ox-carts full of lion hides. In ninety days, I had shot eighty-eight lions and ten leopards—a record which I believe has never been approached and, I sincerely hope, will never be approached again. The natives had filled a hundred-weight drum with lion fat. I had a box full of lion "floating bones." These curved bones vary in size up to four inches and are found in the last shoulder muscle tissue. They are not attached to any other bones in the lion's body and apparently act as regulators, preventing shoulder rack when the lions make their great bounds. They are much in demand among the East Indians, who set them in gold and make ornaments out of them.

Only twenty of the lions I killed had really prime manes. The rest were either lionesses or had manes ruined by the thick brush. If I had been shooting only to get good trophies, I could have obtained more first-rate hides, but I was more interested in destroying cattle killers. Often these beasts had poor manes, for they were old or diseased, which may well be why they had turned to killing cows instead of their natural prey.

When the Masai heard I was leaving, they were greatly distressed. The elders of the tribe assembled and, after much jabbering, came to me with a proposition. They wanted to buy me from the Game Department. After due consideration, they had settled on five hundred cows as the price. As a good wife costs only three cows, I felt highly flattered.

Epitaph on a Jacobite

LORD MACAULAY

≈ ≈ ≈ *The Jacobites were loyal supporters of the exiled Stuart kings of England. After the Revolution of 1688, in which James II, the last Stuart king, was driven from England, the Jacobites either kept their politics secret in England or fled to France and Italy.*

To my true king I offered free from stain
Courage and faith; vain faith, and courage vain.
For him, I threw lands, honours, wealth, away,
And one dear hope, that was more prized than they.
For him I languished in a foreign clime,
Grey-haired with sorrow in my manhood's prime;
Heard on Lavernia Scargill's whispering trees,
And pined by Arno for my lovelier Tees;
Beheld each night my home in fevered sleep,
Each morning started from the dream to weep;
Till God, who saw me tried too sorely, gave
The resting place I asked, an early grave.
Oh thou, whom chance leads to this nameless stone,
From that proud country which was once mine own,
By those white cliffs I never more must see,
By that dear language which I spake like thee,
Forget all feuds, and shed one English tear
O'er English dust. A broken heart lies here.

King Dingaan's Bet

H. RIDER HAGGARD

≈ ≈ ≈ *Deep in the South African wilderness, 125 years ago, Dingaan, king of the warrior Zulu tribe, planned to murder a small band of Boers, pioneers of Dutch descent. Allan Quatermain was a young English hunter engaged to marry one of the Boer girls. Hans was his Hottentot servant.* —From Marie

Dingaan wished to see me. So taking with me the Hottentot Hans and two of the Zulus whom I had hired at Delagoa Bay—for the royal orders were that none of the other white people were to come, I was led through the fence of the vast town in which stood two thousand huts—the "multitude of houses" as the Zulus called it—and across a vast open space in the middle.

On the farther side of this space, where, before long, I was fated to witness a very tragic scene, I entered a kind of labyrinth. This was called *siklohlo,* and had high fences with numerous turns, so that it was impossible to see where one was going or to find the way in or out. Ultimately, however, I reached a great hut named *intunkulu,* a word that means the "house of houses" or the abode of the king, in front of which I saw a fat man seated on a stool, naked except for the *moocha* about his middle and necklaces and armlets of blue beads. Two warriors held their broad shields over this head to protect him from the sun. Otherwise he was alone, although I felt sure that the numerous passages around him were filled with guards, for I could hear them moving.

On entering this place Kambula and his companions flung themselves upon their faces and began to sing praises of which the king took no notice. Presently he looked up, and appearing to observe me for the first time asked:

"Who is that white boy?"

Then Kambula rose and said:

"O king, this is the Son of George, whom you commanded me to capture. I have taken him and the *Amaboona*" (that is, the Boers), "his companions, and brought them all to you, O king."

"I remember," said Dingaan. "The big Boer who was here, and whom Tambusa"—he was one of Dingaan's captains—"let go against my will, said that he was a terrible man who should be killed before he worked great harm to my people. Why did you not kill him, Kambula, although it is true he does not look very terrible?"

"Because the king's word was that I should bring him to the king living," answered Kambula. Then he added cheerfully: "Still, if the king wishes it, I can kill him at once."

"I don't know," said Dingaan doubtfully; "perhaps he can mend guns." Next, after reflecting a while, he bade a shield-holder to fetch someone, I could not hear whom.

"Doubtless," thought I to myself, "it is the executioner," and at that thought a kind of mad rage seized me. "Why should my life be ended thus in youth to satisfy the whim of a savage? And if it must be so, why should I go alone?"

In the inside pocket of my ragged coat I had a small loaded pistol with two barrels. One of those barrels would kill Dingaan—at five paces I could not miss that bulk—and the other would blow out my brains, for I was not minded to have my neck twisted or to be beaten to death with sticks. Well, if it was to be done, I had better do it at once. Already my hand was creeping towards the pocket when a new idea, or rather two ideas, struck me.

The first was that if I shot Dingaan the Zulus would probably massacre Marie and the others—Marie, whose sweet face I should never see again. The second was that while there is life there is hope. Perhaps, after all, he had not sent for an executioner, but for someone else. I would wait. A few minutes more of existence were worth the having.

The shield-bearer returned, emerging from one of the narrow reed-hedged passages, and after him came no executioner, but a young white man, who, as I knew from the look of him, was English. He saluted the king by taking off his hat, which I remember was stuck round with black ostrich feathers, then stared at me.

"O Tho-maas" (that is how he pronounced "Thomas"), said Dingaan, "tell me if this boy is one of your brothers, or is he a Boer?"

"The king wants to know if you are Dutch or British," said the white lad, speaking in English.

"As British as you are," I answered. "I was born in England, and come from the Cape."

"That may be lucky for you," he said, "because the old witch-doctor, Zikali, has told him that he must not kill any English. What is your name? Mine is Thomas Halstead. I am interpreter here."

"Allan Quatermain. Tell Zikali, whoever he may be, that if he sticks to his advice I will give him a good present."

"What are you talking about?" asked Dingaan suspiciously.

"He says he is English, no Boer, O king; that he was born across the Black Water, and that he comes from the country out of which all the Boer have trekked."

At this intelligence Dingaan pricked up his ears.

"Then he can tell me about these Boers," he said, "and what they are after, or could if he were able to speak my tongue. I do not trust you to interpret, you Tho-maas, whom I know to be a liar," and he glowered at Halstead.

"I can speak your tongue, though not very well, O king," I interrupted, "and I can tell you all about the Boers, for I have lived among them."

"*Ow!*" said Dingaan, intensely interested. "But perhaps you are also a liar. Or are you a praying man, like that fool yonder, who is named Oweena?"—he meant the missionary Mr. Owens—"Whom I spare because it is not lucky to kill one who is mad, although he tries to frighten my soldiers with tales of a fire into which they will go after they are dead. As though it matters what happens to them after they are dead!" he added reflectively, taking a pinch of snuff.

"I am no liar," I answered. "What have I to lie about?"

"You would lie to save your own life, for all white men are cowards; not like the Zulus, who love to die for their king. But how are you named?"

"Your people call me Macumazahn."

"Well, Macumazahn, if you are no liar, tell me, is it true that these Boers rebelled against their king who was named George, and fled from him as the traitor Umsilikazi did from me?"

"Yes," I answered, "that is true."

"Now I am sure that you are a liar," said Dingaan triumphantly. "You say that you are English and therefore serve your king, or the *Inkosikaas*" (that is the Great Lady), "who they tell me now sits in his place. How does it come about then that you are travelling with a party of these very *Amaboona* who must be your enemies, since they are the enemies of your king, or of her who follows after him?"

Now I knew that I was in a tight place, for on this matter of loyalty, Zulu, and indeed all native ideas, are very primitive. If I said that I had sympathy with the Boers Dingaan would set me down as a traitor. If I said that I hated the Boers, then still I should be a traitor because I associated with them, and a traitor in his eyes would be one to be killed. I do not like to talk religion, and anyone who has read what I have written in various works will admit that I have done so rarely, if ever. Yet at that moment I put up a prayer for guidance, feeling that my young life hung upon the answer, and it came to me—whence I do not know. The essence of that guidance was that I should tell the simple truth to this fat savage. So I said to him:

"The answer is this, O king. Among these Boers is a maiden whom I love and who betrothed herself to me since we were 'so high.' Her father took her north. But she sent a message to me saying that her people died of fever and she starved. So I went up in a ship to save her, and have saved her, and those who remained alive of her people with her."

"*Ow!*" said Dingaan; "I understand that reason. It is a good reason. However many wives he may have, there is no folly that a man will not commit for the sake of some particular girl who is not yet his wife. I have done as much myself, especially for one who was called Nada the Lily, of whom a certain Umslopogaas robbed me, one of my own blood of whom I am much afraid." *

For a while he brooded heavily, then went on:

"Your reason is good, Macumazahn, and I accept it. More, I promise you this. Perhaps I shall kill these Boers, or perhaps I shall not kill them. But if I make up my mind to kill them, this girl of yours shall be spared. Point her out to Kambula here—not to Tho-maas, for he is a liar and would tell me the wrong one—and she shall be spared."

"I thank you, O king," I said; "but what is the use of that if I am to be killed?"

"I did not say that you were to be killed, Macumazahn, though perhaps I shall kill you, or perhaps I shall not kill you. It depends upon whether I find you to be a liar, or not a liar. Now the Boer whom Tambusa let go against my wish said that you are a mighty magician as

* See the Author's book named *Nada the Lily*.

well as a very dangerous man, one who can shoot birds flying on the wing with a bullet, which is impossible. Can you do so?"

"Sometimes," I answered.

"Very good, Macumazahn. Now we will see if you are a wizard or a liar. I will make a bet with you. Yonder by your camp is a hill called 'Hloma Amabutu,' a hill of stones where evildoers are slain. This afternoon some wicked ones die there, and when they are dead the vultures will come to devour them. Now this is my bet with you. When those vultures come you shall shoot at them, and if you kill three out of the first five on the wing—not on the ground, Macumazahn—then I will spare these Boers. But if you miss them, then I shall know that you are a liar and no wizard, and I will kill them every one on the hill Hloma Amabutu. I will spare none of them except the girl, whom perhaps I will take as a wife. As to you, I will not yet say what I will do with you."

Now my first impulse was to refuse this monstrous wager, which meant the lives of a number of people were to be set against my skill in shooting. But young Thomas Halstead, guessing the words that were about to break from me, said in English:

"Accept unless you are a fool. If you don't he will cut the throats of every one of them and stick your girl into the *emposeni*" (that is, harem), "while you will become a prisoner as I am."

These were words that I could not resent or neglect, so although despair was in my heart, I said coolly:

"Be it so, O king. I take your wager. If I kill three vultures out of five as they hover over the hill, then I have your promise that all those who travel with me shall be allowed to go hence in safety."

"Yes, yes, Macumazahn; but if you fail to kill them, remember that the next vultures you shoot at shall be those that come to feed upon their flesh, for then I shall know that you are no magician, but a common liar. And now begone, Tho-maas. I will not have you spying on me; and you, Macumazahn, come hither. Although you talk my tongue so badly, I would speak with you about the Boers."

So Halstead went, shrugging his shoulders and muttering as he passed me:

"I hope you really *can* shoot."

After he had left I sat alone for a full hour with Dingaan, while he cross-examined me about the Dutch, their movements and their aims in travelling to the confines of his country.

I answered his questions as best I could, trying to make out a good case for them.

At length, when he grew weary of talking, he clapped his hands, whereupon a number of fine girls appeared, two of whom carried pots of beer, from which he offered me drink.

I replied that I would have none, since beer made the hand shake and that on the steadiness of my hand that afternoon depended the lives of so many. To do him justice he quite understood the point. Indeed, he ordered me to be conducted back to camp at once that I might rest, and even sent one of his own attendants with me to hold a shield over my head as I walked so that I should be protected from the sun.

"*Hamba gachlé*" (that is, "Go softly"), said the wicked old tyrant to me as I departed under the guidance of Kambula. "This afternoon, one hour before sundown, I will meet you at Hloma Amabutu, and there shall be settled the fate of these *Amaboona,* your companions."

When I reached the camp it was to find all the Boers clustered together waiting for me, and with them the Reverend Mr. Owen, and his people, including a Welsh servant of his, a woman of middle age who, I remember, was called Jane.

"Well," said the Vrouw Prinsloo, "and what is your news, young man?"

"My news, aunt," I answered, "is that one hour before sundown today I have to shoot vultures on the wing against the lives of all of you. This you owe to that false-hearted hound Hernan Pereira, who told Dingaan that I am a magician. Now Dingaan would prove it. He thinks that only by magic can a man shoot soaring vultures with a bullet, and as he is determined to kill you all, except perhaps Marie, in the form of a bet he has set me a task which he believes to be impossible. If I fail, the bet is lost, and so are your lives. If I succeed I think your lives will be spared, since Kambula there tells me that the king always makes it a point of honour to pay his bets. Now you have the truth, and I hope you like it," and I laughed bitterly.

When I had finished a perfect storm of execration broke from the Boers. If curses could have killed Pereira, surely he would have died upon the spot, wherever he might be. Only two of them were silent, Marie, who turned very pale, poor girl, and her father. Presently one of them, I think it was Meyer, rounded on him viciously and asked him what he thought now of that devil, his nephew.

"I think there must be some mistake," answered Marais quietly, "since Hernan cannot have wished that we should all be put to death."

"No," shouted Meyer; "but he wished that Allan Quatermain should, which is just as bad; and now it has come about that once more our lives depend upon this English boy."

"At any rate," replied Marais, looking at me oddly, "it seems that he is not to be killed, whether he shoots the vultures or misses them."

"That remains to be proved, mynheer," I answered hotly, for the insinuation stung me. "But please understand that if all of you, my companions, are to be slaughtered, and Marie is to be put among this black brute's women, as he threatens, I have no wish to live on."

"My God! does he threaten that?" said Marais. "Surely you must have misunderstood him, Allan."

"Do you think that I should lie to you on such a matter—" I began.

But, before I could proceed, the Vrouw Prinsloo thrust herself between us, crying:

"Be silent, you, Marais, and you too, Allan. Is this a time that you should quarrel and upset yourself, Allan, so that when the trial comes you will shoot your worst and not your best? And is this a time, Henri Marais, that you should throw insults at one on whom our lives hang, instead of praying for God's vengeance upon your accursed nephew? Come, Allan, and take food. I have fried the liver of that heifer which the king sent us; it is ready and very good. After you have eaten it you must lie down and sleep a while."

Now among the household of the Reverend Mr. Owen was an English boy called William Wood, who was not more than twelve or fourteen years of age. This lad knew both Dutch and Zulu, and acted as interpreter to the Owen family during the absence on a journey of a certain Mr. Hulley, who really filled that office. While this conversation was taking place in Dutch he was engaged in rendering every word of it into English for the benefit of the clergyman and his family. When Mr. Owen understood the full terror of the situation, he broke in saying:

"This is not a time to eat or to sleep, but a time to pray that the heart of the savage Dingaan may be turned. Come, let us pray!"

"Yes," rejoined Vrouw Prinsloo, when William Wood translated. "Do you pray, *Predicant,* and while you are about it pray also that the bullets of Allan Quatermain may not be turned. As for me and Allan, we have other things to see to, so you must pray a little harder to cover us as well as yourselves. Now you come along, nephew Allan, or that liver may be overdone and give you indigestion, which is worse for shooting than even bad temper. No, not another word. If you try to speak any more, Henri Marais, I will box your ears," and she lifted a hand like a leg of mutton, then, as Marais retreated before her, seized me by the collar as though I were a naughty boy and led me away to the wagons.

By the women's wagon we found the liver cooked in its frying-pan, as the vrouw had said. Indeed, it was just done to a turn. Selecting a particularly massive slice, she proceeded to take it from the pan with her fingers in order to set it upon a piece of tin, from which she had first removed the more evident traces of the morning meal, with her constant companion, the ancient and unwashen *vatdoek*. As it chanced the effort was not very successful, since the boiling liver fat burnt the vrouw's fingers, causing her to drop it on the grass, and, I am sorry to add, to swear as well. Not to be defeated, however, having first sucked her fingers to ease their smart, she seized the sizzling liver with the *vatdoek* and deposited it upon the dirty tin.

"There, nephew," she said triumphantly, "there are more ways of killing a cat than by drowning. What a fool I was not to think of the *vatdoek* at first. Allemachte! how the flesh has burnt me; I don't suppose that being killed would hurt much more. Also, if the worst comes to the worst, it will soon be over. Think of it, Allan, by to-night I may be an angel, dressed in a long white nightgown like those my mother gave me when I was married, which I cut up for baby-clothes because I found them chilly wear, having always been accustomed to sleep in my vest and petticoat. Yes, and I shall have wings, too, like those on a white gander, only bigger if they are to carry *my* weight."

"And a crown of Glory," I suggested.

"Yes, of course, a crown of Glory—very large, since I shall be a martyr; but I hope one will only have to wear it on Sundays, as I never could bear anything heavy on my hair; moreover, it would remind me of a Kaffir's head-ring done in gold, and I shall have had enough of Kaffirs. Then there will be the harp," she went on as her imagination took fire at the prospect of these celestial delights. "Have you ever seen a harp, Allan? I haven't, except that which King David carries in the picture in the Book, which looks like a broken *rimpi* chair frame set up edgeways. As for playing the thing, they will have to teach me, that's all, which will be a difficult business, seing that I would sooner listen to cats on the roof than to music, and as for making it—"

So she chattered on, as I believe with the object of diverting and amusing me, for she was a shrewd old soul who knew how important it was that I should be kept in an equable frame of mind at this crisis in our fates.

Meanwhile I was doing my best with the lump of liver, that tasted painfully of *vatdoek* and was gritty with sand. Indeed, when the vrouw's back was turned I managed to throw most of it to Hans behind me, who swallowed it at a gulp as a dog does, since he did not wish to be caught chewing it.

"God in heaven! how fast you eat, nephew," said the vrouw, catching sight of my empty tin. Then, eyeing the voracious Hottentot suspiciously, she added: "That yellow dog of yours hasn't stolen it, has he? If so, I'll teach him."

"No, no, vrouw," answered Hans in alarm. "No meat has passed my lips this day, except what I licked out of the pan before breakfast."

"Then, Allan, you will certainly have indigestion, which is just what I wanted to avoid. Have I not often told you that you should chew your bit twenty times before you swallow, which I would do myself if I had any back teeth left? Here, drink this milk; it is only a little sour and will settle your stomach," and she produced a black bottle and subjected it to the attentions of the *vatdoek*, growing quite angry when I declined it and sent for water.

Next she insisted upon my getting into her own bed in the wagon to sleep, forbidding me to smoke, which she said made the hand shake. Thither, then I went, after a brief conversation with Hans, whom I directed to clean my rifle thoroughly. For I wished to be alone and knew that I had little chance of solitude outside of that somewhat fusty couch.

To tell the truth, although I shut my eyes to deceive the vrouw, who looked in occasionally to see how I was getting on, no sleep came to me that afternoon—at least, not for a long while. How could I sleep in that hot place when my heart was torn with doubt and terror? Think of it, reader, think of it! An hour or two, on my skill would hang the lives of eight white people—men, women, and children, and the safety or the utter shame of the woman whom I loved and who loved me. No, she should be spared the worst. I would give her my pistol, and if there were need she would know what to do.

The fearful responsibility was more than I could bear. I fell into a veritable agony; I trembled and even wept a little. Then I thought of my father and what he would do in such circumstances, and began to pray as I had never prayed before.

I implored the Power above me to give me strength and wisdom; not to let me fail in this hour of trouble, and thereby bring these poor people to a bloody death. I prayed till the perspiration streamed down my face; then suddenly I fell into sleep or swoon. I don't know how long I lay thus, but I think it must have been the best part of an hour. At last I woke up all in an instant, and as I woke I distinctly heard a tiny voice, unlike any other voice in the whole world, speak inside my head, or so it seemed to me, saying:

"Go to the hill Hloma Amabutu, and watch how the vultures fly. Do what comes into your mind, and even if you seem to fail, fear nothing."

I sat up on the old vrouw's bed, and felt that some mysterious change had come over me. I was no longer the same man. My doubts and terrors had gone; my hand was like a rock; my heart was light. I knew that I should kill those three vultures. Of course the story seems absurd, and easy to be explained by the state of my nerves under the strain which was being put upon them, and for aught I know that may be its true meaning. Yet I am not ashamed to confess that I have always held, and still hold, otherwise. I believe that in my extremity some kindly Power did speak to me in answer to my earnest prayers and to those of others, giving me guidance and, what I needed still more, judgment and calmness. At any rate, that this was my conviction at the moment may be seen from the fact that I hastened to obey the teachings of that tiny, unnatural voice.

Climbing out of the wagon, I went to Hans, who was seated near by in the full glare of the hot sun, at which he seemed to stare with unblinking eyes.

"Where's the rifle, Hans?" I said.

"*Intombi* is here, baas, where I have put her to keep her cool, so that she may not go off before it is wanted," and he pointed to a little grave-like heap of gathered grass at his side.

The natives, I should explain, named this particular gun *Intombi*, which means a young girl, because it was so much slimmer and more graceful than other guns.

"Is it clean?" I asked.

"Never was she cleaner since she was born out of the fire, baas. Also, the powder has been sifted and set to dry in the sun with the caps, and the bullets have been trued to the barrel, so that there may be no accidents when it comes to the shooting. If you miss the *aasvogels*, baas, it will not be the fault of *Intombi* or of the powder and the bullets; it will be your own fault."

"That's comforting," I answered. "Well, come on, I want to go to the Death-hill yonder."

"Why, baas, before the time?" asked the Hottentot, shrinking back a little. "It is no place to visit till one is obliged. These Zulus say that ghosts sit there even in the daylight, haunting the rocks where they were made ghosts."

"Vultures sit or fly there, also, Hans; and I would see how they fly, that I may know when and where to shoot at them."

"That is right, baas," said the clever Hottentot. "This is not like firing at geese in the Groot Kloof. The geese go straight, like an assegai to its mark. But the *aasvogels* wheel round and round, always on the turn; it is easy to miss a bird that is turning, baas."

"Very easy. Come on."

Just as we were starting Vrouw Prinsloo appeared from behind the other wagon, and with her Marie, who I noticed, was very pale and whose beautiful eyes were red, as though with weeping.

The vrouw asked me where we were going. I told her. After considering a little, she said that was a good thought of mine, as it was always well to study the ground before a battle.

I nodded, and led Marie aside behind some thorn trees that grew near.

"Oh! Allan, what will be the end of this?" she asked piteously. High as was her courage it seemed to fail her now.

"A good end, dearest," I answered. "We shall come out of this hole safely, as we have of many others."

"How do you know that, Allan, which is known to God alone?"

"Because God told me, Marie," and I repeated to her the story of the voice I had heard in my dream, which seemed to comfort her.

"Yet, yet," she exclaimed doubtfully, "it was but a dream, Allan, and dreams are such uncertain things. You may fail, after all."

"Do I look like one who will fail, Marie?"

She studied me from head to foot, then answered:

"No, you do not, although you did when you came back from the king's huts. Now you are quite changed. Still, Allan, you may fail, and then—what? Some of those dreadful Zulus have been here while you were sleeping, bidding us all make ready to go to the Hill of Death. They say that Dingaan is in earnest. It seems that they are sacred birds, and if they escape he will think he has nothing to fear from the white men and their magic, and so will make a beginning by butchering us. I mean the rest of us, for I am to be kept alive, and oh! what shall I do, Allan?"

I looked at her, and she looked at me. Then I took the double-barrelled pistol out of my pocket and gave it to her.

"It is loaded and on the half-cock," I said.

She nodded, and hid it in her dress beneath her apron. Then without more words we kissed and parted, for both of us feared to prolong that scene.

The hill Hloma Amabutu was quite close to our encampment and the huts of the Reverend Mr. Owen, scarcely a quarter of a mile off, I should say, rising from the flat veld on the further side of a little depression that hardly amounted to a valley. As we approached it I noticed its peculiar and blasted appearance, for whereas all around the grass was vivid with the green of spring, on this place none seemed to grow. An eminence strewn with tumbled heaps of blackish rock, and among them a few struggling dark-leaved bushes; that was its appearance. Moreover, many of these boulders looked as though they had been splashed and lined with whitewash, showing that they were the resting place of hundreds of gorged vultures.

I believe it is the Chinese who declare that particular localities have good or evil influences attached to them, some kind of spirit of their own, and really Hloma Amabuta and a few other spots that I am acquainted with in Africa give colour to the fancy. Certainly as I set foot upon that accursed ground, that Golgotha, that Place of Skulls, a shiver went through me. It may have been caused by the atmosphere, moral and actual, of the mount, or it may have been a prescience of a certain dreadful scene which within a few months I was doomed to witness there. Or perhaps the place itself and the knowledge of the trial before me sent a sudden chill through my healthy blood. I cannot say which it was, but the fact remains as I have stated, although a minute or two later, when I saw what kind of sleepers lay upon that mount, it would not have been necessary for me to seek any far-fetched explanation of my fear.

Across this hill, winding in and out between the rough rocks that lay here, there and everywhere like hailstones after a winter storm, ran sundry paths. It seems that the shortest road to various places in the neighbourhood of the Great Kraal ran over it, and although no Zulu ever dared to set foot there between sun-set and rise, in the daytime they used these paths freely enough. But I suppose that they also held that this evil-omened field of death had some spirit of its own, some invisible but imminent fiend, who needed to be propitiated, lest soon he should claim them also.

This was their method of propitiation, a common one enough, I believe, in many lands, though what may be its meaning I cannot tell. As the traveller came to those spots where the paths cut across each other, he took a stone and threw it on to a heap that had been accumulated there by the hands of other travellers. There were many such heaps upon the hill, over a dozen, I think, and the size of them was great. I should say that the biggest contained quite fifty loads of stones, and the smallest not fewer than twenty or thirty.

Now, Hans, although he had never set foot there before, seemed to have learned all the traditions of the place, and what rites were necessary to avert its curse. At any rate, when we came to the first heap, he cast a stone upon it, and begged me to do the same. I laughed and refused, but when we reached the second heap the same thing happened. Again I refused, whereon, before we came to a third and larger pile, Hans sat down upon the ground and began to groan, swearing that he would not go one step farther unless I promised to make the accustomed offering.

"Why not, you fool?" I asked.

"Because if you neglect, it, baas, I think that we shall stop here forever. Oh! You may laugh, but I tell you that already you have brought ill-luck upon yourself. Remember my words, baas, when you miss two of the five *aasvogels.*"

"Bosh!" I exclaimed, or, rather, its Dutch equivalent. Still, as this talk of missing vultures touched me nearly, and it is always as well to conform to native prejudices, at the next and two subsequent heaps I cast my stone as humbly as the most superstitious Zulu in the land.

By this time we had reached the summit, which may have been two hundred yards long. It was hog-backed in shape, with a kind of depression in the middle cleared of stones, either by the hand of man or nature, and not unlike a large circus in its general conformation.

Oh! the sight that met my eyes. All about lay the picked and scattered bones of men and women, many of them broken up by the jaws of hyenas. Some were quite fresh, for the hair still clung to the skulls, others blanched and old. But new or ancient there must have been hundreds of them. Moreover, on the sides of the hill it was the same story, though there, for the most part, the bones had been gathered into gleaming heaps. No wonder that the vultures loved Hloma Amabutu, the Place of Slaughter of the bloody Zulu king.

Of these horrible birds, however, at the moment not one was to be seen. As there had been no execution for a few hours they were seeking their food elsewhere. Now, for my own purposes, I wanted to see them, since otherwise my visit was in vain, and presently bethought myself of a method of securing their arrival.

"Hans," I said, "I am going to pretend to kill you, and then you must lie quite still out there like one dead. Even if the *aasvogels* settle on you, you must lie quite still, so that I may see whence they come and how they settle."

The Hottentot did not take at all kindly to this suggestion. Indeed, he flatly refused to obey me, giving sundry good reasons. He said that this kind of rehearsal was ill-omened; that coming events have a way of casting their shadow before, and he did not wish to furnish the event. He said that the Zulus declared that the sacred *aasvogels* of Hloma Amabutu were as savage as lions, and that when once they saw a man down they would tear him to pieces, dead or living. In short, Hans and I came to an acute difference of opinion. As for every reason it was necessary that my view should prevail, however, I did not hesitate to put matters to him very plainly.

"Hans," I said, "you have to be a bait for vultures; choose if you will be a live bait or a dead bait," and I cocked the rifle significantly, although, in truth, the last thing that I wished or intended to do was to shoot my faithful old Hottentot friend. But Hans, knowing all I had at stake, came to a different conclusion.

"Allemachte! baas," he said, "I understand, and I do not blame you. Well, if I obey alive, perhaps my guardian Snake" (or spirit) "will protect me from the evil omen, and perhaps the *aasvogels* will not pick out my eyes. But if once you send a bullet through my stomach—why, then everything is finished and for Hans it is 'Good night, sleep well.' I will obey you, baas, and lie where you wish, only, I pray you, do not forget me and go away, leaving me with those devil birds."

I promised him faithfully that I would not. Then we went through a very grim little pantomime. Proceeding to the centre of the arena-like space, I lifted the gun, and appeared to dash out Hans' brains with its butt. He fell upon his back, kicked about a little, and lay still. This finished Act 1.

Act 2 was that, capering like a brute of a Zulu executioner, I retired from my victim and hid myself in a bush on the edge of the plateau at a distance of forty yards. After this there was a pause. The place was intensely bright with sunshine and intensely silent; as silent as the skeletons of the murdered men about me; as silent as Hans, who lay there looking so very small and dead in that big theatre where no grass grew. It was an eerie wait in such surroundings, but at length the curtain rang up for Act 3.

In the infinite arch of blue above me I perceived a speck no larger than a mote of dust. The *aasvogel* on watch up there far out of range of man's vision had seen the deed, and, by sinking downwards, sig-nalled it to his companions that were quartering the sky for fifty miles around; for these birds prey by sight, not by smell. Down he came and down, and long before he had reached the neighbourhood of earth other specks appeared in the distant blue. Now he was not more than four or five hundred yards above me, and began to wheel, floating round the place upon his wide wings, and sinking as he wheeled. So he sank softly and slowly until he was about a hundred and fifty feet above Hans. Then suddenly he paused, hung quite steady for a few seconds, shut his wings and fell like a bolt, only opening them again just before he reached the earth.

Here he settled, tilting forward in that odd way which vultures have, and scrambling a few awkward paces until he gained his balance. Then he froze into immobility, gazing with an awful stony stare at the prostrate Hans, who lay within about fifteen feet of him. Scarcely was this *aasvogel* down, when others, summoned from the depths of sky, did as he had done. They appeared, they sank, they wheeled, always from east to west, the way the sun travels. They hovered for a few seconds, then fell like stones, pitched on to their beaks, recovered themselves, waddled forward into line, and sat gazing at Hans. Soon there was a great ring of them about him, all immovable, all gazing, all waiting for something.

Presently that something appeared in the shape of an *aasvogel* which was nearly twice as big as any of the others. This was what the Boers and the natives call the "king vulture," one of which goes with every flock. He it is who rules the roost and also the carcase, which without his presence and permission none dare to attack. Whether this vile fowl is of a different species from the others, or whether he is a bird of more vigorous growth and constitution that has outgrown the rest and thus become their overlord, is more than I can tell. At least it is certain, as I can testify from long and constant observation, that almost every flock of vultures has its king.

When this particular royalty had arrived, the other *aasvogels,* of which perhaps there were now fifty or sixty gathered round Hans, began to show signs of interested animation. They looked at the king bird, they looked at Hans, stretching out their naked red necks and winking their brilliant eyes. I, however, did not pay particular attention to those upon the earth, being amply occupied in watching their fellows in the air.

With delight I observed that the vulture is a very conservative creature. They all did what doubtless they have done since the days of Adam or earlier—wheeled, and then hung that little space of time before they dropped to the ground like lead. This, then, would be the moment at which to shoot them, when for four or five seconds they offered practically a sitting target. Now, at that distance, always under a hundred yards, I knew well that I could hit a tea plate every shot, and a vulture is much larger than a tea plate. So it seemed to me that, barring accidents, I had little to fear from the terrible trial of skill which lay before me. Again and again I covered the hovering birds with my rifle, feeling that if I had pressed the trigger I should have pierced them through.

Thinking it well to practise, I continued this game for a long while, till at last it came to an unexpected end. Suddenly I heard a scuffling sound. Dropping my glance I saw that the whole mob of *aasvogels* were rushing in upon Hans, helping themselves forward by flapping their great wings, and that about three feet in front of them was their king. Next instant Hans vanished, and from the centre of that fluffy, stinking mass there arose a frightful yell.

As a matter of fact, as I found afterwards, the king vulture had fastened on to his snub nose, whilst its dreadful companions, having seized other portions of his frame, were beginning to hang back after their fashion in order to secure some chosen morsel. Hans kicked and screamed, and I rushed in shouting, causing them to rise in a great, flapping cloud that presently vanished this way and that. Within a minute they had all gone, and the Hottentot and I were left alone.

"That is good," I said. "You played it well."

"Good! baas," he answered, "and I with two cuts in my nose in which I can lay my finger, and bites all over me. Look how my trousers are torn. Look at my head—where is the hair? Look at my nose. Good! Played well! It is those *verdomde aasvogels* that played. Oh! baas, if you had seen and smelt them, you would not say that it was good. See, one more second and I, who have two nostrils should have had four."

"Never mind, Hans," I said, "it is only a scratch, and I will make you a present of some new trousers. Also, here is tobacco for you. Come to the bush; let us talk."

So we went, and when Hans was a little composed I told him all that I had observed about the habits of the *aasvogel* in the air, and he told me all that he had observed about their habits on the ground, which, as I might not shoot them sitting, did not interest me. Still, he agreed with me that the right moment to fire would be just before they pounced.

Whilst we were still talking we heard a sound of shouts, and, looking over the brow of the hill that faced towards Umgungundhlovu, we saw a melancholy sight. Being driven up the slope towards us by three executioners and a guard of seven or eight soldiers, their hands tied behind their back, were three men, one very old, one of about fifty years of age, and one a lad, who did not look more than eighteen. As I soon heard, they were of a single family, the grandfather, the father, and the eldest son, who had been seized upon some ridiculous charge of witchcraft, but really in order that the king might take their cattle.

Having been tried and condemned by the *Nyangas*, or witch-doctors, these poor wretches were now doomed to die. Indeed, not content with thus destroying the heads of the tribe, present, and to come, for three generations, all their descendants and collaterals had already been wiped out by Dingaan, so that he might pose as sole heir to the family cattle.

Such were the dreadful cruelties that happened in Zululand in those days.

The doomed three were driven by their murderers into the centre of the depression, within a few yards of which Hans and I were standing.

After them came the head executioner, a great brute who wore a

curiously shaped leopard-skin cap—I suppose as a badge of office—
and held in his hand a heavy kerry, the shaft of which was scored with
many notches, each of them representing a human life.

"See, White Man," he shouted, "here is the bait which the king sends
to draw the holy birds to you. Had it not been that you needed such
bait, perhaps these wizards would have escaped. But the Black One
said the little Son of George, who is named Macumazahn, needs them
that he may show his magic, and therefore they must die today."

Now, at this information I turned positively sick. Nor did it make me
feel better when the youngest of the victims, hearing the executioner's
words, flung himself upon his knees, and began to implore me to spare
him. His grandfather also addressed me, saying:

"Chief, will it not be enough if I die? I am old, and my life does not
matter. Or if one is not sufficient, take me and my son, and let the lad,
my grandson, go free. We are all of us innocent of any witchcraft, and
he is not even old enough to practise such things, being but an unmar-
ried boy. Chief, you, also, are young. Would not your heart be heavy if
you had to be slain when the sun of your life was still new in the sky?
Think, White Chief, at what your father would feel, if you have one,
should he be forced to see you killed before his eyes, that some stranger might use your body to show his skill with a magic weapon by
slaying the wild things that would eat it."

Now, almost with tears, I broke in, explaining to the venerable man
as well as I could that their horrible fate had nothing to do with me. I
told him that I was innocent of their blood, who was forced to be there
to try to shoot vultures on the wing in order to save my white companions from a doom similar to their own. He listened attentively,
asking a question now and again, and when he had mastered my
meaning, said with a most dignified calmness:

"Now I understand, White Man, and am glad to learn that you are
not cruel, as I thought. My children," he added, turning to the others,
"let us trouble this *Inkoos* no more. He only does what he must do to
save the lives of his brethren by his skill, if he can. If we continue to
plead with him and stir his heart to pity, the sorrow swelling in it
may cause his hand to shake, and then they will die also, and their
blood be on his head and ours. My children, it is the king's will that
we should be slain. Let us make ready to obey the king, as men of
our House have always done. White lord, we thank you for your
good words. May you live long, and may good fortune sleep in your

hut to the end. May you shoot straight, also, with your magic tool, Farewell, *Inkoos*," and since he could not lift his bound hands in salutation, he bowed to me, as did the others.

Then they walked to a little distance, and seating themselves on the ground, began to talk together, and after a while to drone some strange chant in unison. The executioners and the guards also sat down not far away, laughing, chatting, and passing a horn of snuff from hand to hand. Indeed, I observed that the captain of them even took some snuff to the victims, and held it in his palm beneath their noses while they drew it up their nostrils and politely thanked him between the sneezes.

As for myself, I lit a pipe and smoked it, for I seemed to require a stimulant, or, rather, a sedative. Before it was finished Hans, who was engaged in doctoring his scratches made by the vultures' beaks with a concoction of leaves which he had been chewing, exclaimed suddenly in his matter-of-fact voice:

"See, baas, here they come, the white people on one side and the black on the other, just like the goats and the sheep at Judgment Day in the Book."

I looked, and there to my right appeared the party of Boers, headed by the Vrouw Prinsloo, who held the remnants of an old umbrella over her head. To the left advanced a number of Zulu nobles and councillors, in front of whom waddled Dingaan arrayed in his bead dancing dress. He was supported by two stalwart body-servants, whilst a third held a shield over his head to protect him from the sun, and a fourth carried a large stool, upon which he was to sit. Behind each party, also, I perceived a number of Zulus in their war-dress, all of them armed with broad stabbing spears.

The two parties arrived at the stone upon which I was sitting almost simultaneously, as probably it had been arranged that they should do, and halted, staring at each other. As for me, I sat still upon my stone and smoked on.

"Allemachte! Allan," puffed the Vrouw Prinsloo, who was breathless with her walk up the hill, "so here you are! As you did not come back, I thought you had run away and left us, like that stinkcat Pereira."

"Yes, *Tante*" (aunt), "here I am," I answered gloomily, "and I wish to heaven that I was somewhere else."

Just then Dingaan, having settled his great bulk upon the stool and recovered his breath, called to the lad Halstead, who was with him, and said:

"O Tho-maas, ask your brother, Macumazahn, if he is ready to try to shoot the vultures. If not, as I wish to be fair, I will give him a little more time to make his magic medicine."

I replied sulkily that I was as ready as I was ever likely to be.

Then the Vrouw Prinsloo, understanding that the king of the Zulus was before her, advanced upon him, waving her umbrella. Catching hold of Halstead, who understood Dutch, she forced him to translate an harangue, which she addressed to Dingaan.

Had he rendered it exactly as it came from her lips, we should all have been dead in five mintues, but, luckily, that unfortunate young man had learnt some of the guile of the serpent during his sojourn among the Zulus, and varied her vigorous phrases. The gist of her discourse was that he, Dingaan, was a black-hearted and bloody-minded villain, with whom the Almighty would come even sooner or later (as, indeed, He did), and that if he dared to touch one hair of her or of her companions' heads, the Boers, her countrymen, would prove themselves to be the ministers of the Almighty in that matter (as, indeed, they did). As translated by Halstead into Zulu, what she said was that Dingaan was the greatest king in the whole world; in fact, that there was not, and never had been, any such a king either in power, wisdom, or personal beauty, and that if she and her companions had to die, the sight of his glory consoled them for their deaths.

"Indeed," said Dingaan suspiciously, "if that is what this man-woman says, her eyes tell one story and her lips another. Oh! Tho-maas, lie no more. Speak the true words of the white chieftainess, lest I should find them out otherwise, and give you to the slayers."

Thus adjured, Halstead explained that he had not yet told all the words. The "man-woman," who was, as he, Dingaan supposed, a great chieftainess among the Dutch, added that if he, the mighty and glorious king, the earth-shaker, the world-eater, killed her or any of her subjects, her people would avenge her by killing him and his people.

"Does she say that?" said Dingaan. "Then as I thought, these Boers are dangerous, and not the peaceful folk they make themselves out to be," and he brooded for a while staring at the ground. Presently he lifted his head and went on: "Well, a bet is a bet, and therefore I will not wipe out this handful, as otherwise I would have done at once. Tell the old cow of a chieftainess that, notwithstanding her threats, I stick to my promise. If the little Son of George, Macumazahn, can shoot three vultures out of five by help of his magic, then she and her servants shall go free. If not, the vultures which he has missed shall feed on them, and afterwards I will talk with her people when they come to avenge her. Now, enough of this *indaba*. Bring those evildoers here that they may thank and praise me, who give them so merciful an end."

So the grandfather, the father, and the son were hustled before Dingaan by the soldiers, and greeted him with the royal salute of *bayète*.

"O king," said the old man, "I and my children are innocent. Yet if it pleases you, O king, I am ready to die, and so is my son. Yet we pray you to spare the little one. He is but a boy, who may grow up to do you good service, as I have done to you and your House for many years."

"Be silent, you white-headed dog!" answered Dingaan fiercely. "This lad is a wizard, like the rest of you, and would grow up to bewitch me and to plot with my enemies. Know that I have stamped out all your family, and shall I then leave him to breed another that would hate me? Begone to the World of Spirits, and tell them how Dingaan deals with sorcerers."

The old man tried to speak again, for evidently he loved this grand-child of his, but a soldier struck him in the face, and Dingaan shouted:

"What! Are you not satisfied? I tell you that if you say more I will force you to kill the boy with your own hand. Take them away."

Then I turned and hid my face, as did all the white folk. Presently I heard the old man, whom they had saved to the last that he might witness the deaths of his descendants, cry in a loud voice:

"On the night of the thirtieth full moon from this day I, the far-sighted, I, the prophet, summon thee, Dingaan, to meet me and mine in the Land of Ghosts, and there to pay—"

Then with a roar of horror the executioners fell on him and he died. When there was silence I looked up, and saw that the king, who had turned a dirty yellow hue with fright, for he was very superstitious, was trembling and wiping the sweat from his brow.

"You should have kept the wizard alive," he said in a shaky voice to the head slayer, who was engaged in cutting three more nicks on the handle of his dreadful kerry. "Fool, I would have heard the rest of his lying message."

The man answered humbly that he thought it best it should remain unspoken, and got himself out of sight as soon as possible. Here I may remark that by an odd coincidence Dingaan actually was killed about thirty moons from that time. Mopo, his general, who slew his brother

Chaka, slew him also with the help of Umslopogaas, the son of Chaka. In after years Umslopogaas told me the story of the dreadful ghost-haunted death of this tyrant, but, of course, he could not tell me exactly upon what day it happened. Therefore I do not know whether the prophecy was strictly accurate.*

The three victims lay dead in the hollow of the Hill of Death. Presently the king, recovering himself, gave orders that the spectators should be moved back to places where they could see what happened without frightening the vultures. So the Boers, attended by their band of soldiers, who were commanded to slay them at once if they attempted to escape, went one way, and Dingaan and his Zulus went the other, leaving Hans and myself alone behind our bush. As the white people passed me, Vrouw Prinsloo wished me good luck in a cheerful voice, although I could see that her poor old hand was shaking, and she was wiping her eyes with the *vatdoek*. Henri Marais, also in broken tones, implored me to shoot straight for his daughter's sake. Then came Marie, pale but resolute, who said nothing, but only looked me in the eyes, and touched the pocket of her dress, in which I knew the pistol lay hid. Of the rest of them I took no notice.

The moment, that dreadful moment of trial, had come at last; and oh! the suspense and the waiting were hard to bear. It seemed an age before the first speck, that I knew to be a vulture, appeared thousands of feet above me and began to descend in wide circles.

"Oh, baas," said poor Hans, "this is worse than shooting at the geese in the Groote Kloof. Then you could only lose your horse, but now—"

"Be silent," I hissed, "and give me the rifle."

The vulture wheeled and sank, and sank and wheeled. I glanced toward the Boers, and saw that they were all of them on their knees. I glanced at the Zulus, and saw that they were watching as, I think, they had never watched anything before, for to them this was a new excitement. Then I fixed my eyes upon the bird.

Its last circle was accomplished. Before it pounced it hung on wide, outstretched wings, as the others had done, its head toward me. I drew a deep breath, lifted the rifle, got the foresight dead upon its breast, and touched the hair-trigger. As the charge exploded I saw the *aasvogel* give a kind of backward twist. Next instant I heard a loud clap, and a surge of joy went through me, for I thought that the bullet had found its billet. But alas! it was not so.

The clap was that of the air disturbed by the passing of the ball and

* For the history of the death of Dingaan, see the Author's *Nada the Lily*.

the striking of this air against the stiff feathers of the wings. Anyone who has shot at great birds on the wing with a bullet will be acquainted with the sound. Instead of falling the vulture recovered itself. Not knowing the meaning of this unaccustomed noise, it dropped quietly to earth and sat down near the bodies, pitching forward in the natural way and running a few paces, as the others had done that afternoon. Evidently it was quite unhurt.

"Missed!" gasped Hans as he grasped the rifle to load it. "Oh! why did you not throw a stone on to the first heap?"

I gave Hans a look that must have frightened him; at any rate, he spoke no more. From the Boers went up a low groan. Then they began to pray harder than ever, while the Zulus clustered round the king and whispered to him. I learned afterwards that he was giving heavy odds against me, ten to one in cattle, which they were obliged to take, unwillingly enough.

Hans finished loading, capped and cocked the rifle, and handed it to me. By now other vultures were appearing. Being desperately anxious to get the thing over one way or another, at the proper moment I took the first of them. Again I covered it dead and pressed. Again as the gun exploded I saw that backward lurch of the bird, and heard the clap of the air upon its wings. Then—oh horror!—this *aasvogel* turned quietly, and began to mount the ladder of the sky in the same fashion as it had descended. I had missed once more.

"The second heap of stones has done this, baas," said Hans faintly, and this time I did not even look at him. I only sat down and buried my face in my hands. One more such miss, and then—

Hans began to whisper to me.

"Baas," he said, "those *aasvogels* see the flash of the gun, and shy at it like a horse. Baas, you are shooting into their faces, for they all hang with their beaks toward you before they drop. You must get behind them, and fire into their tails, for even an *aasvogel* cannot see with its tail."

I let fall my hands and stared at him. Surely the poor fellow had been inspired from on high! I understood it all now. While their beaks were towards me, I might fire at fifty vultures and never hit one, for each time they would swerve from the flash, causing the bullet to miss them, though but by a little.

"Come," I gasped, and began to walk quickly round the edge of the depression to a rock, which I saw opposite about a hundred yards away. My journey took me near the Zulus, who mocked me as I passed, asking where my magic was, and if I wished to see the white people killed presently. Dingaan was now offering odds of fifty cattle to one against me, but no one would take the bet even with the king.

I made no answer; no, not even when they asked me "if I had thrown down my spear and was running away." Grimly, despairingly, I marched on to the rock, and took shelter behind it with Hans. The Boers, I saw, were still on their knees, but seemed to have ceased praying. The children were weeping; the men stared at each other; Vrouw Prinsloo had her arm about Marie's waist. Waiting there behind the rock, my courage returned to me, as it sometimes does in the last extremity. I remembered my dream and took comfort. Surely God would not be so cruel as to suffer me to fail and thereby bring all those poor people to their deaths.

Snatching the rifle from Hans, I loaded it myself; nothing must be trusted to another. As I put on the cap a vulture made its last circle. It hung in the air just as the others had done, and oh; its tail was towards me. I lifted, I aimed between the gathered-up legs, I pressed and shut my eyes, for I did not dare to look.

I heard the bullet strike, or seem to strike, and a few seconds later I heard something else—the noise of a heavy thud upon the ground. I looked, and there with outstretched wings lay the foul bird dead, stone dead, eight or ten paces from the bodies.

"Allemachte! that's better," said Hans. "You threw stones on to *all* the other heaps, didn't you, baas?"

The Zulus grew excited, and the odds went down a little. The Boers stretched out their white faces and stared at me; I saw them out of the corner of my eye as I loaded again. Another vulture came; seeing one of its companions on the ground, if in a somewhat unnatural attitude, perhaps it thought that there could be nothing to fear. I leaned against my rock, aimed, and fired, almost carelessly, so sure was I of the result. This time I did not shut my eyes, but watched to see what happened.

The bullet struck the bird between its thighs, raked it from end to end, and down it came like a stone almost upon the top of its fellow.

"Good, good!" said Hans with a guttural chuckle of delight. "Now, baas, made no mistake with the third, and 'als sall recht kommen' (all shall be well)."

"Yes," I answered; "*if* I make no mistake with the third."

I loaded the rifle again myself, being very careful to ram down the powder well and to select a bullet that fitted perfectly true to the bore. Moreover, I cleared the nipple with a thorn, and shook a little fine powder into it, so as to obviate any chance of a miss-fire. Then I set on the cap and waited. What was going on among the Boers or the Zulus I do not know. In this last crisis of all our fates I never looked, being too intent upon my own part in the drama.

By now the vultures appeared to have realized that something unusual was in progress, which threatened danger to them. At any rate, although by this time they had collected in hundreds from east, west, north, and south, and were wheeling the heavens above in their vast, majestic circles, none of them seemed to care to descend to prey upon the bodies. I watched, and saw that among their number was that great king bird which had bitten Hans in the face; it was easy to distinguish him, because he was so much larger than the others. Also, he had some white at the tips of his wings. I observed that certain of his company drew near to him in the skies, where they hung together in a knot, as though in consultation.

They separated out again, and the king began to descend, deputed probably to spy out the land. Down he came in ever-narrowing turns, till he reached the appointed spot for the plunge, and, according to the immemorial custom of these birds, hung a while before he pounced with his head to the south and his great, spreading tail towards me.

This was my chance, and rejoicing in having so large a mark, I got the sight upon him and pulled. The bullet thudded, some feathers floated from his belly, showing that it had gone home, and I looked to see him fall as the others had done. But alas! he did not fall. For a few seconds he rocked to and fro upon his great wings, then commenced to travel upwards in vast circles, which grew gradually more narrow, till he appeared to be flying almost straight into the empyrean. I stared and stared. Everybody stared, till that enormous bird became, first a mere blot upon the blue, and at length but a speck. Then it vanished altogether into regions far beyond the sight of man.

"Now there is an end," I said to Hans.

"*Ja,* baas," answered the Hottentot between his chattering teeth. "There is an end. You did not put in enough powder. Presently we shall all be dead."

"Not quite," I said with a bitter laugh. "Hans, load the rifle, load it quick. Before they die there shall be another king in Zululand."

"Good, good!" he exclaimed as he loaded desperately. "Let us take that fat pig of a Dingaan with us. Shoot him in the stomach, baas; shoot him in the stomach, so that he too may learn what it is to die slowly. Then cut my throat, here is my big knife, and afterwards cut your own, if you have not time to load the gun again and shoot yourself, which is easier."

I nodded, for it was in my mind to do these things. Never could I stand still and see those poor Boers killed, and I knew that Marie would look after herself.

Meanwhile, the Zulus were coming towards me, and the soldiers who had charge of them were driving up Marais' people, making pretence to thrust them through with their assegais, and shouting at them as we do to cattle. Both parties arrived in the depression at about the same time, but remained separated by a little space. In this space lay the corpses of the murdered men, and the two dead *aasvogels*, with Hans and myself standing opposite to them.

"Well, little Son of George," puffed Dingaan, "you have lost your bet, for you did but kill two vultures out of five with your magic, which was good as far as it went, but not good enough. Now you must pay, as I would have paid had you won."

Then he stretched out his hand, and issued the dreadful order of "*Bulala amalongu!*" (Kill the white people). "Kill them one by one, that I may see whether they know how to die, all except Macumazahn and the tall girl, whom I will keep."

Some of the soldiers made a dash and seized the Vrouw Prinsloo, who was standing in front of the party.

"Wait a little, King," she called out as the assegais were lifted over her. "How do you know that the bet is lost? He whom you call Macumazahn hit that last vulture. It should be searched for before you kill us."

"What does the old woman say?" asked Dingaan, and Halstead translated slowly.

"True," said Dingaan. "Well, now I will send her to search for the vulture in the sky. Come back thence, Fat One, and tell us if you find it."

The soldiers lifed their assegais, waiting the king's word. I pretended to look at the ground, and cocked my rifle, being determined that if he spoke it, it should be his last. Hans stared upwards—I supposed to avoid the sight of death—then suddenly uttered a wild yell, which caused everyone, even the doomed people, to turn their eyes to him.

He was pointing to the heavens, and they looked to see at what he pointed.

This was what they saw. Far, far above in that infinite sea of blue there appeared a tiny speck, which his sharp sight had already discerned, a speck that grew larger and larger as it descended with terrific and ever-growing speed.

It was the king vulture falling from the heavens—dead!

Down it came between the Vrouw Prinsloo and the slayers, smashing the lifted assegai of one of them and hurling him to the earth. Down it came, and lay there a mere mass of pulp and feathers.

"O Dingaan," I said in the midst of the intense silence that followed, "it seems that it is I who have won the bet, not you. I killed this king of birds, but being a king it chose to die high up and alone, that is all."

Dingaan hestitated, for he did not wish to spare the Boers, and I, noting his hesitation, lifted my rifle a little. Perhaps he saw it, or perhaps his sense of honour, as he understood the word, overcame his wish for their blood. At any rate, he said to one of his councillors:

"Search the carcase of that vulture and see if there is a bullet hole in it."

The man obeyed, feeling at the mass of broken bones and flesh. By good fortune he found, not the hole, for that was lost in the general destruction of the tissues, but the ball itself, which having pierced the thick body from below upwards, had remained fast in the tough skin just by the backbone where the long, red neck emerges from between the wings. He picked it out, for it was only hanging in the skin, and held it up for all to see.

"Macumazahn has won his bet," said Dingaan. "His magic has conquered, though by but a very little. Macumazahn, take these Boers, they are yours, and begone with them out of my country."

To a Poet a Thousand Years Hence

JAMES ELROY FLECKER

I who am dead a thousand years,
  And wrote this sweet archaic song,
Send you my words for messengers
  The way I shall not pass along.

I care not if you bridge the seas,
  Or ride secure the cruel sky,
Or build consummate palaces
  Of metal or of masonry.

But have you wine and music still,
  And statues and a bright-eyed love,
And foolish thoughts of good and ill,
  And prayers to them who sit above?

How shall we conquer? Like a wind
  That falls at eve our fancies blow,
And old Mæonides the blind
  Said it three thousand years ago.

O friend unseen, unborn, unknown,
  Student of our sweet English tongue,
Read out my words at night, alone:
  I was a poet, I was young.

Since I can never see your face,
  And never shake you by the hand,
I send my soul through time and space
  To greet you. You will understand.

Index to Authors and Titles